Ps 0401

DR. ROBERT E. GRAETZ

The Design of

ELECTRIC CIRCUITS

in the Behavioral Sciences

The Design of

ELECTRIC

in the

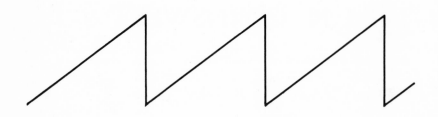

JOHN WILEY AND SONS, INC.

New York • London • Sydney

CIRCUITS

Behavioral Sciences

TOM N. CORNSWEET

Associate Professor of Psychology

University of California, Berkeley

Library of Congress Catalog Card Number: 63-18622
Printed in the United States of America

to my patient professors,
Thomas A. Ryan and Lorrin A. Riggs

Preface

People beginning research in the behavioral sciences frequently find themselves faced with an unexpected and distressing problem. They need apparatus. Many institutions are fortunate enough to have a machine shop, complete with machinist to design and build mechanical equipment, and some schools have facilities for the design and construction of electric apparatus as well. Even when a department has mechanics and technicians, there is frequently someone among the faculty or graduate student body who is in great demand because he can design electric circuits. This harried expert is asked two questions over and over again: "How did you ever learn all this?" and "Is there any place where I can learn it?"

The answer to the first question is usually that the expert has learned from experience. The answer to the second is much more difficult. Courses given in electrical engineering schools are almost always too theoretical and complex to be of direct value to experimenters who have not had the necessary background. Courses offered by technical schools, such as television repair training schools, are just the opposite. They are oriented so specifically toward radio and television that they are of little help in general circuit design. Textbooks for engineering and technical courses have the same shortcomings.

This book has been written specifically for researchers in the behavioral sciences, and particularly for those who have little or no knowledge of electricity. It is my hope that it will provide them with a clearer understanding of the basic principles of electricity and will enable them to apply these principles directly to their experimental work.

vii

Having read the book and solved the problems in it, the reader should be equipped to design and build any electric circuits short of those involving electron tubes. He should also have an appreciation of the functions for which more complex electronic circuits are used.

It is obviously important for the scientist to have this kind of information to build and understand the experimental equipment he uses. But for many areas within the behavioral sciences there is another salient need for a familiarity with electrical principles. Many theories of behavior are based on the activity of neurones, neural circuits, and neuro-muscular feedback loops, and many behavior models are constructed of electric elements. To understand these theories and models, as well as to generate new ones, the student will find it helpful to be familiar with the topics discussed in this book.

TOM N. CORNSWEET

Berkeley, California
July 1963

Contents

ix

Chapter 1

Introduction to circuit elements

For an adequate understanding of the subject matter of this book, it is essential not only that the text be read and understood but especially that the reader complete all of the problems. The importance of solving the problems cannot be overstated. Some of the points in the text will seem quite obvious, and it is hoped that all of them will seem logical and understandable. However, it has been the author's repeated experience in teaching this material that people may feel that they understand it completely and yet are unable to put into practice even some of the simpler principles. If the reader really has no need to solve the problems in order to understand them, then the problems will be very easy for him. If the reader finds them hard, then they must have been needed.

The general method of presentation in this book is to put basic principles and practical applications in close juxtaposition. It is certainly true that an understanding of such principles is essential to the design of new circuits, but, at the same time, understanding is not always sufficient for the successful application of these principles. Frequently, the applications must be specifically explained. A complete mastery of the concept of electric resistance helps very little in building a piece of apparatus if the builder does not know what a resistor looks like or what to do about the wires sticking out of each end. The following pages, therefore, contain almost as many pictures of actual circuit parts as circuit diagrams, and as much concrete description of elements which go into electric apparatus as discussion of the properties of electricity flowing through conductors.

The examples discussed and the problems to be solved are drawn primarily from the behavioral sciences. Some of the most common circuit problems will be discussed specifically, so that the reader may use the solutions presented directly if he insists. However, this book is not intended as a handbook of solutions to common circuit problems and will not serve that function very well.

Many of the problems given require the building of actual electric circuits, and a note about shock hazards might be in order here. None of the circuits to be built at the beginning of this book requires more than 12 volts to operate it. It is virtually impossible to get a real shock from these circuits. In fact, except for very few circuits which will be specifically pointed out, it is difficult even to feel a shock when trying very hard to do so. There is no need, therefore, to fear electrocution; each circuit capable of giving any shock at all will be so identified.

It will be necessary to borrow or buy a number of circuit parts in order to solve the problems presented. These parts can be bought at any radio supply store, but they are all common enough so that many of them can probably be found around the laboratory. A list of these parts follows:[1]

1. A 100-foot spool of solid (not stranded) hookup wire (#22 solid-type MW plastic-insulated wire, or equivalent).
2. Ten feet of lamp cord.
3. Ten alligator clips (screw connection).
4. A 1-pound spool of rosin core solder.
5. Four terminal strips (at least four terminals each), lugtype, for soldering. To be screwed to board.
6. Four pilot light bulbs (6 volts, type 47).
7. Two sockets for above light bulbs.
8. One battery, Burgess-type 5156 "B or C" (3, 4½, 6, 9, 10½, 16½, 22½ volts) clip terminals (or equivalent).
9. One male wall plug.
10. Two resistors (5 watts, 30 ohms each).
11. One potentiometer (10 watts, 50 ohms, wire-wound).
12. One potentiometer (4 watts, 5000 ohms, wire-wound).
13. Two set screw knobs for potentiometers.
14. Two capacitors (at least 150 microfarads, 50 volts, electrolytic).
15. Two microswitches, SPDT.
16. One toggle switch, DPDT.

[1] The terms used in this list may not be familiar to you, but an electronics salesman will recognize them and give you what you need.

17. One relay, 115 volts a-c, at least 4PDT, not enclosed (with visible working parts).

18. One relay, SPDT, sensitive (e.g. with at least 1000-ohm coil resistance, closes on 10 volts or less, closes on 10 milliamperes or less), not enclosed (with visible working parts).

19. One toy motor (3 volts).

If none of these items can be borrowed, they should not cost more than a total of about $25.00, and may be much cheaper at surplus stores.

The following tools should be available:

1. A medium-sized screw driver.

2. A small soldering iron.

3. One pair of long-nosed pliers with wire cutters or, preferably, one pair of long-nosed pliers and a separate pair of wire cutters.

4. One ohm-volt-ammeter.

It would be most efficient if all these items were on hand before the book proper is begun rather than trying to locate each part or tool when it is first required. Many of the items listed above should be mounted on a board for convenience in setting up circuits. Find a

Fig. 1.1 A board with mounted circuit elements.

piece of wood about one foot square, and mount on it each of the components listed below.

1. All four terminal strips.
2. Two of the flashlight bulbs in their sockets.
3. Battery.
4. Both potentiometers (variable resistors).
5. Both microswitches.
6. Toggle switch.
7. Both relays.
8. Motor.

The particular locations of each of these components is not important. Figure 1.1 shows a photograph of such a board.

To speed up construction of some of the simpler circuits, "clip leads" are convenient. A clip lead is a wire with an alligator clip at each end. Make five clip leads by connecting alligator clips to each end of five 12 inch-long pieces of hookup wire.

THE CONCEPT OF ELECTRICITY

When you pet a cat on a dry day, both you and the cat get shocked. The reason for this is that there are loosely bonded electrons on the surface of your skin, and with your first stroke some of them are rubbed off onto the cat's fur. The cat now has more electrons than normal, and you have fewer (the cat is negatively charged, you are positive). The excess electrons on the cat's fur redistribute themselves so that the charges are most dense at the tip of each hair. When you begin the next stroke, some of these electrons jump back to your hand, illustrating the fact that electrons are repelled by other electrons, and attracted by atoms that have fewer electrons than normal. The sparks that you feel and hear (and can see in a dark room) are groups of electrons jumping the gap between the tips of the cat's hairs and your hand.

Current and Voltage

If you were to connect a wire between a petted cat and the hand that did the petting, electrons would flow through the wire from the cat to the hand. This flow of electrons is called electric *current*. The more electrons flowing past any point in the wire in a given time, the higher the current.

If more electrons are rubbed off in the first place, the "charge" on the cat and the hand is higher, and the tendency for electrons to flow in the wire is greater. The "tendency" for current to flow between two points is called the *voltage* between the two points. From these crude definitions, it is clear that the higher the voltage, the greater the current, other conditions being equal.

Suppose that there were a means of continuously supplying a voltage between two points, and that the two points were connected together by a wire; then current would continuously flow in the wire. But it will lead to some confusion later if you picture current as the flow of a series of individual electrons from one end of the wire to the other. What actually happens is this. Any good conductor of electricity, e.g., the wire, contains many loosely bonded electrons. When an electron enters one end of the wire, it displaces a second electron from one of the nearby atoms. This second electron displaces a third, and so on. This means that, when one electron enters one end of a wire, another, different electron leaves the other end. Electric current is conducted along wire in a manner very analogous to the way in which a sound wave is conducted through the air. The energy in an electric current travels much faster than do the individual electrons. Individual electrons in a conductor travel in the order of magnitude of 100 feet per second, but the energy itself travels so fast that conduction in essentially all circuits can be considered instantaneous.[1] This is one reason why it is usually better to think of electric current in a conductor as a flow of electric energy rather than of electrons themselves.

Cat fur is not a particularly convenient supplier of electric energy. The sources you will use most frequently are batteries and wall sockets. Since batteries are easier to understand and involve many of the same principles as wall sockets, batteries will be discussed first.

Batteries

There are many different types of batteries. The kind you are probably most familiar with is the one used in flashlights. It is one of a type called dry cells, because it contains no liquids. Look at Fig. 1.2, or better still, a flashlight battery. It consists of a zinc can containing chemicals and a carbon rod. There is usually a paper jacket over the can, except at the bottom where the zinc is exposed, and at the top where the end of the carbon is covered by a brass shell. The chemicals operate on the can and the carbon rod in such a way as to

---

[1] Conduction time does become an important consideration in certain extremely high-frequency circuits, e.g., some radar circuits, but it is unusual for a behavioral scientist to have need for such a circuit.

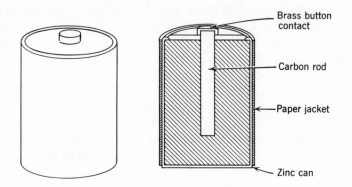

Fig. 1.2   Cross section through a typical flashlight.

generate voltage between them.   That is, the zinc has an excess of electrons (it is negative) and the carbon has fewer electrons than normal (it is positive).   If a wire were connected between the carbon rod and the can, current would flow through the wire until the battery ran down.   A flashlight bulb contains just such a wire.   Current running through the wire heats it up to the point where it emits light (the wire, or filament, is enveloped in an inert gas so that it does not burn up).

The terminals of flashlight batteries are such that it is difficult to make connections directly to them.   When such batteries are used, they are typically mounted in holders like the one in Fig. 1.3a.   But dry-cell batteries working on identical principles do come in more versatile packages.   Some of them are shown in Fig. 1.3b.   The zinc can and the carbon rod are connected to screw terminals [(1) in Fig. 1.3b], clips (2), or a socket (3), so that they are easier to connect to other circuit elements.   Dry-cell batteries can be obtained to give voltages anywhere from 1.5 volts to 300 volts, or more.   For the moment, we will consider only the 1.5-volt type.

Resistance

Suppose you **were** to connect a wire from one terminal of a 1.5-volt battery to the other.   The wire has a property known as electric *resistance*.   Resistance means just what you would intuit it to mean. The more resistance a conductor has, the harder it is for current to get through it—fewer loosely bonded electrons are available.   When a wire is connected between the terminals of the battery, and if the

(*a*)

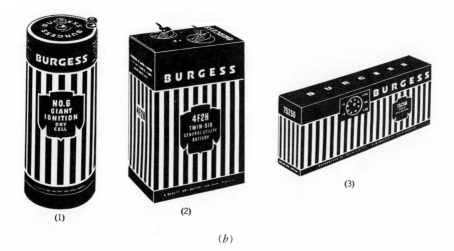

(1)   (2)

(3)

(*b*)

Fig. 1.3 (*a*) Holders for flashlight batteries. (*b*) Various batteries; (1) with screw terminals; (2) clips; and (3) a socket. (*Courtesy* Burgess Battery Co.)

wire has a higher resistance, less current will flow.   An ordinary wire
has a very low resistance, so that if you actually did connect it from
one terminal of the battery to the other, so much current would flow
that the chemicals in the battery would be exhausted very rapidly.

A Simple Circuit

In order to get a feel for what voltage, current, and resistance mean,
it is worthwhile to set up a simple electric circuit.   You will need
three clip leads, one light bulb and socket, the 50 ohm variable resistor
(potentiometer), and the battery.   The circuit can be schematically
represented by a diagram, Fig. 1.4a.   In this diagram straight lines

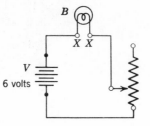

(a)

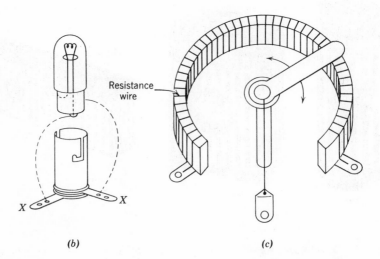

(b)   (c)

Fig. 1.4   (a) Circuit diagram for varying the brightness of a light bulb.   V represents the battery, B the bulb, and the zig-zag line a variable fifty ohm resistor.
(b) The internal connections of the bulb and socket.   (c) The anatomy of the
variable resistor (potentiometer).

represent connections (by clip leads), and the series of short lines labeled V represents the battery.

The figure enclosed in the circle, labeled B, represents the light bulb and its socket. Figure 1.4b illustrates the bulb and socket connections. Voltage impressed between the two metal tabs, or terminals, on the socket causes current to flow in one terminal, through the lead-in wires and the lamp filament, and out the other terminal.

The zig-zag line in Fig. 1.4a represents the resistor. Examine the resistor. If it has a cover on it, take the cover off so that you can see the parts inside. The resistive element itself is a long wire wrapped around a cylindrical core, Fig. 1.4c. There are three metal tabs on the outside of the resistor. The two outside tabs are connected to the two ends of this resistance wire. The middle tab is connected to an arm called the slider, or wiper, which slides along the resistance coil. On the circuit diagram, the two outside tabs are represented by the two ends of the zig-zag, and the middle tab—the slider—is represented by the arrow.

Connect up the circuit, as shown in Fig. 1.5.[1] If you have done this correctly, the brightness and color of the light bulb will change as the slider of the resistor is moved. Now consider why this should be. The actual resistance through which current must flow is the resistance of the light bulb plus that of the wire between one end of the resistor and the slider. When the slider is moved from one end to the other, the effective length of resistance wire changes, and so the amount of resistance in the circuit changes. Because the voltage generated in the battery is constant, that is, the "tendency" for current to flow in the circuit does not change, the amount of current actually flowing will decrease when the amount of resistance increases. The brightness of the bulb decreases correspondingly when the current through it decreases.

This circuit is often used to control the brightness of slide projectors, house lights, etc. (although it should be noted that the color is changed along with brightness, which is undesirable under many experimental conditions). The only difference between your circuit and one that might be used to control the intensity of a projected subliminal stimulus, for example, is that a physically bigger resistor would be needed to handle the large current of a projector bulb.

---

[1] One of the battery terminals is marked "+" and the others may be marked "—." These symbols represent the polarity of the battery, a concept that will be discussed later. For this particular circuit, the polarity of the battery is irrelevant. Either terminal of the battery may be connected to the bulb and the other to the resistor.

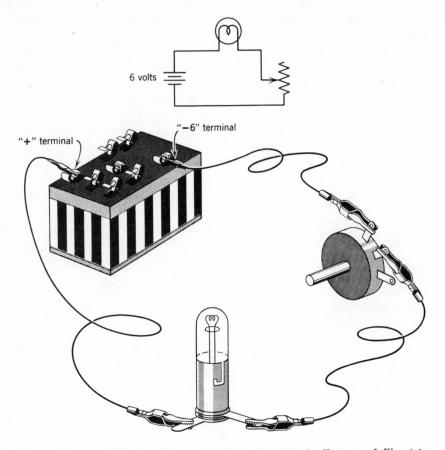

6 volts

"−6" terminal

"+" terminal

Fig. 1.5 The connections as represented in the circuit diagram of Fig. 1.4*a.*
That diagram is redrawn at the top of this figure.

Be sure that you can predict, by looking at the resistor, whether the
bulb should get brighter or dimmer as the slider is turned, say, clockwise. Then change the circuit so that the opposite will be true.

Do not dismantle the circuit yet (but disconnect one of the wires
to the battery, so that it will not run down).

METERS

In the simple circuit you have just built, the light bulb acts as a sort
of meter, crudely indicating the amount of current flowing in the

circuit.   A device which measures, quantitatively, the amount of current flowing in a circuit is called an ampere meter, or *ammeter*.   It is called this because, as will be discussed later, electric current is commonly measured in units called amperes.   It is important for anyone working with electric apparatus to understand the fundamental principles underlying the operation of ammeters.   The following section discusses these principles.

Principles of Meter Operation

When electrons flow through a wire, they cause the wire to heat up. Light bulbs and electric heaters are examples of this.   Current flowing through a wire also generates a magnetic field around the wire.   If current flows through a wire that is wound into a coil, a magnetic field will be formed around the entire coil.   As the current through the coil is increased, the strength of the magnetic field is increased in direct proportion.   If two magnetic fields are juxtaposed, they will either attract or repel each other, depending upon the relationship of their polarities, and this effect forms the basis for the actions of almost all ammeters.

The typical ammeter consists of a permanent magnet and a small coil of wire which pivots.   The coil is mounted in the magnetic field of the permanent magnet and is held in position by springs (Fig. 1.6).

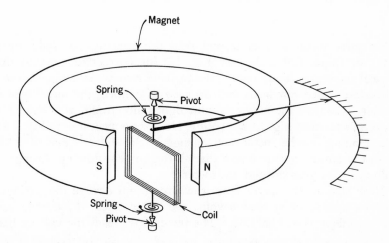

Fig. 1.6 Essential parts of a typical meter movement.

When current is passed through the coil, a magnetic field is generated around the coil. This field is pushed at one end and pulled at the other by the field of the permanent magnet, and the coil therefore turns on its pivots. As the coil turns farther and farther, the springs exert an increasing force in the opposite direction; that is, they tend more strongly to return the coil to its original position. The coil moves until the magnetic and spring forces are equal. The higher the current through the coil, the stronger will be the magnetic forces, and the farther the coil will turn. A pointer which moves across a scale is connected rigidly to the coil. Thus the strength of the current can be read by the position of the pointer on the scale. The two ends of the coil are connected to terminals on the outside of the meter so that any current to be measured may be passed through the coil. To determine how much current is flowing in some circuit, the ammeter must be connected into the circuit in such a way that either all or some known proportion of the unknown current flows through the meter coil.

Meters used to measure voltage (voltmeters) and resistance (ohmmeters) operate on exactly the same principles. In fact, a single meter movement, that is, magnet and coil, can be used to measure current, voltage, or resistance. You need only to change the circuit external to the movement itself in order to accomplish this. The meter that you have contains one movement and the switches on the front panel connect the appropriate built-in circuits to it. These conversion circuits are important and will be explained later.

Use of the "Multimeter"

Set your meter so that it will read d-c current, 500 milliamperes (ma) or more, full scale (see Fig. 1.7 for correct settings on three typical meters). Your meter should have two wires plugged into it. These are called test leads and are used to connect the meter into the circuit. Connect the meter in your light-bulb circuit, as in the circuit diagram shown in Fig. 1.8a. (*Note:* Do *not* connect it as in Fig. 1.8b.) The reading on the meter will change as the slider is moved. Note from the circuit configuration that all the current flowing through the bulb must also pass through the meter.[1]

Now remove the meter from the circuit and change the settings to read on a scale of at least 6 volts, d-c. Reconnect the circuit, using the voltmeter as in Fig. 1.8b. The meter now reads the voltage being

---

[1] *Warning:* Do not experiment with the meter. Follow the instructions carefully. The meter can be badly damaged by improper connections.

Fig. 1.7   Three typical volt-ohm-ammeters set to read at least 500 milliamperes d-c full scale. This setting may be made with a single knob on some meters, by two knobs on others (one for 500 milliamperes and another for d-c), or, on still others, by a combination of a knob setting and the placement of the two test leads in the appropriate sockets.

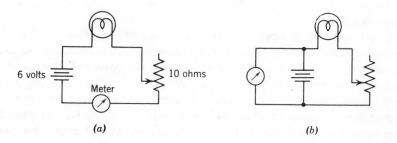

Fig. 1.8   (a) Circuit diagram for the measurement of the amount of current flowing through the light bulb. (b) Circuit diagram for measuring the voltage of the battery when it is lighting the bulb.

put out by the battery. Notice that the voltage does not change when the resistance slider is moved.

Remove the meter again and change the settings so that it reads ohms $\times$ 1. The meter is now internally connected to read resistance in the standard units, ohms. Inside the meter case there are several batteries and they have now been connected to the coil and test leads so that some of the voltage from the batteries appears between the test leads. Touch the two leads together. If the meter is working properly, the needle will swing up toward the full-scale reading which, on the ohms scale, is *zero* ohms. There is a knob on the meter that says something like "ohms adjust."[1] Turn this knob until the meter reads zero ohms when the test leads are touching each other. This procedure assumes that the resistance of the test leads themselves is zero, and for all practical purposes it is. If the needle will not go all the way to zero (full scale), the meter needs new batteries.

Now *make sure that your battery is disconnected* from your 50 ohm variable resistor, and connect the test leads between the slider and one end of the resistor. Read the resistance from the meter for several settings of the slider. The ohm scale on the meter is the reverse of the volt and ampere scales. When the resistance is zero, the battery in the meter drives enough current through the meter coil to cause it to swing to full scale. The "ohms adjust" knob gives this current the proper value. Now, when a resistance is connected between the test leads, it reduces the amount of current that can flow through the meter so that the needle swings back toward less current, indicating more resistance. (The light bulb in your first circuit indicated the amount of current and, at the same time, the amount of resistance, much as an ohmmeter would. The dimmer the bulb, the higher the resistance.)

The principles of operation of meters, as outlined above and in the following chapters, are well worth mastering. It is certainly possible to use meters without understanding how they operate, but it is safer, both for the meters and for the interpretation of their readings, if the basic principles are understood. Examples of common misuses of meters will be given in several other sections of this book. At present, however, it is worth mentioning a few aspects of meter use that may not be obvious.

---

[1] There is another adjustment on the meter, usually a screw head, which either says "zero adjust" or is mounted just about over the pivot of the needle. That is *not* the adjustment referred to above. It merely adjusts the position of the needle, mechanically, so that the meter reads zero on the volt and ampere scales when the test leads are not connected to anything.

It can do a meter a great deal of harm to have it set on the wrong scale when it is connected into the circuit. For instance, if it is set on a scale whose maximum reading is 1 volt, and you connect it across 6 volts, two things can happen to damage the meter. First, the needle will swing up to full scale very quickly and bang against the stop at that end of the scale. This can put a permanent bend in the needle. A second, more serious, consequence is that more current will flow through the meter coil than it can safely carry and the coil may burn out. In general, always make sure before you connect a meter into a circuit that it is set to a scale higher than the maximum possible value of whatever is to be measured.

It does a meter no harm to be run backwards so long as it is set on a safe scale. For example, set the meter to read at least 6 volts full scale and connect the test leads to the battery, one to the terminal marked "+," and the other to the one marked "4½v." If you have done this correctly, the meter will read 4.5 volts. If you have the test lead connections reversed, the meter needle will read *less than zero*. This reversed condition will not hurt the meter. Therefore, if you do not know in advance which lead to connect to which terminal, just try out either combination and the right one will give you a reasonable reading.

Never try to measure the current in a battery. You may, out of idle curiosity, wonder how much current there is in your 22½-volt battery, so you may set your meter to read amperes and connect the test leads, one to each side of the battery. This will cause the meter to burn out immediately. What you have *actually* asked the meter is, "How much current will flow when the meter is connected across the battery?" and, since an ammeter has very little resistance to current flow, an enormous amount of current will begin to flow, more than the meter is built to handle. The question of how much current is in a battery is an unanswerable one, not just technically, but logically. It is like asking how fast the water in the Pacific Ocean will flow.

Table 1.1.　Electrical Units and Symbols

Name	Circuit Symbol	Common Units	Unit Symbol or Abbreviation
Voltage		volt	v
		millivolt (10^{-3} volt)	mv
		microvolt (10^{-6} volt)	μv
		kilovolts (10^3 volts)	kv
Current	none	ampere	amp or a
		milliampere(10^{-3} ampere)	ma
		microampere (10^{-6} ampere)	μa
Resistance	Fixed ohm		Ω
	Variable or		

Chapter 2

Ohm's law and power

There are two formulas presented in this chapter, and it is essential that both be mastered. The first is Ohm's law and it will be discussed now; the second, the calculation of power, will be discussed later in the chapter.

OHM'S LAW

What is commonly called Ohm's law is the mathematical expression for the relationship already mentioned between the amount of current, voltage, and resistance in any given circuit or part of a circuit. When resistance is constant, the higher the voltage the higher the current. When voltage is held constant, the lower the resistance the higher the current. That is

$$I = \frac{E}{R}$$

where I = the current, in amperes,
E = the voltage, in volts,
R = the resistance, in ohms.

It can be stated in two other equivalent forms:

$$E = IR \qquad R = \frac{E}{I}$$

You really need to remember only one of these forms because, knowing one, either of the others is immediately derivable. Be sure to notice that even if all forms are forgotten they can be easily figured out just by realizing the fact that higher voltages and lower resistances give higher currents.

The best way to learn the implications of Ohm's law is to solve problems.

PROBLEM 1.   Given the circuit in Fig. 2.1, find the current that will flow around it.

Solution.   Ohm's law holds when I is in amperes, E in volts, and R in ohms. $I = E/R$, $I = 10$ volts/20 ohms $= 0.5$ ampere.

PROBLEM 2.   What must R be changed to in the above circuit in order that 3 amperes flow in the circuit?

Solution. $R = E/I = {}^{10}\!/_3 = 3\frac{1}{3}$ ohms.

PROBLEM 3.   How large is the voltage across R in the circuit in Problem 1?

Solution. $E = IR$. I has been found to be 0.5 ampere.   Therefore, $E = 0.5 \times 20 = 10$ volts.   But looking at the circuit again, it is true by definition that the voltage across R is 10 volts without bothering with Ohm's law.   Straight lines in a circuit diagram always represent connections between points.   Therefore, the circuit diagram essentially says that the battery is connected across the resistor R.   Since there are 10 volts between the terminals of the battery, there must be 10 volts across the resistor.

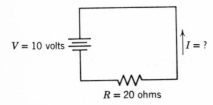

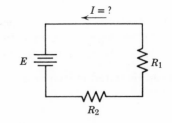

Fig. 2.1 Circuit diagram for Problems 1, 2, and 3.

Fig. 2.2 Circuit diagram for Problems 4, 5, and 6.

PROBLEM 4.   Solve for the current I in the circuit of Fig. 2.2, given $E = 10$ volts, $R_1 = 8$ ohms, and $R_2 = 6$ ohms.

Solution.   The solution of this problem requires some additional discussion about circuits in general.   In the first place, the number of amperes flowing through R_1 is the same as through R_2, through the connections (represented by the straight lines) and through the battery. If you think about what electric current is, you will see why this must be true.   Any given electron entering one end of, say R_1, will cause another electron to leave the other end of R_1, which, in turn, will cause one electron to enter and another to leave R_2, the battery, etc.   If more current were to flow in any one part of the circuit than in some other part, electrons would begin to pile up somewhere.   This piling up would produce an increase in the voltage at that point, which, in turn, would mean an increase in the tendency for current to flow at that point.   And since current and voltage are directly proportional to each other, the resulting increase in current would just balance out the rate of piling up.   Thus, the current must be the same through R_1, R_2, and the battery.

By similar reasoning, the effect of putting two resistors into the circuit, end to end as in this problem, is the same as putting in one resistor whose resistance is the sum of the two separate ones.   When resistors are connected end to end, they are said to be in *series* with each other.   The solution of the problem is: $I = E/R = 10/(6 + 8) =$ $^{10}\!/_{14} = 0.715$ ampere.

PROBLEM 5 (Fig. 2.2). $E = 10$ volts

$$R_1 = 8 \text{ ohms}$$

Find the value of R_2 which will allow 0.5 ampere to flow in the circuit.

Solution. $R = \dfrac{E}{I}$

$$8 + x = \frac{10}{0.5}$$

$$x = 20 - 8 = 12 \text{ ohms}$$

PROBLEM 6 (Fig. 2.2). $E = 10$ volts

$$R_1 = 8 \text{ ohms}$$

$$R_2 = 6 \text{ ohms}$$

Find the voltage across R_1 and the voltage across R_2.

Solution. $E = IR$

$$I = \frac{10 \text{ volts}}{(6 + 8) \text{ ohms}} = 0.715 \text{ ampere}$$

Therefore

$$E = 0.715 \times 8 = 5.72 \text{ volts across } R_1$$

$$E = 0.715 \times 6 = 4.28 \text{ volts across } R_2$$

Note that the voltage across R_1 plus that across R_2 equals 10 volts. From the circuit diagram this makes sense. This problem illustrates a point which is very important and at the same time difficult for many people really to understand. Whenever a current flows through a resistance, a voltage will appear across that resistance. The magnitude of the voltage will equal the current multiplied by the resistance. Such a voltage has exactly the same mathematical properties as a voltage generated by a battery. Recognition of voltages generated in this way often permits solving problems which otherwise have only very circuitous solutions. Problems of this sort will be given in the next chapter.

PROBLEM 7. Put together the circuit in Fig. 2.3. Now calculate the voltages across R_1 and R_2, as in Problem 6, and check your answer by measuring the voltages. Measure the voltage across R_1 by setting the meter to read volts on the appropriate scale (at least 6 volts full scale) and then connect the test leads, one to each end of R_1. The voltage across R_2 is measured in the same way. Next, calculate the amount of

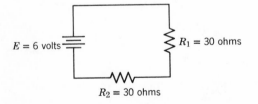

Fig. 2.3   Circuit to be constructed for Problem 7.

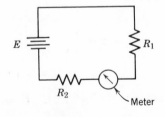

Fig. 2.4   Circuit diagram for the measurement of the amount of current flowing in the circuit given in Problem 7.

current that will flow in the circuit and check your answer by measuring the current. Set the meter to read d-c amperes on the appropriate scale (at least 500 milliamperes full scale).[1] Then disconnect the circuit any place and connect it back together again through the meter, as in Fig. 2.4.

POWER

The rate at which a system does work is called the power of the system. In electric systems, power is used to light lamps, run motors, heat resistors, shock rats, etc. The amount of power is usually measured in units called *watts* (or milliwatts, or microwatts). The formula for the calculation of watts should be learned. It is as follows:

$$\text{Power (in watts)} = E \text{ (in volts)} \times I \text{ (in amperes)}$$

$$W = E \times I$$

When part of an electric circuit is damaged because of improper circuit connections, the damage can almost always be attributed to heat, e.g., a misconnected meter may literally "burn out." So will a light bulb run at too high a voltage. The amount of power that a circuit element can consume without burning up may be specified in watts. Some circuit elements, for example, some resistors, have their maximum tolerable wattage printed on them. When a resistor carries somewhat more than rated wattage, its resistance begins to change. At still higher wattages, the resistor may burn up.

Other circuit elements, such as most relays, have their maximum rating specified in current rather than watts. This rating system can be converted to watts though, because the resistance of the relay will also be stated, and since

$$W = EI$$

and, from Ohm's law,

$$E = IR$$

then

$$W = I^2R$$

Similarly, the wattage rating may sometimes be used to calculate the amount of current flowing through an element. Consider a regular 100-watt household light bulb. This 100-watt rating means that, when

[1] One milliampere = $\frac{1}{1000}$ amperes, and is abbreviated ma. Therefore, 500 ma = 0.5 amp.

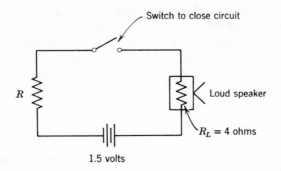

Switch to close circuit

R

Loud speaker

R_L = 4 ohms

1.5 volts

Fig. 2.5 Circuit to produce audible clicks. Changing the value of R changes the loudness of the clicks.

the light bulb is connected across the normal house voltage, which is typically 115 volts, the light bulb will carry 0.87 ampere.[1]

$$W = EI$$

$$100 = 115I$$

$$I = \tfrac{100}{115} = 0.87 \text{ ampere}$$

Household bulbs are sometimes incompletely labeled. It must be assumed that they are designed for 115 volts in order to make the above calculations. When a device such as a resistor or a flashlight bulb is designed for a maximum voltage other than 115 volts, the voltage is usually specified. Given any two of the four parameters—resistance, voltage, current, watts—the other two may be calculated.

Problems   (Answers to problems begin on page 302.)

1. A slide projector is used to present stimuli in an experiment. Preliminary trials during which the projector is run from a variable voltage supply (to be explained later) show that the stimulus is at the proper intensity when the voltage across the projector is 60 volts and the current through it is 2 amperes. A variable voltage supply is too expensive to tie up permanently in your experiment. Therefore, determine the resistance

[1] The resistance of a lamp when it is cold is considerably different from its resistance when the rated voltage is applied across it. Since the wattage rating of a lamp is the wattage it dissipates when it is hot (e.g., at rated voltage), these formulas will not yield correct values when the lamp is being run at any voltage other than its rated voltage.

and wattage of the resistor which, when put between the 115-volt wall socket and the projector, would cause it to run at the desired intensity.

2. You wish to present a subject with a series of clicks at five different loudness levels, the levels being at approximately equal sensory intervals. Such will be the case when the amplitudes of the clicks are in the ratios 1:2:4:8:16 (so long as they are not at either extreme of the loudness range). When a battery is first connected across a loudspeaker, a click is sounded the amplitude of which is approximately proportional to the amount of current flowing through the loudspeaker. Therefore, clicks of different loudnesses can be generated by closing the circuit in Fig. 2.5 with different values of R. Assume that you have found, for a loudspeaker whose resistance is 4 ohms, that the loudest click you need occurs when $R = 11$ ohms. Find the values of the four other resistors that must be substituted for the 11-ohm one in order to produce clicks at the desired loudnesses.

Chapter 3

Simple circuits

All electric circuits fall into one of three classes: series, parallel, and series-parallel. Each of these will be examined in this chapter.

SERIES CIRCUITS

All of the circuits discussed up to this point have been series circuits. The defining characteristic of a series circuit is that the current in all of its parts is equal. This property of series circuits has already been pointed out in some of the problems in Chapter 2. The current must be the same in all parts of a series circuit because there is only one path in which the current can flow.

Connect up the series circuit shown in Fig. 3.1. In this circuit the two bulbs and the battery are all said to be "in series." If the two light bulbs are identical and the current through each of them is the same, then the voltage across A must equal the voltage across B

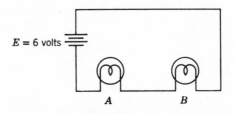

Fig. 3.1 Series circuit. A and B are 6-volt flashlight bulbs.

($E_A = IR_A$, $E_B = IR_B$, and since $R_A = R_B$, E_A must equal E_B). There-fore, since the voltage across both bulbs combined is 6 volts, the voltage across each must be 3 volts. But the bulbs are designed to be run at 6 volts each, so they will be much dimmer in this circuit than they would be in normal operation.

PARALLEL CIRCUITS

Now connect up the circuit in Fig. 3.2a. This is called a parallel circuit; the two bulbs are said to be in parallel with each other. In this case, there are two different paths for the current to flow in. One path is around the loop containing the battery and bulb A, and the other is around the loop containing the battery and bulb B. The current cannot be the same in all parts of this circuit because the current in the connector labeled X must equal the sum of the currents in Y and Z. Note that both light bulbs are brighter than when they were in series because there are a full 6 volts across each light bulb in this circuit.

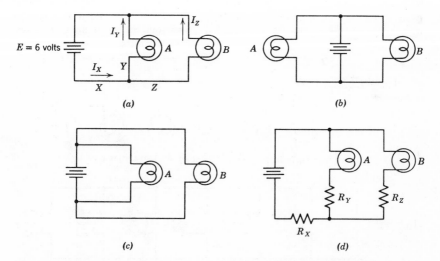

Fig. 3.2   (a) Parallel circuit. A and B are 6-volt flashlight bulbs. (b) Another configuration of the identical circuit to that in Fig. 3.2a. (c) A third configura-tion of the identical circuit to that in Figs. 3.2a and 3.2b. (d) The circuit dia-gram for the circuit in Fig. 3.2a when the wires connecting the elements have appreciable resistance. R_X represents the resistance of the wires in the branch which contains the battery, R_Y the resistance of the wires in the branch con-taining A, and R_Z the resistance of the wires in the branch containing B.

Diagrams of Fig. 3.2*b* and Fig. 3.2*c* are *exactly* equivalent to Fig. 3.2*a*. This is a very important point. It follows from the fact that straight lines in circuit diagrams merely represent connections between points; they *do not* represent the wires themselves. The information contained in each of the three diagrams is the same, namely, that each light bulb is connected across the battery. It does appear that bulb *B* is connected in one case to bulb *A* (Fig. 3.2*a*), whereas in the others it is connected directly to the battery. But this would make a difference only if the wires actually making the connections had appreciable resistance. Since there are no resistances (other than the bulbs themselves) shown in the diagrams, the diagrams explicitly exclude that case. If the wires actually had appreciable resistance, the resistance would be represented as in Fig. 3.2*d*. If you do not clearly grasp this argument, you should actually connect up the two "different" circuits.

Each light bulb in the circuit in Fig. 3.2*a* may be considered to be completely independent of the other. This can be demonstrated by the fact that disconnecting either of the light bulbs from the circuit has no effect upon the brightness of the other.[1] Since this is true—

[1] Christmas tree lights may be bought in either series or parallel strings. The series string can be diagrammed as in Fig. 3.3. Each bulb is rated at $^{115}/_6 \approx 20$ volts in this 6-bulb string. If any one bulb burns out, all the bulbs will be ex-

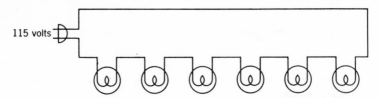

Fig. 3.3   The diagram of a series string of six Christmas tree lights.

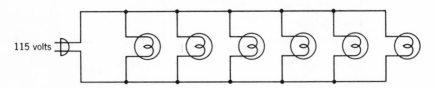

Fig. 3.4   The diagram of a parallel string of six Christmas tree lights.

tinguished because there is no path for the current to flow in. Then the game of finding the bad bulb begins.

Parallel strings can be diagrammed as shown in Fig. 3.4. In this case, each bulb is rated at 115 volts, and if any one of them burns out, the others remain lit.

that is, since each light bulb can be considered to be operating by itself across its rated voltage (6 volts)––then the battery must be delivering twice as much current as it would if only one bulb were connected across it. At this point Ohm's law should be reconsidered ($I = E/R$). Since E, the voltage, does not change whether one or two bulbs are connected across the battery, then, because the current coming out of the battery is twice as great, the effective resistance of the two bulbs "in parallel" must be one half of the resistance of each of them separately. This is a special case of the general principles stated in the following discussion.

Figure 3.5 shows three different circuit diagrams. In Fig. 3.5a, $I = E/R = 6/30 = 0.2$ ampere. In Fig. 3.5b, $I = 6/80 = 0.075$ ampere. In this circuit the two resistors are said to be in series with each other and with the battery. Whenever two resistors are in series with each other, the effective resistance of the combination of the two is the sum of the resistance of each alone. The resistance of any number of resistors in series is the sum of all the individual resistances. This should make intuitive sense because it should be just as difficult for current to get through two resistors of, say 30 ohms each, when the

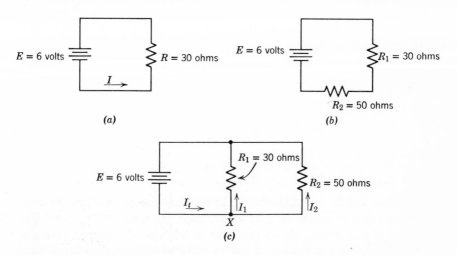

(a)   (b)   (c)

Fig. 3.5   (a) A simple series circuit. (b) A circuit containing two resistors and a battery in series. (c) A simple parallel circuit.

current must pass through one and then the other (when they are in series), as it would be for current to get through one 60-ohm resistor.

Figure 3.5c shows two resistors in parallel and the pair of resistors in series with the battery. The various currents in the circuit can be found as follows. It has already been pointed out that disconnecting R_2 will not change the current flowing through R_1, and disconnecting R_1 will not change the current through R_2. Therefore, the current through R_1, i.e., I_1, can be calculated as if there were no R_2, and vice versa. $I_1 = E/R = \frac{6}{30} = 0.2$ ampere. $I_2 = \frac{6}{50} = 0.12$ ampere. Now look at the point in the diagram labeled X. The current I_t here divides up into I_1 and I_2. Since there is no place for I_t to go except through R_1 and R_2, and since there is no place for I_1 and I_2 to come from except from the battery, I_t must be equal to the sum of I_1 and I_2.

$$I_t = I_1 + I_2 = 0.2 + 0.12 = 0.32 \text{ ampere}$$

The effective resistance of the parallel combination of R_1 and R_2 can now be calculated. The "effective" or "equivalent" resistance of the parallel combination equals the resistance of that single resistor which could be substituted for the parallel combination without affecting the rest of the circuit. For example, if two 30-ohm resistors are in *series*, their equivalent resistance is 60 ohms. In the present example, we know that $E = 6$ volts, and $I_t = 0.32$ ampere. Therefore, to compute the equivalent resistance of the parallel pair, we must determine the value of a single resistor that will give these voltage and current values when it is substituted for the parallel pair.

$$I = \frac{E}{R}$$

$$0.32 = \frac{6}{R}$$

$$R = \frac{6}{0.32} = 18.75 \text{ ohms}$$

In other words, an 18.75-ohm resistor put in the place of the 30- and 50-ohm resistors in circuit 3.5c would have the same effect as did the original combination. From this kind of analysis, the general formula for the equivalent resistance of any number of individual resistors may be derived. It is:

$$\frac{1}{R_{\text{equiv}}} = \frac{1}{R_1} + \frac{1}{R_2} + \frac{1}{R_3} \cdots$$

The equivalent resistance of any number of resistors in *parallel* is always less than the resistance of the lowest valued resistor in the group.
It is convenient to know one special case of this equation. When-

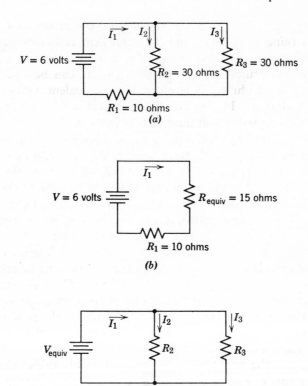

Fig. 3.6 (*a*) A series-parallel circuit. The parallel pair (R_2 and R_3) is in series with R_1 and the battery. (*b*) A circuit equivalent to the one of Fig. 3.6*a*. (*c*) Another circuit equivalent to that of Fig. 3.6*a*.

ever resistors of equal resistance are put in parallel, their equivalent resistance is simply this:

$$R_{\text{equiv}} = \frac{R}{n}$$

where R is the resistance of each, and n is the number of resistors. For instance, the equivalent resistance of two 30-ohm resistors in parallel is 15 ohms, of three 30-ohm resistors in parallel, 10 ohms, etc.

SERIES-PARALLEL CIRCUITS

Any circuit having some elements in parallel and some in series is called a series-parallel circuit. A simple example of this sort of circuit is shown in Fig. 3.6a.   In order to compute the values of I_1, I_2, and I_3, the first thing to do is to find the equivalent resistance of the two 30-ohm resistors in parallel.   Once this is done and this equivalent resistance is substituted for the parallel pair, I_1 can be easily found. $R_{equiv} = {}^{30}\!/_{2} = 15$ ohms.   Therefore, the equivalent circuit in Fig. 3.6b can be drawn.   In this circuit $I_1 = E/R = {}^{6}\!/_{25} = 0.24$ ampere. Thus I_1 in the original circuit must be 0.24 ampere.

Computing I_2 and I_3 (Fig. 3.6a) may be a little more confusing.   If the voltage across R_2 and R_3 were known, the I's could be computed as in the previous example.   In other words, if an equivalent circuit like that in Fig. 3.6c could be drawn, it would be easy to compute I_2 and I_3.   The question is: What is V_{equiv}?   Look back at the circuit in Fig. 3.6b.   The voltage across R_{equiv} can be computed easily from Ohm's law. $E = IR = 0.24 \times 15 = 3.6$ volts.   This is V_{equiv} in the circuit of Fig. 3.6c.   Thus $I_2 = E/R = 3.6/30 = 0.12$ ampere, and I_3, by the same calculation, is also 0.12 ampere.   This must be correct because I_1 must equal $I_2 + I_3$; $0.24 = 0.12 + 0.12$.   There is another way to arrive at the same conclusion.   The current through R_1 is 0.24 ampere.   Therefore the voltage across R_1 must equal $I \times R = 0.24 \times 10 = 2.4$ volts.   Since there are only 6 volts in the circuit altogether and 2.4 of them are used up in R_1, then 3.6 volts must be what is left to appear across the two parallel resistors.   Possibly this is a confusing way to determine V_{equiv}, but it is an attack on the problem which should be clearly understood.   Once mastered, it is the most convenient way of analyzing many circuits.

Examine the circuit in Fig. 3.7a.   When the slider is at the extreme upper end of the variable resistor, the full battery voltage is applied to the motor and the circuit may be represented as in Fig. 3.7b.   When the slider is pushed all the way to the lower end of the resistor, the circuit may be represented as in Fig. 3.7c.   In Fig. 3.7c there is no source of voltage in the loop containing the motor, and the voltage across the motor must thus be zero volts.   (The mere fact that the loop containing the motor is connected at one point to the loop containing the battery is not sufficient to cause current to flow in the motor loop.   There is no "reason why current should flow" in the motor loop, i.e., there is no voltage in the motor loop.)

Moving the slider in Fig. 3.7a from one end of the resistance to the other causes the voltage across the motor to change continuously from full voltage to zero voltage.   The diagram shown in Fig. 3.7d represents the circuit when the slider is one-quarter of the way from the top to the bottom.   Note that this circuit is identical in form to the circuit of Fig. 3.6*a*, and the value of the voltage across the motor may be found by the procedures discussed in connection with Fig. 3.6.

The circuit in Fig. 3.7*a* is called a voltage-divider circuit (since the battery voltage is divided into two parts, one part appearing across the motor and the other across the remainder of the variable resistor) and is used very extensively to produce adjustable voltages. You have already used a variable resistance in series with a light bulb to change its brightness. The voltage divider circuit may be used in the same way, and has the very great advantage that it permits variation of the voltage continuously down to zero volts. The practical importance of this circuit is so great that its properties should be thoroughly mastered. One of the following set of problems involves the voltage-divider circuit. If you have difficulty with the problem, you should make up similar ones and solve them until you become familiar with the circuit.

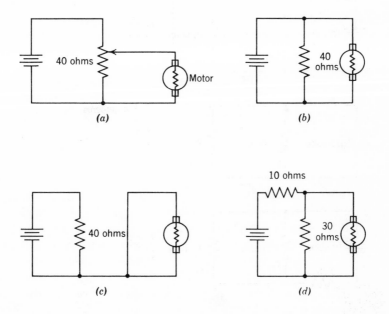

Fig. 3.7 (*a*) A circuit to provide a voltage across a motor which may be varied from zero volts to the full battery voltage. (*b*) The circuit in Fig. 3.7*a* when the slider is all the way up. (*c*) The circuit in Fig. 3.7*a* when the slider is all the way down. (*d*) The circuit in Fig. 3.7*a* when the slider is one quarter of the way down.

Problems

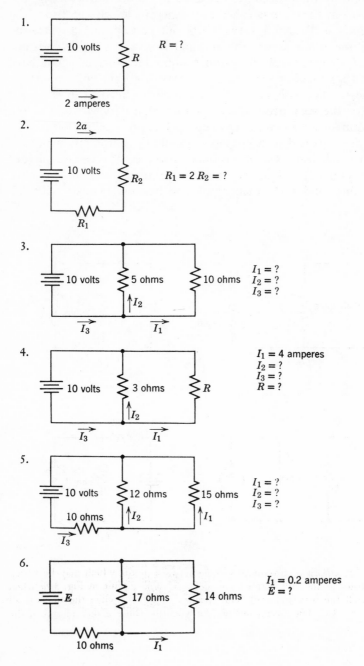

1.

   10 volts R $R = ?$

   2 amperes

2.

   $2a$

   10 volts R_2 $R_1 = 2\,R_2 = ?$

   R_1

3.

   10 volts   5 ohms   10 ohms $I_1 = ?$
                                      $I_2 = ?$
              I_2 $I_3 = ?$

   I_3 I_1

4.

   10 volts   3 ohms R $I_1 = 4$ amperes
                                 $I_2 = ?$
              I_2 $I_3 = ?$
                                 $R = ?$
   I_3 I_1

5.

   10 volts   12 ohms   15 ohms $I_1 = ?$
                                       $I_2 = ?$
   10 ohms I_2 I_1 $I_3 = ?$
   I_3

6.

   E 17 ohms   14 ohms $I_1 = 0.2$ amperes
                                 $E = ?$

   10 ohms I_1

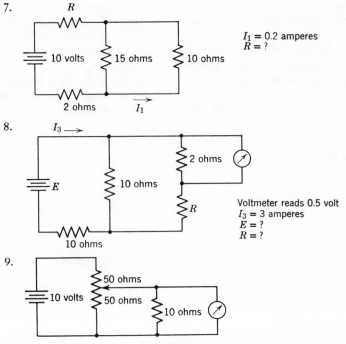

7.

10 volts
R
15 ohms
10 ohms
2 ohms
I_1

$I_1 = 0.2$ amperes
$R = ?$

8.
$I_3 \longrightarrow$

E
10 ohms
2 ohms
R
10 ohms

Voltmeter reads 0.5 volt
$I_3 = 3$ amperes
$E = ?$
$R = ?$

9.

10 volts
50 ohms
50 ohms
10 ohms

What is the voltmeter reading?

10. Given a 100-watt and a 500-watt light bulb, run in parallel from the wall supply, what current will be drawn from the supply?

11. Given a clock that operates on 0.1 watt and 6 volts, what value of resistance must be placed in series with it to run it from the 115-volt wall supply?

12. Plot V as a function of the position of the slider on the variable resistance in this circuit diagram, for $R_1 = 10$ ohms and for $R_1 = 10,000$ ohms. Note the shapes of these two curves. (In general, the greater the load resistance (R_2) is relative to the variable resistance (R_1), the more nearly linear is the curve.)

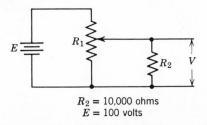

E
R_1
R_2
V

$R_2 = 10,000$ ohms
$E = 100$ volts

13. You are given a meter movement whose coil resistance is 100 ohms, and which will give a full-scale deflection when 1 milliampere is flowing through it. Make a box which holds the movement and some other circuit

elements, and on which two input terminals are mounted. Draw a different circuit diagram for what must be inside the box in order that it perform each of the following:

  a. The meter reads full scale when 1 volt is impressed across the input terminals. (The box is then a 1-volt full-scale voltmeter.)

  b. The meter reads full scale when 100 volts are across the input terminals.

  c. The meter reads full scale when 10 milliamperes are flowing in one terminal and out the other. (The box is then a milliammeter, 10 milliamperes, full scale.)

  d. The meter reads full scale when 1 ampere is flowing in one terminal and out the other.

Chapter 4

Circuit elements

In the first chapter the construction of flashlight batteries was discussed. The flashlight battery is one of a class called dry cells (as contrasted to wet cells, e.g., automobile batteries). Nearly all dry batteries consist of one or more cells each of which is identical in principle to the flashlight battery. The #6 dry cell shown in Fig. 4.1 is a single cell just like a flashlight battery, only bigger. Instead of having to connect a circuit to the bottom of the zinc can and to a button at the top of the cell, the carbon rod and the zinc can are connected to screw terminals on the top of the #6 cell so that connections to circuits are easier.

As long as a dry battery contains only one cell, its voltage is always close to 1½ volts, no matter how large it is. For instance, this #6 cell and the very small battery that fits into pencil-type flashlights (see Fig. 4.1) are both rated at 1½ volts. However, the larger the battery, the more current it can deliver before it runs down. If a battery is to be used to light a flashlight bulb continuously for long periods of time, it is better to use a larger cell. Some output curves for determining how much power can be drawn from a cell of any particular size are given in Appendix I.

Dry-cell batteries also go bad even when current is not being drawn from them. The "shelf life" of a battery is the length of time it will retain its usefulness when it is standing unused. The shelf life of any particular type of battery may be as short as a few months or as long as several years. The approximate expiration date is some-

35

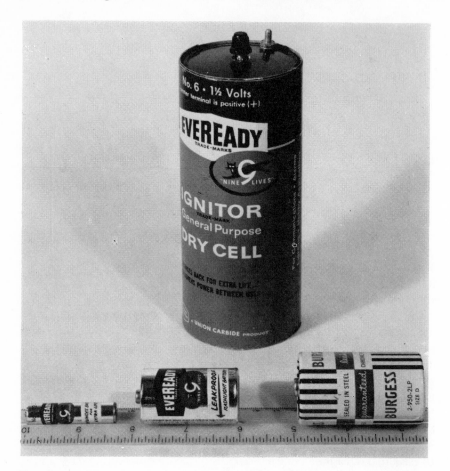

Fig. 4.1 Various 1½–volt dry cells. (*Courtesy* Helen E. Howell, Berkeley, Calif.)

times printed on the bottom of the battery, and should be looked for when the battery is purchased.

Cells in Series

Many dry-cell batteries will deliver more than 1½ volts. The one used in your circuits, for instance, delivers from 3 to 22½ volts, depending on which terminals are used. Any dry battery that delivers more than 1½ volts consists of a combination of several dry cells connected together inside the battery casing. (The word "battery"

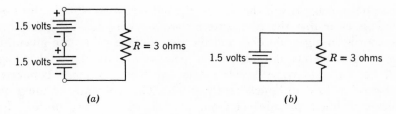

Fig. 4.2 (a) Two 1½-volt cells connected in series across a 3-ohm resistor.
(b) A single cell connected across the same resistor.

refers to a set of one or more individual cells.) To illustrate how
this is accomplished, consider the circuit in Fig. 4.2a. Two dry cells,
each delivering 1½ volts, are connected in series with each other
across the resistor. The total voltage across the combination of the
two batteries is 3 volts. This can be understood in the following
way. If just one cell were connected across the resistor, as in Fig.
4.2b, the current flowing would be 1.5/3 = 0.5 ampere. That is,
if *either* of the two batteries in Fig. 4.2a were connected alone across
the resistor, 0.5 ampere would flow. When both are connected up
"end to end," the total tendency for current to flow will be the sum
of the two individual tendencies; that is, 3 volts will be across the resistor, and 1 ampere will flow. It is generally true that the equivalent
voltage of any combination of batteries connected *in series* is simply
the sum of the individual voltages.

To connect two batteries in series means to connect them so that
any current flowing through one must also flow through the other.
Batteries may be connected in series in either of two ways (Fig. 4.3).

In Fig. 4.3a, the connected terminals have opposite polarity, and
the total voltage across the combination will be the sum of the two
voltages. In Fig. 4.3b, the connected terminals have the same polarity.

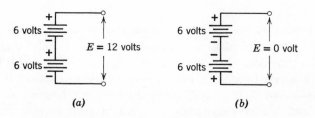

Fig. 4.3 (a) Two 6-volt cells connected in series to give a total of 12 volts.
(b) The same two cells connected in series (bucking) to give a total of 0 volt.

The total voltage is still the sum of the individual voltages in this case, but it is clear that the two batteries are working against each other; the sum is an algebraic one, and the two voltage values are given opposite signs. Thus, if each battery delivers 6 volts, the total voltage will be $+6 + (-6) = 0$ volt. The two voltages when connected this way are said to "buck" each other. The technique of using one voltage to buck, or subtract from another, can be very useful. Examples of such circuits will be discussed later.

Inside the battery that you have been using, there are 15 small individual cells connected to each other in series. The circuit diagram for this battery is shown in Fig. 4.4

The small circles in the figure represent the clips on the top of the battery. The plus sign on the diagram and on your battery is merely a convention to indicate that this terminal has too few electrons as compared with each of the other terminals. That is, if a resistor were connected between the "+" terminal and the terminal marked "−3," electrons would flow from the "−3" terminal to the "+" terminal. This state is described by saying that the "+" terminal is 3 volts positive with respect to the "−3" terminal, *or* that the "−3" terminal is 3 volts negative with respect to the "+" terminal. Note that the "−3" terminal will therefore be 3 volts positive with respect to the "−6" terminal, 6 volts positive with respect to the "−9" terminal, etc. This is an important concept. Voltage is always meas-

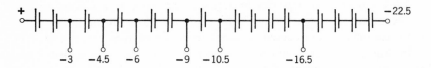

Fig. 4.4 Circuit diagram of the battery on your circuit board. The small circles represent the battery clips.

ured between two points. It is meaningless to say, for example, that the "−3" volt terminal is negative. It is negative only *with respect to* the plus terminal. It is positive with respect to the 6-volt terminal. To light a 6-volt bulb, it is just as satisfactory to connect it between the −10½− and −16½−volt terminals on your battery as between the "+" and −6−volt terminals. In fact, if your battery should run low during your circuit building, just use a different pair of terminals.

The direction of flow of electrons makes no difference to most circuit elements. For instance, a flashlight bulb will light equally brightly no matter which way the current is flowing. Resistors offer the same resistance to current flowing one way as to current flowing the opposite way. For such circuit elements, it therefore makes no difference which terminal of the battery is positive and which is negative. One circuit element already discussed which does discriminate between directions of current flow is a meter. The needle of a voltmeter will move in the opposite direction when the direction of current through it is reversed. For this reason a meter can be used to determine the polarity of a voltage.

One of the test lead connections to the meter is marked plus. When this connection is positive with respect to the other, the meter will read normally. Otherwise, the needle will move below zero on the voltage scale. To determine which of two battery terminals is positive with respect to the other, connect a voltmeter between them. If the pointer moves in the right direction, the terminal connected to the "+" of the meter is positive with respect to the one connected to the other meter lead.

Cells in Parallel

The equivalent voltage of several batteries in *series* is the sum of the individual voltages. Batteries can also be connected in *parallel*, as in

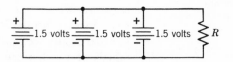

Fig. 4.5   Three 1½-volt batteries in parallel across a resistor. The total voltage across the resistor is 1½ volts.

Fig. 4.5. In this case, the voltage across the resistor is still 1½ volts. Voltages of batteries in parallel do *not* add. In fact, adding batteries of equal voltage in parallel does not affect the circuit in any way at all.[1] Adding several cells in parallel is exactly equivalent to using a bigger cell. As more and more batteries are added to the circuit, all that happens is that each battery will last longer, for the following

[1] This statement is true for the circuit as it is drawn. Adding batteries in parallel will affect the current slightly in any real circuit for reasons to be discussed in the next section.

reason. The voltage across the resistor does not increase. But since an increasing number of batteries share in delivering that same current, each battery has to deliver less current than if there were no other batteries in parallel.

Internal Resistance

Whenever a battery is connected into a circuit so that it causes current to flow around the circuit, current must also be considered to be flowing through the battery itself. In the simplest case of an ordinary series circuit (e.g., a flashlight bulb connected across a battery), it has already been stated that the current is the same in all parts of the circuit, and that includes the battery. It is also true that anything which is conducting current shows some electric resistance. Therefore, whenever a battery is used in a circuit, the internal resistance of the battery itself will affect the circuit. To understand this, consider the battery as composed of two hypothetically separate aspects: the first is its voltage-delivering aspect, the second is its internal resistance. These may be correctly diagrammed as if they were in series with each other, as in Fig. 4.6. In this figure, R_i represents the internal resistance, and the actual terminals of the battery are represented by the small circles.

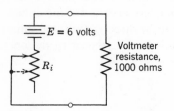

Fig. 4.6   Diagram of a 1000-ohm voltmeter connected across the terminals of a 6-volt battery. The small circles represent the battery terminals, and the variable resistor R_i represents the internal resistance of the battery.

Notice that the internal resistance is represented as a variable one. When a battery is new, its resistance is so very low that it can be neglected for almost all practical purposes. That is why battery resistance has been neglected in all the preceding discussions. However, when a battery runs down, instead of considering that its voltage-generating aspect has been reduced, it is much more useful to consider that its voltage generator is unchanged and that its internal resistance increases (as in the dotted line, Fig. 4.6). The following discussion will illustrate why this is an important consideration.

Suppose that you want to measure the voltage of a battery as it appears between the battery terminals. The voltmeter draws a certain amount of current out of the battery through R_i. Assume that the resistance of the voltmeter is 1000 ohms, as in Fig. 4.6.   If the battery is new, R_i is close to zero and the full 6 volts will appear across the meter.   However, if the battery is old, R_i increases to, say, 1000 ohms. The current through the circuit will then be $E/R = 6/2000 = 0.003$ amperes.   Therefore, the voltage across $R_i = I \times R = 0.003 \times 1000 = 3$ volts.   In other words, as the battery runs down, more of its voltage will be lost internally so that less is available at the terminals. More important, as the current being drawn from the battery increases, the voltage available at its terminals decreases.   This is because the voltage lost internally is $I \times R_i$, so that increasing I will increase the amount of voltage lost.   A misunderstanding of this point frequently leads to great difficulties when batteries are used in circuits.   To illustrate, suppose that a reaction time clock is being started and stopped by a 6-volt battery and that the apparatus suddenly fails to work.   The first thought for the troubleshooter is that the battery has run down.   He disconnects the battery from the clock and connects a voltmeter across the battery terminals, finds that it reads a full 6 volts, and concludes that the battery is not the source of the trouble.   As long as he uses a good meter to measure the voltage of the battery, he is sure to read close to 6 volts even if the battery is almost completely dead.   The resistance of a good voltmeter is very high.   This means that the current being drawn from the battery when it is connected across the voltmeter is much less than when it is actually being used in the circuit.   Thus the voltage available at the battery terminals is much greater when it is being measured than when it is supposed to be turning on and off the clock.

The only reliable way to test whether or not a battery is delivering enough voltage to do what it is supposed to do, is to measure the

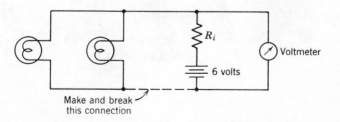

Fig. 4.7   Circuit to demonstrate the effect of the internal resistance of the battery on your circuit board.   The resistor R_i represents the internal resistance of the battery.   When the dotted connection is made and broken, the reading of the voltmeter will change slightly.

voltage across the battery terminals when the battery is actually connected up as it normally is in the circuit. Demonstrate this fact by connecting up the circuit in Fig. 4.7, setting the meter to read at least 6 volts full scale. Leaving the meter connected across the battery, connect and disconnect the pair of flashlight bulbs, and note that the voltage on the meter changes a little. The extent of this change in voltage increases as the battery runs down, and this sort of procedure is actually used to test the freshness of batteries.

Wet cells will be discussed here only briefly. They are much more unwieldy and inconvenient than dry cells, and thus are not used as frequently. They do have one great advantage over dry cells in that they can be recharged once they have run down. For this reason, wet cells are used whenever large amounts of current are needed for long periods of time and normal house current is not suitable.

FIXED RESISTORS

You have already had some experience with both fixed and variable resistors. Figure 4.8 shows a selection of fixed resistors. The physical size of a resistor has little relation to the value of its resistance. For example, the resistor labeled a has a resistance of 5,000,000 ohms, and that labeled b 10 ohms. The physical size of a resistor primarily determines the amount of wattage it can carry without burning up.

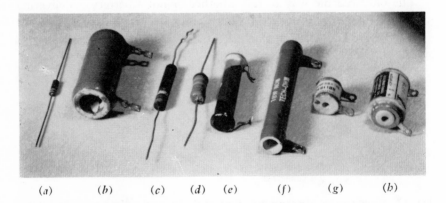

(a) (b) (c) (d) (e) (f) (g) (h)

Fig. 4.8 Various fixed resistors. (a) 5,000,000 ohms, ¼ watt. (b) 10 ohms, 100 watts. (c), (d), (e) show other composition resistors. (f), (g), and (h) are wire-wound resistors. (*Courtesy* Helen E. Howell, Berkeley, Calif.)

The resistor labeled *a* is a ¼-watt resistor. To find its current capacity:

$$\text{watts} = E \times I = I^2 R$$

$$I^2 = \frac{W}{R} = \frac{\frac{1}{4}}{5 \times 10^6} = 5 \times 10^{-8}$$

$$I = 2.24 \times 10^{-4} \text{ ampere}$$

$$= 0.224 \text{ milliampere}$$

This resistor can carry no more than about 0.2 milliampere before it becomes overheated.

To find the maximum voltage that may be impressed across it,

$$\text{watts} = EI$$

$$E = \frac{W}{I}$$

$$E = \frac{\frac{1}{4}}{2.24 \times 10^{-4}}$$

$$E = 1120 \text{ volts}$$

The highest voltage that can be safely placed across this resistor is about 1120 volts. Any voltage higher than that will drive more current through the resistor than it is designed to handle.

The large resistor labeled *b* will dissipate 100 watts without overheating. Since it has a resistance of 10 ohms, it can carry about 3 amperes.

Resistors that look like *c, d, e,* and *a* are cheap and very common in radio circuits. The wires extending from each end are connected inside the resistor to the two ends of a cylinder of special composition, and the cylinder itself is the resistive element. The composition is coated with a plastic jacket to protect it, and there are bands of color on this jacket. The colors of the bands indicate the resistance according to a standard code which is given in Appendix II. These composition resistors can be obtained in a range of resistance from about 1 ohm to about 20,000,000 ohms (20 megohms), and in wattages from about ¹⁄₁₀th watt to about 2 watts.

The other resistors in Fig. 4.8 are all "wire wound." The wires or tabs extending from each end connect to the two ends of a length of special resistance wire. This resistance wire is made of alloys that have considerably greater resistance per unit length than those used for ordinary wire. Usually the wire is wound around some kind of core and is often covered on the outside by a paper or plastic jacket. Wire-wound resistors can be obtained in resistances varying from less than 1 ohm to about 100,000 ohms (or 100 kilohms, 100 K) and in an almost unlimited variety of wattages. They are more expensive than carbon resistors, but the precision and reliability of their resistance values can be considerably greater than for any other kind of resistor. It is for this reason that they are used extensively in meter circuits. There are a few other types of fixed resistors used for very special purposes which are not encountered often enough to be worth discussing here.

VARIABLE RESISTORS

The resistive element in variable resistors is also either of composition or wire. You have already examined one of your variable resistors; it is probably wire wound. Only variable resistors with

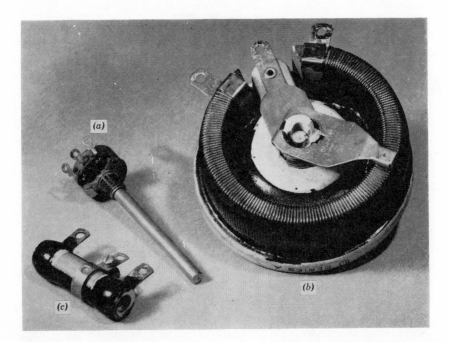

Fig. 4.9   Variable resistors. (*Courtesy* Helen E. Howell, Berkeley, Calif.)

fairly high maximum resistance can be made from resistive composition (greater than about 500 ohms), and variable resistors whose maximum resistance is greater than about 100,000 ohms are almost always of composition.

Three variable resistors are pictured in Fig. 4.9. Type *a* is probably like the one on your circuit board. Type *b* is similar, but it can carry larger amounts of current. Type *c* is more difficult to adjust, and is generally used when the resistance will have to be changed only infrequently.

WIRE

There is a very large variety of wire available at any electrical supply store. Much of it has specialized uses (e.g., television lead-in wire), but there are three types of wire that are of general usefulness in experimental work. "Hook-up" wire is extensively used for hooking up circuits. The most convenient hook-up wire consists of a single strand of copper wire, tinned (coated with another metal which is easy to solder to), and covered with an insulating layer of plastic. Such wire comes in a variety of colors which facilitate tracing the wire after it has been hooked up. It is also available with a cloth insulation, but this type is much less convenient to use because the insulation is more difficult to remove.

Hook-up wire also comes in multiple-stranded form. Instead of the conducting element consisting of one single wire, a number of smaller wires are twisted around each other to form the conductor. These strands are not insulated from each other so they act electrically as a single wire. The collection of strands is then insulated with plastic or cloth. About the only advantage of multiple-stranded over single-stranded hook-up wire is that multiple-stranded wire is more flexible. If two parts move with respect to each other and must be electrically connected, stranded wire is preferable. The only real disadvantage of multiple-stranded hook-up wire is that it is more difficult to use in making connections. Most electrical connections require the hook-up wire to run through a small hole in a "terminal lug." Trying to push 16 strands of fine wire through one small hole can drive you to hysterical aphonia and mutism. Pushing one larger strand through the same hole is easy.

To prevent the individual strands in multistranded wire from separating, they may be twisted together and coated with solder (as will be explained in Chapter 5). The end of the wire thus essentially becomes a single, thick strand which will not fray, but, at the same time, is appreciably stiffer than a true single-strand wire of equivalent current-carrying capacity.   (Some of the procedures for making actual electrical connections will be discussed in Chapter 5.)

Hook-up wire consists of a single conducting path (which itself may be composed of one or several separate wires) and an insulating coating.   Cables which consist of any number of conducting paths, each insulated from the others, are also available.   Probably the most familiar cable is known as "lamp cord."   This is the wire that connects lamps to wall sockets and forms the typical type of extension cord. It contains two conducting paths, each path multiple-stranded and each surrounded by rubber insulation.   Cables with as many as 50 separate conducting paths are readily available commercially.

For most purposes, the choice of particular wire size and type of insulation is made purely on the basis of convenience.   Sometimes, however, the wire must be selected more carefully.   For example, the insulation on typical hook-up wire will not withstand extremely high voltages (e.g., above 1000 volts).   Should your circuit include voltages higher than this, you would choose wire whose insulation is specifically designed to withstand very high voltages.   The voltage rating of wire is one of its normal specifications, so that it is easy to choose the appropriate wire from a catalogue.[1]   ·

Another, more common, need for special wire arises when the circuit must carry a large amount of current.   Suppose that you wished to light three 1000-watt, 115-volt floodlights through an extension cord.

For each lamp:

$$W = E \times I \qquad I = \frac{W}{E} = \frac{1000}{115} \text{ volts} = \text{about 9 amperes}$$

Three lamps, all across the same extension cord (in parallel) would draw 27 amperes.   (Draw the circuit diagram for this situation and verify this solution.)   Ordinary extension cords made of lamp cord are rated at about 5 amperes.   They begin to get too hot when they carry much more.   Therefore, a heavier wire must be used for the floodlights.   Wire size is often specified by a code rather than by actual dimensions, and this code together with the corresponding current capacities is included in Appendix IV.   Actually, there are few occasions that require special wire.   Most apparatus can be built with almost any kind.

[1] A list of some of the electrical suppliers who furnish catalogues is included in Appendix III.

FUSES

When a piece of equipment is damaged by electricity, the damage is almost always caused by excessive heat, and the excessive heat is almost always produced by excessive current flow. A fuse is a device which protects equipment or wiring by burning itself out before the equipment does. This is a worthwhile protection so long as the fuse is cheaper than the equipment it protects—and fuses are very cheap. They consist of a wire, usually made of low-melting-point metal, mounted in some kind of holder. Figure 4.10 shows some different types of fuses. All have the same basic construction and are used in the same way. Suppose that you were building an apparatus which contained an expensive amperemeter and you wanted to make sure that any accidental misconnections or misuse would not destroy the meter. Assume that the meter reads 1 ampere full scale. Circuit elements other than fuses can usually tolerate 100% overloading. Thus, for short periods, the meter can probably carry 2 amperes, but not much more. A fuse whose rating is, say, 1.5 amperes is put *in series* with the meter, as shown in Fig. 4.11. In this circuit all the current that will flow through the meter must also flow through the fuse. The 1.5-ampere rating on the fuse means that it will melt if more than 1.5 amperes are run through it. Now suppose that in some remote part of the apparatus, something goes wrong which greatly increases the voltage across the meter and fuse. A large current would begin

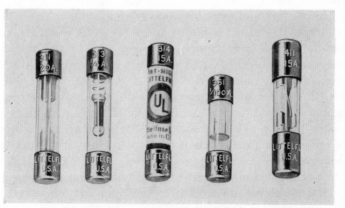

Fig. 4.10 Various fuses. (*Courtesy* Littelfuse, Inc.)

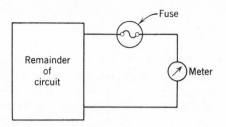

Fig. 4.11   Diagram showing how a fuse must be connected to protect a meter.

to flow. However, before this large current can damage the meter, the fuse will melt and, consequently, the meter will be disconnected from the circuit. Notice that a fuse must be placed *in series* with the element that it is protecting.

Fuses also protect the wiring that supplies power to the wall socket. If the equipment plugged into a socket were to draw enough current to heat the wires leading to the socket, the building might catch on fire. Fuses placed in series with the wiring melt at currents lower than those which would cause the wire to overheat.

Fuses are readily available with ratings from as low as $\frac{1}{500}$ ampere up to hundreds of amperes.

WALL SOCKETS

Some laboratories are supplied with a source of 115 volts d-c (direct current), accessible through wall sockets similar to the sockets in homes. For most purposes, the power supplied to these laboratory sockets is just the same as power from 115 volts worth of batteries. One of the socket connections is positive with respect to the other, and the supply is usually fused so that it can deliver up to 20 or 30 amperes before the fuse blows.

Most laboratories do not have such a d-c supply, but in the United States almost all are supplied with 115 volts a-c (alternating current), also accessible through wall sockets. Alternating current is current that keeps changing its direction of flow, in contrast to direct current which always flows in the same direction. If you were to connect a very fast-acting voltmeter between the two terminals of an a-c wall socket, the needle would wobble to the right and left of zero as the voltage and current reversed direction. In almost every region of the United States, a-c reverses with a very constant and precise fre-

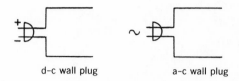

d-c wall plug   a-c wall plug

Fig. 4.12   Circuit diagram symbols for d-c and a-c wall plugs.

quency of 60 cycles per second, i.e., current reverses itself 120 times a second.   This is much too fast for an ordinary voltmeter to follow, so that if you actually connected a voltmeter across the socket, the needle would not wobble.

If the voltmeter were set to read "volts d-c," it would read the average value of the a-c voltage,[1] which is zero.   When the meter is changed to read "volts a-c," a special circuit in the meter, of a type to be discussed later, converts the a-c into d-c, and the meter reads the value of this d-c.   Figure 4.12 shows the circuit diagram symbols used to represent plugs that go into wall sockets for a-c and d-c.

Many pieces of apparatus will work equally well on a-c or d-c.   An incandescent light bulb for example will light just as brightly (it will get just as hot) whether the current heating it is changing direction or not.   But there are some circuit elements that are designed to operate on a-c only, and that can be badly damaged when plugged into d-c by mistake.   Devices to be operated on a-c only are usually so labeled.

[1] Since a-c is the abbreviation for alternating current, the term a-c voltage is not a very good one. It should be a-v. But a-c in ordinary usage has come to mean just alternating.   Thus, both a-c volts and a-c current are common phrases.

Chapter 5

Soldering

There are many superstitions about the best way to solder electric connections. The author's particular set is presented here. If the reader can find someone who is experienced with soldering techniques and willing to spend half an hour or so instructing, he is probably better off than trying to learn the actual manual skill from this chapter. This chapter is included in case such a person is not available.

In the few circuits that you have already connected up, clip leads were used. Clip leads are convenient when only a few temporary connections must be made and when those connections are changed frequently. But when more than three or four clip leads are used in the same circuit, they begin to bump into each other, fall off, and become a general nuisance.

It is usually more convenient, and much less frustrating in the long run, to make circuit connections by soldering. At first this will seem inefficient when clip leads are so quick and easy, but as soon as you gain some proficiency at soldering, you will find that procedure well worth the trouble for almost all circuits.[1] Therefore, put away your clip leads, and use only soldered connections for the remaining circuits in this book.

There are four basic items used in soldering: the iron, rosin core solder (*not acid core*), soldering paste, and a file. Collect those items now and plug in the soldering iron. Any small- or medium-sized

[1] In special cases, other forms of connections are more suitable than either clip leads or soldered joints. For example, snap connections are becoming very popular now in Skinner box control panels.

soldering iron will do when you are learning; but don't try to use a soldering *gun* until you are proficient with an iron.

Solder will not stick to some metals (e.g., aluminum). Many others, copper, for instance, must be very clean before solder will adhere to them. For a soldering iron to work effectively, its tip must be well coated with solder, and most tips are made of copper. Therefore, the first step in preparing to solder is to clean the tip of the iron thoroughly and then coat it with solder. If the iron is brand new, and the tip looks very clean, you will need only to let the iron heat up, dip the tip in soldering paste, and then apply solder to the tip. Wait until the iron is very hot, then push the whole tip right down into the soldering paste. This will produce a cloud of steam and a lot of hissing, but will not do any damage. The paste acts as a cleaner, dissolving away the thin layer of oxides and dirt that coats the copper. Immediately after this brief dipping, touch the end of the solder to the tip of the iron and melt enough solder so that the tip is completely tinned, i.e., covered with a layer of solder. You do not need to cover the entire copper area but only the surfaces that you will use later for the actual soldering. Now give the iron a shake to slip off the excess solder and it is ready for use.

If the iron is not brand new, the chances are that the tip will be somewhat corroded. In this case, first file or steel-wool the tip until as much of the usable surface is clean and unpitted as possible. Then proceed as described above to tin the iron.[1]

Another soldering device that is quite common is the soldering gun, so called because it has a pistol grip and looks like a gun. It is turned on by a trigger and heats very rapidly. However, as soon as the trigger is released, it cools rapidly. Soldering guns are excellent to use in situations where only a single connection must be soldered occasionally, but for work involving more continuous soldering, an iron is preferable.

Soldering irons consist of a handle, a tip, and an electrical heating element that heats up the tip. They may be plugged into a-c or d-c. Soldering guns have a built-in transformer and must, for reasons to be discussed later, be plugged into a-c only.

To practice soldering on a relatively easy connection, solder two pieces of hook-up wire to the two lugs of a light bulb socket, using the following procedure.

[1] A few irons have special tips that are not supposed to corrode, and that should not be filed down. If you buy a new iron of this kind, it will say so on the box. If you are using a borrowed iron, be sure to check on this. If you cannot find out, the chances are very good that it is an ordinary copper tip.

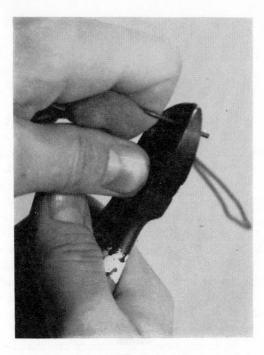

Fig. 5.1   Use of the wire cutter to strip insulation.

First, cut a piece of hook-up wire longer than you will need. Then strip a short piece of insulation from each end of the wire. You will probably find this very difficult. It is fairly simple to cut off a piece of insulation with a knife, but, in the long run, this is an inefficient procedure. There are devices specifically designed to strip insulation, but they are often unavailable. It is best to learn now how to strip insulation with a pair of wire cutters. You must develop this technique on your own, and it will probably take a lot of practice. The technique in general is to clamp the cutters around the wire (Fig. 5.1) just tightly enough to grip the insulation, but not so tight as to dig into the wire itself. This is easier if the flatter side of the cutters is facing the near end of the wire, as shown in Fig. 5.1. The wire should *not* make a bend at the cutter. Then pull the cutters and the wire in opposite directions. If you have exactly the right pressure on the cutters, the insulation will break and a short piece of it will slip off the end of the wire, leaving the wire intact and undented. If the wire is dented by the cutters, it is likely to break when bent near the dent.   It usually takes novices at least a half hour's practice to be able to strip wire properly and reliably.

Having stripped both ends of a length of hook-up wire, you are ready to make the first connection.   Put one bare end of the wire through the hole in one of the terminals, and bend the wire so that it does not fall out (Fig. 5.2a).

The basic principle in soldering is to get the *parts to be soldered* hot (not just the solder).   Press the *tinned* tip of the soldering iron against the terminal and wire, and try to get as large an area of contact with the iron as possible.   This procedure heats up the parts to be soldered.   As you are holding the iron against the terminal, touch the end of the solder to the *terminal*, not to the iron.   When the solder melts easily and flows onto the terminal, the joint is as hot as it should be.   Now, while still holding the iron against the joint, touch the solder to the terminal until just enough melts off to run smoothly around the joint.   The solder should run in and fill gaps between the wire and the terminal, coating both.   If it does not, the joint is not hot enough or the terminals are dirty.   *After* the solder has run, the iron may be removed from the joint, and the solder will harden

(a)   (b)

Fig. 5.2   (a) Lamp socket with hook-up wire ready to be soldered.   (b) After having been soldered.   (*Courtesy* Helen E. Howell, Berkeley, Calif.)

Fig. 5.3   At the left, a solder joint which was not sufficiently hot. The solder did not flow smoothly; in the middle, a joint with too much solder; at the right, a well-soldered connection. (*Courtesy* Helen E. Howell, Berkeley, Calif.)

quickly. The joint should now look neat, and there should be just enough solder on it so that the connection is clearly a good one. There is no need to use so much solder that a drop of it hangs below the terminal. Figure 5.3 illustrates good and bad solder joints.

The procedure just described is different from what most novice solderers would expect, and the steps are worth enumerating. Given a tinned, clean iron and clean joint:

1. Heat the joint with the iron until the *joint*, not the iron, melts solder.

2. Melt solder on to the joint by touching it to the joint, not to the iron.

3. Melt on just enough solder to cover the joint.

4. After you have stopped adding solder, keep the iron on the joint until the solder flows smoothly.

5. *Then* remove the iron.

The most common errors in soldering are (1) a poor connection because the parts were not clean enough for the solder to adhere well; (2) a poor connection because the parts were not hot enough to allow the solder to flow smoothly; and (3) too much solder (the bulb of solder thus formed sometimes makes a connection between the soldered joint and some other part of the circuit where such a connection is not desired).

There are only a few types of connections in which the procedure outlined may not be followed exactly. If one of the parts to be soldered will not withstand high temperatures (e.g., transistors, to be discussed later), the procedure must be modified, either by using joints that require no solder or by using a "heat sink." The latter procedure is quite simple. Just clamp a pair of pliers to the metal between the joint and the delicate part, and keep it there while soldering (Fig. 5.4). The pliers tend to dissipate the heat, keeping the temperature of the sensitive element down.

If either of the parts to be joined has a copper surface or is dirty, it may be necessary to use soldering paste. In this case, if paste is not

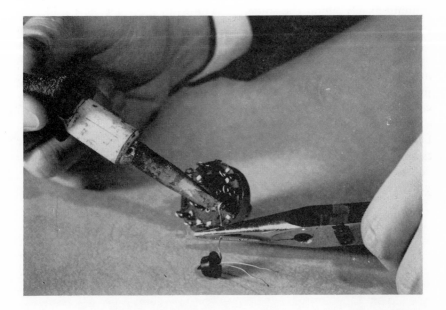

Fig. 5.4 Use of the long-nosed pliers as a heat sink to protect the soldered part (a transistor in this photograph) from overheating. (*Courtesy* Helen E. Howell, Berkeley, Calif.)

used, the solder may run but will not "wet" or adhere well to the surfaces of the joint. If a *little* paste is added to the joint (this may be done easily by dipping the end of the solder into the paste before applying the solder to the joint), the solder should adhere more easily. Do not use any more paste than is necessary for adhesion, and be sure that you heat the joint thoroughly and keep it heated for a short time *after* the solder is taken away. This is necessary for the following reason. Soldering paste, when melted, flows over the metal more quickly than the solder and coats the surfaces before the solder gets there. When paste is melted and then allowed to cool, it forms a hard layer similar to varnish, and the layer has a high electric resistance. If the solder joint cools too soon after the application of the paste and solder, this layer may remain between the joint and the solder. The joint may look perfect and yet have poor electrical characteristics (it is called a "cold-solder joint"). As long as the joint is kept hot for a moment after the solder and paste have been withdrawn, the paste boils to the surface of the solder and will not form an insulating layer.

The solder you are using is rosin cored. This means that the solder is in the form of a tube filled with a rosin compound (or, in so-called multicored solders, the rosin is distributed among several small holes running axially along the solder). The rosin itself acts as a soldering paste, and insufficient heat may result in a cold-solder joint even when additional paste in not used.

Solder with an acid core can also be purchased. The acid is a much more effective cleaner but will gradually corrode the surfaces of the joint. Acid-core solder should never be used for making electric connections.

Much practice is usually required before soldering becomes easy and fast, and even more is needed to perfect insulation stripping. Both are essential, however, for the construction of electric circuits. In the course of wiring the circuits discussed in the remainder of this book, you should get a lot of practice in both skills.

Chapter 6

Switching and switches

MANUAL SWITCHES

Nearly everyone has had some experience with the device called a knife switch shown in Fig. 6.1. The function of this switch is evident from its appearance. It is used to make and break electric connections. Such a switch might be used in the simple circuit of Fig. 6.2 to turn on or off the light bulb.

Fig. 6.1 An "on-off" knife switch. (*Courtesy* Helen E. Howell, Berkeley, Calif.)

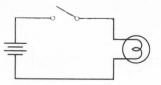

Fig. 6.2 Circuit using the switch in Fig. 6.1 to turn on and off a light bulb.

Fig. 6.3 Two "on-off" toggle switches. The two terminals extending from the body of each of the switches correspond to the two terminals of the knife switch shown in Fig. 6.1. The bodies of the switches and the handles are electrically insulated from the terminals. They are called single-pole, single-throw (or SPST) switches. (*Courtesy* Helen E. Howell, Berkeley, Calif.)

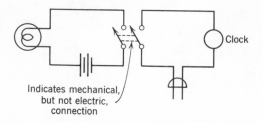

Indicates mechanical,
but not electric,
connection

Clock

Fig. 6.4 Circuit to turn on and off two separate subcircuits simultaneously.

Another common switch that performs the same function is the toggle switch shown in Fig. 6.3.   In this type there are two terminals extending from the bottom, and the switch either connects them together or disconnects them, depending upon which way the handle is thrown.   Neither the body of the switch nor the handle is electrically connected to either of the two terminals.   Any switch that makes or breaks one pair of contacts is called a single-pole, single-throw (or SPST) switch.

Frequently more than one circuit must be turned on or off at the same time.   For example, consider the circuit in Fig. 6.4.   This circuit is intended to measure the total time the light bulb is on.   Therefore, the clock and the bulb should be connected and disconnected simultaneously.   A switch to do this is shown in Fig. 6.5.   It consists es-

Fig. 6.5 A knife switch to perform the switching operation depicted in Fig. 6.4. The bar between the two "knives," the handle mounted on it, and the body of the switch are electric insulators. Thus the two sides are mechanically but not electrically connected to each other. (*Courtesy* Helen E. Howell, Berkeley, Calif.)

Fig. 6.6 A toggle switch that performs the same function as the knife switch in Fig. 6.5 It is a double-pole, single-throw (or DPST) switch. (*Courtesy Helen E. Howell, Berkeley, Calif.*)

sentially of two knife switches connected together *mechanically*, but *not* electrically. The same handle operates both switches. Figure 6.6 shows a toggle switch of the same type. Note that there are four terminals extending from the bottom of this toggle switch. The terminals on toggle switches are arranged in the same way as for the

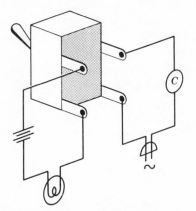

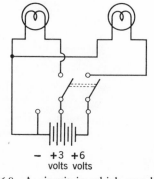

− +3 +6
volts volts

Fig. 6.7 Connections for the circuit in Fig. 6.4, when the switching operation is performed by a DPST toggle switch.

Fig. 6.8 A circuit in which two bulbs turn on and off simultaneously, one brighter than the other. The switch is DPST.

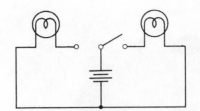

Fig. 6.9   A circuit in which *either* one bulb *or* another is lit.

corresponding knife switch.   Thus, on this switch, the actual terminals would be connected as shown in Fig. 6.7.   Any switch that makes
or breaks two pairs of contacts is called a *double-pole*, single-throw
(or DPST) switch.

PROBLEM.   Design a circuit containing two lights, one brighter than
the other, which turn on and off simultaneously, by using only your
battery, a switch, and two flashlight bulbs and sockets.

Solution.   The solution is diagrammed in Fig. 6.8.

The simple "on-off" switch first mentioned in this chapter may be
said to perform a "yes-no" operation.   The bulb is either lit or not lit.
The second—double—switch performs an "and" operation as well;
that is, the switch causes bulb A and B to light or not to light.

Another common form of switching requirement is the "or" operation, in which either one circuit *or* another is activated.   A good example of the "or" circuit is the one used for probability-matching
experiments, in which one or the other of two lights will be turned
on, and the subject is required to guess which it will be.   Figure 6.9
shows a circuit constructed to perform this "or" operation, and Fig.
6.10 shows the corresponding knife switch and toggle switch.[1]   Any
switch that connects a single terminal with either one or the other of
two terminals is called a single-pole, double-throw (or SPDT) switch.

The first switch mentioned in this chapter was designated as a single-

---

[1] A probability-matching experiment requires that part of the time both lights
be off.   If a knife switch were used, the arm could be put in a vertical position
when neither is to be on.   Most toggle switches, however, do not have such a
"center-off" position.   When the lever is thrown, they flip from one set of connections directly to the other.   If such a toggle switch were used in the circuit
of Fig. 6.9, there would be no way to turn off *both* lights.   Therefore, should a
toggle switch be used in the apparatus, a second switch, A in Fig. 6.11, must be
added to the circuit.   The action of this circuit may be described by saying that
"if A is closed, then either bulb 1 or bulb 2 is on."

Fig. 6.10 A knife switch and toggle switch to perform the "either-or" operation in Fig. 6.9. They are single-pole, double-throw (or SPDT) switches. (*Courtesy* Helen E. Howell, Berkeley, Calif.)

pole, single-throw (or SPST) switch. It is single-pole because it operates on only one circuit, and it is called single-throw because that circuit may be either on or off. (This is clearer when contrasted with other types of switches.) The second type of switch described was the double-pole, single-throw (or DPST) switch, so called because

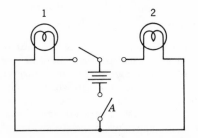

Fig. 6.11 A circuit in which either bulb 1 or bulb 2 or neither 1 nor 2 is lit.

two electrically independent circuits are either on or off. The "or" switch is called single-pole, double-throw (SPDT). If instead of selecting one or the other of two bulbs, one of four were to be chosen, an SP4T switch would be required.   A SP17T switch and circuit diagram for lighting any one of four bulbs are shown in Fig. 6.12.   (Note that this switch has a mechanical structure different from the switches discussed thus far. The common contact rotates across the others, and the switch is called a rotary switch.)

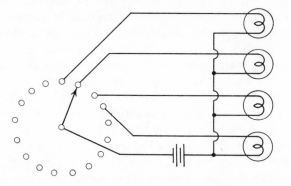

Fig. 6.12 A single-pole, seventeen-throw (or SP17T) switch, and a diagram of a circuit using such a switch to select any one of four bulbs. (*Courtesy* Helen E. Howell, Berkeley, Calif.)

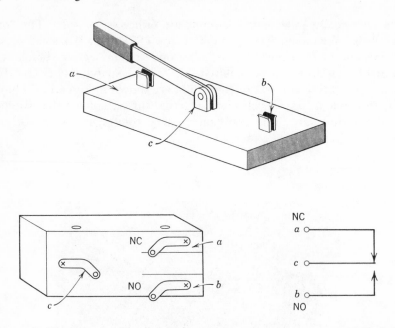

Fig. 6.13 The relationship between operating elements on a SPDT knife switch, a SPDT microswitch, and a circuit symbol for a SPDT microswitch. The terminals marked *c* are called the "common" terminals.

The microswitches on your board are SPDT switches. Figure 6.13 shows the relationship between a SPDT knife switch and the terminals on your microswitch, together with a circuit diagram symbol for a SPDT microswitch. Note that there are two important differences between the knife and the microswitch. First, the knife switch has no spring in it, so it stays where it is put, whereas the microswitch snaps back to its resting position as soon as pressure is released. The microswitch is therefore said to give "momentary" contact. Second, whereas the knife switch may be left in a middle position where neither circuit is closed, the microswitch is always in either one position or the other (except for an extremely short transit time). Because of these two factors, one of the terminals on the switch is labeled "normally closed" (or NC) and another "normally open" (or NO). This means that the unlabeled, or "common," terminal is *normally* connected to the NC terminal, but when the handle is pressed, the common terminal shifts over and connects with the NO terminal. When the pressure is released, it shifts back to the NC terminal.

The toggle switch on your board is a double-pole, double-throw (or DPDT) switch. Figure 6.14*a* shows such a toggle switch and its corresponding knife switch. This versatile contact configuration may be used as a SPST, SPDT, DPST or DPDT switch simply by using the appropriate terminals. Each of these switches is diagrammed again in Fig. 6.14*b*. The DPDT switch might be used as such when either light *A* or light *B* must be on and the "on" time for each must be recorded. The circuit in Fig. 6.15 would meet this need.

In the preceding discussion and figures, knife switches are used to illustrate the various classes of switching action because their functions are clear from their structure. However, knife switches are rarely used when actual circuits are constructed. They are bigger, less positive in action, and more exposed than toggle switches. Almost the only time they are required in behavioral instrumentation is when large amounts of current are to be turned on and off (large knife switches can carry larger currents than most toggle switches).

SPST

SPDT

DPST

DPDT

(b)

(a)

Fig. 6.14 (*a*) A double-pole, double-throw (DPDT) knife switch and toggle switch. (*b*) Diagrams of some of the switches discussed. (*Courtesy* Helen E. Howell, Berkeley, Calif.)

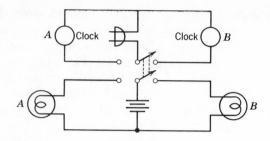

Fig. 6.15 A circuit to perform the following operation. Either (light A and clock A) or (light B and clock B).

Single switches of the types discussed above may be used when *either* one *or* another *element* is to operate (e.g., SPDT), or when one *element and* another operate (e.g., DPST), or combinations of "either-or" and "and" circuits. A different class of switching operations requires the use of combinations of separate switches. For example, suppose that a bulb is to be lighted when either one or another of two switches is closed. This simple circuit is shown in Fig. 6.16, where two SPST switches are connected in parallel. Whenever a *single circuit element* or *group of elements* is to operate when *either* one *or* another of two *switches* is thrown, the two switches may be connected in parallel. This frequently occurs in apparatus used in situations where the subject normally controls the events but the experimenter wants to be able to control them as well. For example, an animal in a Skinner box may get reinforced for pressing a bar, but the experimenter would like to deliver a reinforcement when he chooses as well. In almost all Skinner boxes, the bar is mechanically connected in such a way that pressure on it operates a microswitch. Therefore, in order to permit the experimenter to control the same events that the rat controls, a switch similar to the one which is

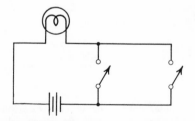

Fig. 6.16 A circuit in which either of two switches will operate the bulb.

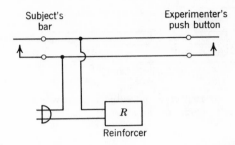

Fig. 6.17   A circuit to permit either the subject or the experimenter to deliver a reinforcement.

closed by a bar press is connected in parallel with the bar switch and mounted on the experimenter's control panel, as shown in Fig. 6.17.

Suppose, instead, that the bar press opens a normally closed switch, as in Fig. 6.18a, and that the experimenter wishes to be able to perform the same operation manually.   In this case, the experimenter may use a second, normally closed, switch connected in *series* with the animal's switch, as shown in Fig. 6.18b.   Whenever each and any one of two or more switches is to perform the same operation, the switches are all connected in parallel if they are normally open, and all connected in series if they are normally closed.

Now consider the case where an element or set of elements is only to operate if *all* of two or more switches are closed at the same time. For example, in the Skinner box it is usually necessary for the experimenter to be able to determine when a bar press will be reinforced. The circuit in Fig. 6.19 is such that the animal will only be reinforced when both the experimenter's switch and the bar switch are closed. In this case, the two switches are normally open and connected in

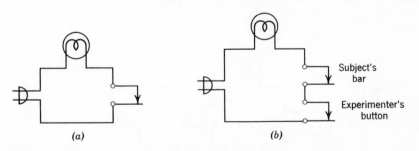

Fig. 6.18   (a) A circuit to turn off a lamp when the bar is pressed.   (b) The circuit modified so that either the subject or the experimenter may turn off the lamp.

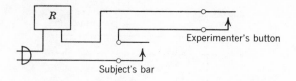

Fig. 6.19 A circuit to reinforce the subject only when both the subject's bar and the experimenter's switch are closed.

series. If, instead, the switches are normally closed and a bulb is to go off only when all are open at the same time, the switches must be in parallel, as shown in Fig. 6.20.

Design and build the following circuits, soldering all connections. (Of course, you do not need to solder the connections to the clips on the battery.)   When performing these exercises, *always draw a complete circuit diagram on paper before you make any electric connections*. Even if this seems unnecessary to you, it constitutes practice that will be indispensable in designing and building more complicated circuits.

PROBLEM.   Either bulb (6 volts) or motor (3 volts) on.   (To run the motor, connect 3 volts between the two leads or terminals mounted on the motor. Most toy motors are supplied with leads. If these leads are bent frequently, they will break off at the motor end. To avoid this, connect each lead to a separate terminal on one of the mounted terminal strips, as shown in Fig. 6.21. Thereafter, any connection to the motor may be made by soldering wires to the terminal strip.)

Solution. Virtually every problem in electric circuit design has a number of correct solutions. Two are presented in Fig. 6.22.

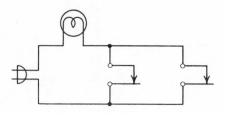

Fig. 6.20 A circuit to turn off the lamp only when both the subject's bar and the experimenter's switch are opened.

Fig. 6.21 Terminal strip connections to the motor. (*Courtesy* Helen E. Howell, Berkeley, Calif.)

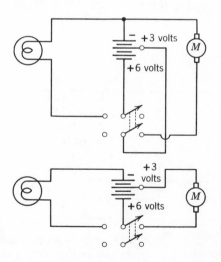

Fig. 6.22 Two correct solutions to the problem of either bulb or motor on.

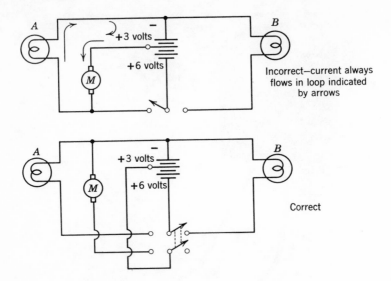

Fig. 6.23 A correct and an incorrect solution to the problem of either light *A* and the motor on, or light *B* on.

PROBLEM.   Either light *A* and the motor on, or light *B* on.

Solution.   See Fig. 6.23.

PROBLEM.   Either bulb *A* or bulb *B* on.   If *A* is lit, the motor may be turned on by closing the microswitch; if *B* is lit, the motor cannot be turned on.

Solution.   See Fig. 6.24.

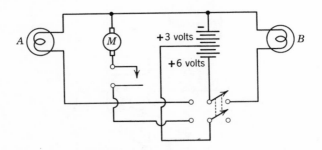

Fig. 6.24 A solution to the problem of either bulb *A* or bulb *B* on. Note that this circuit is identical to the correct one in Fig. 6.23, except for the addition of a microswitch in series with the motor.

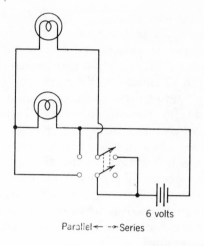

6 volts

Parallel← —→Series

Fig. 6.25 A solution to the problem of two bulbs in either series or parallel.

PROBLEM.   Two bulbs in either series or parallel (across 6 volts).

Solution.   See Fig. 6.25.

PROBLEM.   Build a circuit to locate the position of the slider on your 50-ohm variable resistor such that the resistance is divided in half.

Solution.   See Fig. 6.26.   When the slider divides the resistance in half, the bulb will not change brightness when the switch is thrown. The principle illustrated by this circuit is a very basic one, and extensive applications of it will be discussed in Chapter 17.

The descriptions and designations given above apply to all kinds of switches.   That is, a 3PDT switch may be a knife switch, a toggle switch, etc.   These designations merely state what might be called

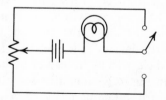

Fig. 6.26 A solution to the problem of finding the mid-point of a variable resistor.

the logical operations of the switch. The differences between types of switches within any one *operational category* (e.g., DPDT) are related to the amounts of current and voltage that they may safely handle, their size, etc. There are so many switch shapes that it is not worthwhile to begin to enumerate them. If you cannot actually see the insides of a switch to ascertain what sorts of connections it makes, it is usually possible to guess quite accurately from looking at the terminals of the switch. For example, if there are six terminals extending from a strange switch, it is a very good bet that it is a DPDT switch. To be sure, it is always possible to check just which terminals are connected together by putting an ohmmeter between the various pairs of terminals and operating the handle. If there is an infinite resistance between two terminals when the switch is in one position, and a very low resistance when the switch is changed, the change connected the two terminals.

SOLENOIDS

It has already been pointed out, in the discussion of meters, that current flowing through a coil of wire generates a magnetic field around the coil. A useful form of such an electromagnet is called a solenoid. This is a coil of wire wrapped around a metal core which has a hole in it. A rod of iron slides in and out of the hole. If the rod is initially just part way in the hole and current is passed through the coil, the rod will be pulled into the core. Thus, if the handle of a camera shutter were attached to the rod for example, the shutter could be operated by remote control.

RELAYS

A solenoid permits the performance of a mechanical operation by remote control. If the iron rod of a solenoid were mechanically connected to the handle of a toggle switch, the switch could then be operated by remote control. This is the principle of operation of a class of extraordinarily useful devices called relays. In general, a relay is a switch that is operated electrically instead of by hand.

The relay shown in Fig. 6.27 should be somewhat similar to one of the relays on your board. The part labeled "coil" consists of a large number of turns of wire wrapped around an iron core. There are two, and only two, wires or terminals coming from this coil. They

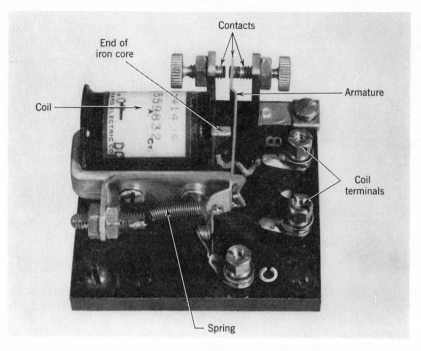

Fig. 6.27 A sensitive, SPDT relay, similar to the one on your circuit board. (*Courtesy* Helen E. Howell, Berkeley, Calif.)

are connected one to each end of the wire forming the coil. When a current is passed through the coil (by connecting a voltage between the two terminals), the iron core becomes an electromagnet just as the coil in a meter movement forms a magnet (Chapter 1). The magnetic field produced pulls on the armature, or clapper, and the armature acts like the handle of a switch, changing the connections between the contacts. The standard relay behaves more like a microswitch, or "momentary" switch, than like a standard toggle switch, in that the contacts normally stay in one position, and are in the other position only while the armature is actually being held by the magnetic field. As soon as current stops flowing through the coil, the spring returns the armature and the contacts to their resting or "normal" position. The relay shown in this figure is a single-pole, double-throw relay. In other words, it performs the same operations as a SPDT switch. Circuit symbols for this relay and the corresponding switches are shown in Fig. 6.28. Note the similarity between the three representations.

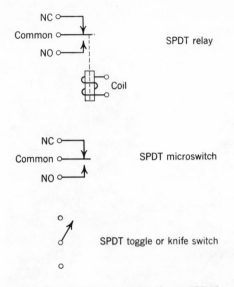

Fig. 6.28   A comparison of the circuit symbols for a SPDT relay, SPDT micro-switch, and SPDT toggle or knife switch. The dashed line on the relay symbol represents the fact that current through the coil magnetically pulls the common contact toward the coil.

Almost all relays consist of a magnet coil and a set of contacts, some of which are moved by the magnetic field. These two parts are *not* electrically connected together when the relay comes from the factory. The only connections between the contacts and the coil are mechanical and magnetic ones. For some particular circuit requirements it is necessary to make an electric connection between the coil and some of the contacts, but such a connection must be made by you. It is not there to start with. This statement is emphasized because it is an extremely common error for people learning circuit design to assume that such a connection is built into the relay.

Relays may be purchased with coils suitable for all sorts of currents and voltages, and with contact arrangements of an almost infinite variety. Circuits consisting of virtually nothing but relays can be made to do an enormous number of things. For example, many of the early, large digital computers used relay circuits exclusively to perform their mathematical operations. The vacuum tubes, transistors, ferrite cores, etc., which are now being used in computers function like very fast and small relays. The rest of this chapter will consider some of the ways in which relays are used.

Relays are sometimes employed to permit a very weak signal to control a much stronger signal. For example, suppose that a light is to be turned on in a room whenever it gets dark outside. Photocells will be discussed in more detail in Chapter 16, but for this purpose it is sufficient to state that certain types of cells will generate a voltage which is proportional to the light intensity incident on them; that is, they act like variable-voltage batteries. However, the power output of photocells is relatively small. A photocell would have to be enormous and expensive in order to deliver enough power to light a light bulb; but many photocells will deliver enough power to operate a sensitive relay. If the photocell is connected across the coil of a sensitive relay, as in Fig. 6.29a, the photocell will drive current through the relay. When the incident light exceeds some critical level, sufficient current will be driven through the relay to pull in its armature. The contacts on the relay, in turn, may handle enough power to light the bulb. When the circuit is connected as shown in Fig. 6.29b, a strong light on the photocell will make the lamp turn on. In this manner, the small power of the photocell controls the relatively large power of the lamp.

If the photocell is placed outside the room, and the bulb inside, then, according to the circuit in Fig. 6.29b, the bulb will turn on whenever it is light outside. But the original problem was to turn on the bulb when it got *dark* outside. Therefore, the circuit should be changed to the one shown in Fig. 6.29c. In the first case (Fig. 6.29b), the bulb was connected across a normally open pair of contacts on the relay. Now it is connected across a normally closed pair, so that the bulb goes on when the relay goes off, and vice versa.

In this circuit diagram, a DPDT relay is shown, although only one set of contacts is used. Actually, all that is needed for this circuit is a normally closed SPST relay. The DPDT relay was deliberately shown to point out what is perhaps obvious—that for any given circuit, the particular contact configuration required specifies the *minimum* contact requirement for the relay; any relay with *at least* this number of contacts will be satisfactory. In fact, it is usually a good idea to have extra contacts on a relay because, should it become necessary to add elements to a circuit which were not originally anticipated, these elements may often be connected through the extra contacts.

A second common use of relays is to convert a single-pole switch into a multiple-pole switch. Consider a typical rat T-maze apparatus. Suppose that, as soon as the rat leaves the start box, a clock is to start and a light is to go on. An easy and reliable way to get a signal when a rat enters or leaves a section of a maze

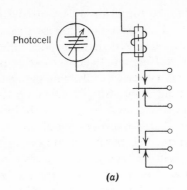

(a)

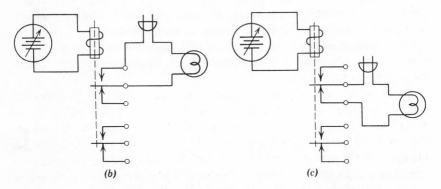

(b)   (c)

Fig. 6.29 (a) A photocell connected so that an increase in incident light will close the relay. (b) A circuit in which an increase in incident light turns on a lamp. (c) A circuit in which a decrease in light turns on the lamp.

is illustrated in Fig. 6.30. The floor is hinged, and one end rests on the arm of a microswitch. The sensitivity of the microswitch and the lever arrangement are such that the weight of the rat on the floor will close the microswitch. In the T-maze, this kind of arrangement can be built into the start-box floor. Then, as soon as the rat leaves the start box, the *normally closed* contacts *close*. If the microswitch were a DPDT switch, then two such circuits would be closed as soon as the rat left the start box; one circuit might be used to start the clock and the other to turn on the light. However, microswitches more complex than SPDT are expensive and generally hard to get. It is easier and cheaper to use the normally closed contacts of an ordinary SPDT microswitch to turn on and off a double-pole relay, and then use the two pairs of contacts on the relay to operate the clock and the light.

PROBLEM.   Draw a circuit diagram for a circuit in which the release in pressure on a SPDT microswitch causes a lightbulb to light and a clock to start.   Then build the circuit, substituting two flashlight bulbs for the bulb and the clock.

Solution.   There are many solutions to this problem.   The simplest, shown in Fig. 6.31, is to connect the bulb and clock in series across the microswitch.   This solution is fine theoretically, but it is not very practical.   First of all, most clocks require 115 volts a-c to run them, as do most light bulbs.   In order to run the two in series, 220 volts a-c are needed, a voltage not usually available.   Second, most clocks require only a very small current, whereas most light bulbs require a relatively large one.   Since the current through any two elements in series with each other must be the same in each element, either the light bulb would be very dim or the clock would burn.

A second easy solution to the problem is shown in Fig. 6.32, where the bulb and the clock are in parallel.   This is a practical solution

Fig. 6.30   A method for detecting the presence or absence of a rat in a particular region of an alley.   The rat's weight depresses the microswitch lever.

only if the clock and the bulb happen to have the same rated voltage (e.g., 115 volts a-c). The series and parallel solutions are thus applicable only in special cases. To illustrate the problem in its general form, assume that the clock runs on 115 volts and the bulb on 6 volts. Under these conditions, neither the series nor the parallel solution will work, and a different type of solution, requiring a relay, is suggested.

Figure 6.33 is a diagram of a circuit that will work. Notice that this diagram contains three more or less separate subcircuits. Actually, there are no *electric* connections between any of these three subcircuits, but there are mechanical and magnetic connections. Look at them one at a time. Subcircuit *A* is a circuit in which the microswitch, the relay, and a source of power are in series. Releasing the pressure on the microswitch causes its normally closed contacts to close, allowing current to flow through the coil of the relay, pulling in the relay armature. Subcircuit *B* contains a bulb, a power source, and a pair of normally open contacts, all in series. When the contacts close, the bulb will light. The contacts are mechanically connected to the relay so that, when the relay armature pulls in, they close. When the microswitch pressure is released, current flows through the relay coil, the armature is pulled in, the contacts close, and the light goes on.

Subcircuit *C* allows the clock to start at the same time as the bulb lights, by using a second pair of normally open contacts on the same relay.

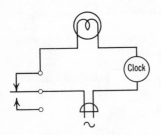

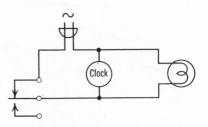

Fig. 6.31 A simple circuit to turn on a light and clock when a rat leaves the start box of an alley. This solution will only work if (1) the rated currents of the clock and bulb are equal and (2) the voltage across the plug equals the sum of the rated voltages of the clock and bulb.

Fig. 6.32 Another circuit to turn on the clock and bulb when the rat leaves the start box. This solution will only work if the bulb and clock have equal rated voltages.

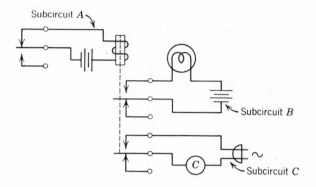

Fig. 6.33 A circuit to turn on a clock and bulb when the rat leaves the start box, regardless of the ratings of the bulb and clock. The only function of the relay in this circuit is to provide more contacts than the microswitch contains.

Now try to draw the circuit diagram just discussed without looking back at it. An efficient procedure is to begin by drawing the symbols for each of the elements that you know must be in the circuit, namely, a microswitch, a relay coil, a clock, and a light bulb. Then begin to connect them up so that each operates properly.

Each of the separate subcircuits is drawn with its own power supply. This is a convenient way to go about designing the circuit. When the circuit is actually built, however, it may turn out that the same power supply will be used in several subcircuits; in this case, the final circuit diagram should show that this is true (cases like this will be illustrated and discussed later). But in the initial stages of designing any circuit, it is much easier to represent a separate power supply for each circuit element that requires power.

The circuit diagram in Fig. 6.33 fulfills the logical requirements of the first part of this problem. However, the problem also includes the building of such a circuit, substituting two flashlight bulbs for the clock and the light. That requires some changes, not in the logical but in the practical aspects of the circuit diagram.

First of all, there is only one relay on your board that has enough contacts on it and the rating of the coil of that relay is 115 volts a-c. Therefore, a new symbol for 115 volts a-c must be substituted for battery 1.[1] The two light bulbs both require the same voltage, and they might as well be run off the same battery, especially since you only

[1] Your relay has many more contacts than need be used for this problem. It is easiest if the unneeded contacts are simply omitted from the circuit diagram.

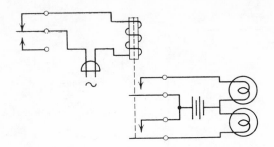

Fig. 6.34 A circuit in which release in pressure on the microswitch turns on two bulbs.

have one battery. The circuit diagram should be changed to indi-cate this. These two changes are shown in Fig. 6.34.[1]

Connect up this circuit on your board. Here, for the first time, you must be careful because, when the circuit is plugged in, there will be enough voltage across the relay and the switch to give a good shock. In general, never touch any terminals or bare wires when the circuit is plugged into the wall socket.

A convenient way to bring 115 volts a-c to your circuit board is as follows. Connect the wall plug to one end of your lamp cord. Then, at the other end of the cord, solder the two conducting paths to a pair of terminals on one of the terminal strips mounted on your board, as shown in Fig. 6.35. Thereafter, when the plug is plugged into the wall, the two terminals may be regarded as the source of 115 volts a-c.

[1] Because your two bulbs happen to require the same voltage, the circuit could be greatly simplified over the one in Fig. 6.34, but then the point of the problem would be lost.

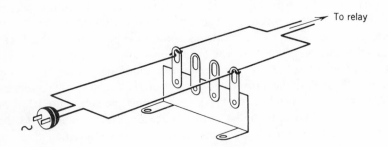

Fig. 6.35 A convenient way to make the wall-socket voltage available on your circuit board.

Caution: Finish the circuit and check the connections against the diagram before you plug it in. Then, as a final check, measure the resistance between the two prongs of the wall plug with an ohmmeter (again, *before* it is plugged into the wall). The ohmmeter should show an infinite resistance when the switch is in the position where the relay is off, and a resistance of at least a few hundred ohms (the resistance of the relay coil) when the switch is in the other position. This test is a good one to use generally when you are about to plug in a new circuit. If you have made a wiring mistake which causes the resistance across the plug to be very low (e.g., 1 ohm), and you were to plug the circuit into the wall, a very large current would flow (e.g., 115 amperes), and a fuse would blow out.

Another convenient way to check a new circuit is to connect a large light bulb in series between the circuit and the wall socket, as shown in Fig. 6.36. The bulb should be of such a wattage that, in order for it to light, it must conduct a current larger than that normally drawn by the circuit to be tested (e.g., if the circuit is supposed to draw 1 ampere, the bulb should be 500 watts or more). If the circuit has been correctly wired and then plugged in, the bulb will not light and will just add a small resistance to the circuit. However,

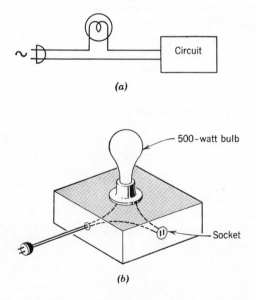

(a)

(b)

Fig. 6.36 (*a*) The insertion of a large bulb in series with a circuit to protect the supply fuses. (*b*) A unit for convenient testing of new circuits.

if there is a short circuit in the wiring, the bulb will light fully and no damage will be done.

Problems

1. Given a single 3-volt battery, a 3-volt motor that reverses direction of rotation when the direction of current through it is reversed (e.g., the motor on your circuit board), and a DPDT switch, design a circuit to drive the motor either clockwise or counterclockwise, depending on the position of the switch.

2. Given two bulbs, A and B, design a circuit which lights A when a selector switch is in one position; B when in another position; and A and B when in a third position.

3. Given two bulbs, A and B, and three push buttons, design a circuit so that pushing one button will light A, another B, and the third A and B.

4. Given a Skinner box with two adjacent bars, design a circuit so that the experimenter will have a selector switch which allows him to reinforce the pressing of (a) bar A alone (i.e., A and B together will not be reinforced); or (b) bar B alone; or (c) bars A and B simultaneously.

5. Design a circuit to measure choice reaction time. The experimenter closes his key, which lights either bulb A or bulb B, and starts the clock. The subject has two keys and presses one if A lights, the other if B lights. The subject's keys, when pressed, stop the clock. The subject holds his key down until he is told to release it.

a. Design the circuit so that any response, correct or incorrect, will stop the clock.

b. Design it so that only a correct response stops the clock.

6. Design and build a circuit, using the components on your board, which will cause a 6-volt bulb to go on and the 3-volt motor to go off, when the shaft of the 5000 ohm variable resistor is turned through about 90 degrees.

7. A subject is presented with three toggle switches, A, B, and C, and a push button. He is to learn which pair of switches is correct for each of a number of different stimuli (e.g., when he is shown a square, he is to turn on A and B, when shown a circle, B and C, etc.). He is shown a figure, throws the two switches he thinks are correct, then pushes the button. If he was correct, the button lights a bulb, and if wrong, it sounds a buzzer. Design the circuit so that the experimenter can select the pair of "correct" switches before each trial, and the rest is automatic.

Chapter 7

Complex switching circuits

This and the following chapters will examine some of the more complex and interesting switching circuits commonly used in experiments on behavior. All of the subsequent examples and problems will be typical of those which come up repeatedly in research. Many of the examples deal with learning experiments on animals because complex switching circuitry is even more extensively used in research on rats and pigeons in Skinner boxes than in the study of human behavior. Probably this is a result of the fact that by verbal instruction it is possible to throw into operation a human subject's own built-in, logical machinery, thus replacing a lot of relays.

This chapter contains many problems, and it is important to solve them all. Solving a problem means drawing the solution on real paper. It often *seems* possible to read a problem and arrive at a solution without actually writing anything down. However, thinking up a way of solving a problem is easy. Solving it is the hard part.

PROBLEM. John has a ball that weighs 3 pounds. It is hollow, and made of rubber weighing 63 pounds per cubic foot. The ball just barely floats in water. How thick are its walls?
Solution. Use division.

HOLDING RELAYS

There is one particular relay circuit that is used very extensively. It is called the holding, or lockup, circuit, and is used when a circuit element must remain activated after the activating circuit is turned off. In essence, a relay is made to close as soon as a switch is operated, hold itself closed even after the switch is opened, and release only when a second switch is operated. The basic circuit is illustrated in the following example.

Suppose you are given the problem of designing a circuit to measure the length of time it takes a rat to run from point X in a straight alley to another point Y farther down the alley. First, some device must be used to sense when the rat passes each of the two points. In solving the present problem, we will use the method mentioned in the previous chapter of hinging a section of the floor at X and another at Y, so that the rat's weight will momentarily operate a SPDT microswitch at each of the two points.[1] The clock commonly used for this type of timing consists of an electric motor driving the hands through an electric clutch. The motor runs constantly, but the hands turn only so long as the clutch is engaged. The clutch operates as long as a small current is being passed through it, and disengages as soon as the current is turned off. To time a rat, then, a circuit is needed which will cause a current to begin to flow through the clutch when one SPDT switch (at X) is momentarily operated, and stop flowing when another (at Y) is operated. Neither microswitch alone could operate the clutch in the desired way because, during the time the rat is between X and Y, both switches are open so that the clutch would not be engaged.

Suppose, instead, that the clutch is turned on and off through a relay. Now, if the relay could be made to close when switch X is closed, hold itself closed even after switch X is opened, and release when switch Y is operated, the problem would be almost solved. (The clutch could then be turned on and off by a pair of contacts on the relay.) Figure 7.1a shows the clutch connected through a relay, and the relay connected directly to one of the microswitches. This circuit is no improvement over connecting the clutch directly through the microswitch. As soon as X is closed by the rat's running over that section of the alley, the relay closes, allowing current to flow in the clutch circuit. However, as soon as the rat leaves that section of the alley, the microswitch will open again, the relay will thus be released, and the clutch is turned off.

Now examine Fig. 7.1b. This circuit is identical with that of Fig. 7.1a, except for the addition into the circuit of a second pair of normally open contacts on the relay. These contacts are connected in parallel with the normally open contacts of the microswitch. The

[1] There are better ways (e.g., photoelectric cells) which will be discussed later.

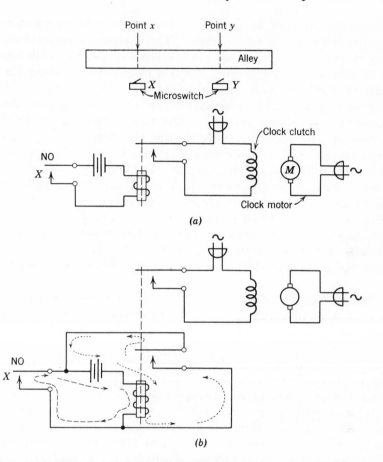

Fig. 7.1 (a) Preliminary circuit for measuring the time a rat spends in going from X to Y in a straight alley. This circuit will not work. (b) A circuit that will start the clock when the rat passes X, and will hold the clock running indefinitely. The dashed and dotted arrows indicate the loops of the basic holding relay circuit.

action of the circuit is as follows. At first, the microswitch and the relay are open so that no current flows anywhere (except, of course, through the clock motor). (Be sure that it is clear from the diagram that no current can flow. Try to find a closed path from one side of a power source to the other side of the same source. If there is no such path, then there can be no current flow, but as soon as there is such a path, there must be current flow.)

Now the rat steps on the hinged alley section, closing the normally open contacts of the microswitch. This furnishes a path for current to flow through the relay coil (dashed arrows), and the resulting magnetic field will cause the relay armature to pull down, closing the two pairs of normally open contacts. The top pair activates the clutch. The lower pair provides a second path for the current to flow through the relay coil (dotted arrows). This time, when the rat leaves the section and the microswitch opens again, the relay will stay closed because there is still a path allowing current to flow through the coil. With the microswitch open, current will flow only along the dotted lines. Under these conditions, the relay is, in a sense, holding itself closed and once it has been closed, microswitch X no longer has any effect at all. The clock will start running when the rat first crosses the hinged section of the alley and will keep running indefinitely, as the circuit is now drawn. Even if the rat were to retrace and go back and forth several times over this alley section, the clock would be unaffected.

Set up the circuit diagrammed in Fig. 7.2a on your board. In this circuit, a flashlight bulb and socket substitute for the clutch in Fig. 7.1b. The relay is your 115-volt a-c relay, and switch X is one of the microswitches. (Observe the same precautions as were discussed in the previous chapter: remember that 115 volts can be painful.[1]) If the circuit is connected up correctly, the light should go on when you first press the microswitch and stay on after you let go.

Now the bulb is lit (the clock is running). How do you turn it off? There are several ways. First, you can unscrew the bulb. This is the equivalent of putting a switch in the clutch circuit and opening it. Suppose that this switch were actually the second microswitch Y in the alley, connected as in Fig. 7.2b. That is, the normally closed pair is connected in series with the clutch. When the rat hits section X, the relay closes and the clock starts. When he hits section Y, the clock stops. If at that moment the clock could be read very quickly, the circuit problem would be solved. But as soon as the rat leaves section Y, the clock will start up again. Prove this by unscrewing the bulb and then putting it back again.

If the section Y switch could actually turn off the power to the *relay*, then the relay would stay open even after the section is returned to its normally closed condition, because the only things keeping the relay closed are its own contacts. In the circuit on your board, turn off the light by pulling out the wall plug. Now when the plug

---

[1] The microswitch lever is electrically insulated from its terminals and is, therefore, safe to touch.

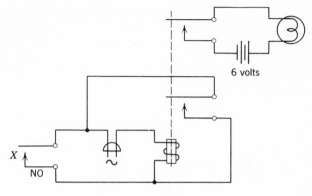

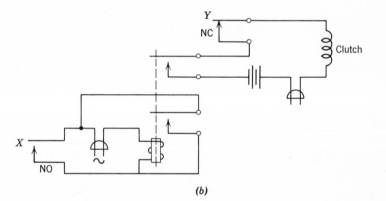

Fig. 7.2 (*a*) Diagram of circuit to be built on your board. The bulb in this circuit is analogous to the clock in the timing circuit under discussion. (*b*) One way (an ineffective one) to turn off the clock in the timing problem.

is connected again, the light will remain off and the whole circuit is restored to its initial condition.

On your board, connect up the normally closed contacts of the second microswitch as shown in Fig. 7.3. This switch will now do what you were doing when you momentarily disconnected the wall plug. If the circuit is working properly, the light will turn on when switch X is momentarily pressed, and stay on until switch Y is momentarily pressed.

This circuit, the holding relay circuit, is very fundamental to switching circuit design. It is used as it has been presented here or with only slight modifications in a very large proportion of the switching

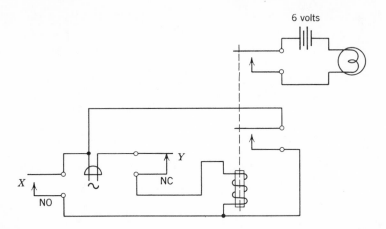

Fig. 7.3 Diagram of a circuit to be built on your board. The bulb lights when X is pressed and extinguishes when Y is pressed. If the microswitches were mounted in a straight alley and a clock were substituted for the bulb, the circuit would allow the measurement of the rat's running speed.

circuits found in behavioral research. For this reason, it is worth-while for you to draw the circuit diagram in Fig. 7.3 over and over again until it becomes almost automatic. Be sure you understand its principles of operation. This will save you considerable time when you are solving many of the remaining problems in this book.

If the circuit in Fig. 7.3 were used in a straight alley way, it would permit the measurement of the total time between the first crossing of X and the first crossing of Y (i.e., stepping on Y again would not restart the clock). Consider instead the problem of designing a circuit to measure the total time the animal spends in the portion of the alley between X and Y. In other words, if he runs out of this portion, past Y, and then turns around and runs back into it once more, the clock should start again.

Since this is probably the most difficult problem yet presented, it may be a good one with which to illustrate the sort of process used by people skilled at circuit design to solve relatively complicated problems.

Many of the processes involved in arriving at solutions to this kind of problem are difficult to verbalize in a coherent way. If prodded, people who are skilled at circuit design frequently will say that they knew by intuition where to start and what things to try. Intuition is probably an excellent word to describe what happens. Most people using such intuition will readily agree that it is developed through a combination of some intelligence and a lot of experience. Here, an attempt will be made to enumerate some of the submerged logic involved.

The first step in arriving at a solution is to state the circuit requirements as explicitly as possible. In this particular problem, the circuit must:

1. Start the clock any time the animal (*a*) crosses X going toward Y or (*b*) crosses Y going toward X.

2. Stop the clock any time he (*a*) crosses X going away from Y or (*b*) crosses Y going away from X.

(For any problem there are a number of solutions. For example, this problem may be easily solved, in theory at least, by hinging the entire section between X and Y and resting it on a microswitch. In practice, it is difficult to make a large section of alley operate that way. The solutions presented herein are chosen both because they are practical and because they illustrate various important aspects of circuit design. If you arrive at a solution different from one in the text— and this happens very often—that does not necessarily mean that yours is incorrect.)

Examination of the apparatus requirements listed above indicates that the circuit must sense the direction in which the rat is traveling as well as his presence when he is at point X or point Y. If there were two short, hinged floor sections at X, and if the circuit could determine the order in which these two sections were traversed, it would indicate which way the animal was going when he went by X, and either of the sections might also indicate his presence at X. In other words, it may be that if there were four hinged floor sections, each with a microswitch, two at X and two more at Y, it would be possible to solve the problem. A guess about what kinds of circuit elements might solve the problem can be considered the second step in the solution.

The third step might then be to see whether or not such a collection of elements really can be made to work. To do this, it is probably most efficient to begin by representing, on a large sheet of paper, each of the possible elements without any particular regard for how they will be connected up. Such a drawing is shown in Fig. 7.4.

The clock will run so long as there is current flowing through its clutch coil, and it becomes clear from looking at Fig. 7.4 and considering the original problem that the clutch must be operated through something that is not yet represented. This is true because, although

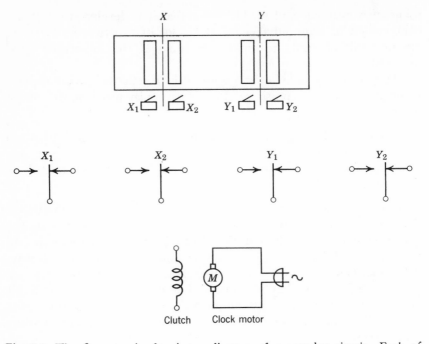

Fig. 7.4   The first step in drawing a diagram of a complex circuit. Each of the known elements is represented.

the clutch must remain activated when the rat is, say, halfway between X and Y, there is nothing drawn yet that will act that way.   As in the preceding problem, a holding relay circuit is strongly indicated. A relay is thus drawn in with at least enough contacts to hold itself, and connected so as to operate the clutch (Fig. 7.5).   Now the clutch no longer need be considered.   The problem is to get the relay to be on all the time the rat is between X and Y.   If this is done, the clock will necessarily do the same.

Figuring out additional connections requires consideration of the step-by-step operation of the circuit.   Let the rat come out of the start box and begin to walk up the alley.   The clutch is to engage, that is, the relay is to close, when the rat passes X.   Therefore, either microswitch X_1 or X_2 must close the relay.   Try X_1 first, as in Fig. 7.6a.   With this circuit, when the rat walks past X and stands between X and Y, the clock keeps running (the relay is connected to hold itself on).   Now, if the rat turns around and crosses X again, the clock is supposed to go off.   Since X_2 is left over, try its normally closed contacts to turn off the clock (Fig. 7.6*b*). This will stop the clock all right when the rat recrosses X_2 going toward the start box, but two other things are wrong. First, if he goes a little farther and crosses X_1 too, the clock will go back on again. Second, after he leaves the start box in the first place, he will start the clock at X_1, but stop it again as he goes by X_2. Therefore, try reversing the roles of X_1 and X_2 to see if that works any better (Fig. 7.7). Now, when the rat crosses X_1 going toward Y, nothing happens. When he crosses X_2, the clock starts. If he then turns around and recrosses X_2 going the wrong way, nothing happens. But as soon as he crosses X_1 going the wrong way, the clock stops. When he again turns around and recrosses X going toward Y, the clock starts once more. So far, then, this circuit is operating according to plan. All that remains is to make

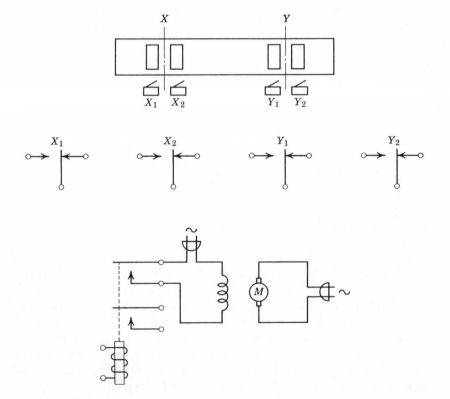

Fig. 7.5 The next design step. The problem requires that the clock be operated from a relay. The relay must have enough contacts left over to hold itself closed. Such a relay is represented.

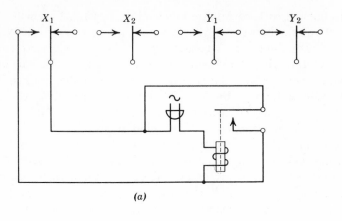

(a)

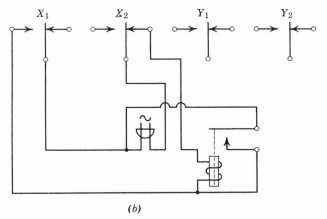

(b)

Fig. 7.6 (a) The circuit drawn so that X_1 closes the relay. (b) The same circuit with the addition that X_2 opens the relay.

the switches at Y operate in a similar, but *opposite*, manner. In other words, it would seem plausible, as a first guess, to make Y_1 start the clock and Y_2 stop it. (Crossing Y toward X should do the same thing as crossing X toward Y.) The circuit in Fig. 7.8 is connected this way and will solve the problem. In this circuit, either Y_1 or X_2 will start the clock, and either X_1 or Y_2 will stop it. The clock will always be running when the rat is between X and Y because the rat must have most recently closed either X_2 or Y_1 to get there. And any time the rat leaves the section between X and Y, the clock must be stopped because the rat must have most recently opened either X_1 or Y_2.

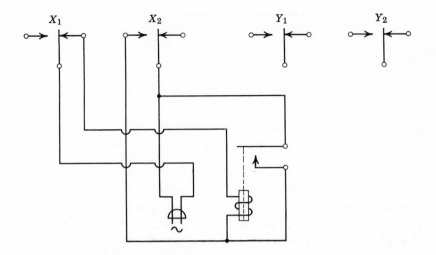

Fig. 7.7 The same circuit as in Fig. 7.6*b* except that the functions of X_1 and X_2 are reversed; that is, X_2 closes the relay and X_1 opens it.

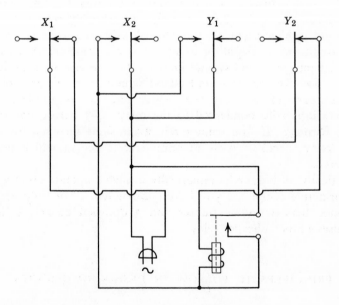

Fig. 7.8 The circuit of Fig. 7.7, with the additions that Y_1 (as well as X_2) closes the relay, and Y_2 (as well as X_1) opens it.

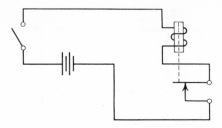

Fig. 7.9   Circuit diagram for a buzzer.

The next problem illustrates another modification of a holding relay circuit. A relay that is turned on and off repeatedly at a fairly fast rate will buzz. In the holding relay circuit, the relay holds itself on. If instead a relay is connected in such a way that it turns itself *off*, then it must buzz. This is shown in the circuit of Fig. 7.9. Before the switch is closed, the relay is open, so that the normally closed contacts of the relay are closed. As soon as the switch is closed, current will flow through the relay contacts and through the relay coil, causing the relay armature to pull in. But when the armature pulls in far enough to open the normally closed contacts, the circuit through the relay coil is broken, so the armature is released. This allows the contacts to close again, and the cycle automatically repeats itself.

Connect up this circuit on your board, using the sensitive relay (not the 115-volt one). Begin by using as low a voltage across the relay as is convenient (say 3 volts), and increase it, if necessary, until the relay buzzes. Be sure that you understand which terminals are connected to which parts of the relay (i.e., which terminals on the body of the relay are internally connected to the relay coil) before you connect up the battery. If you cannot tell about some terminal by looking at the relay, check it with an ohmmeter to see to which part it is connected.

Practically all buzzers commercially available operate on exactly the same principle as the one you have constructed. The only important difference between your buzzer and a doorbell buzzer is that the latter uses a much cheaper relay.

SOME PRINCIPLES TO FOLLOW IN DESIGNING CIRCUITS

There are three principles which an experienced circuit designer uses automatically as he designs a new circuit. These principles are also useful in checking a novice's diagram, and you should apply them to each of your circuits when they are in the design stage as well as after you think the circuit diagram is complete.

Principle 1

Every possible path of current from one side of each power source to the other side of the same source should contain some resistance.

Trace each such path in Fig. 7.10.   Each path should contain some circuit element which has resistance (e.g., a relay coil).   If a path contains only a pair of closed relay contacts, for example, an infinite current will be drawn from the power source.   The use of this principle is illustrated in Fig. 7.10.

Each circuit should be checked in this way under all its conditions of normal operation.   That is, if during circuit operation, a relay is

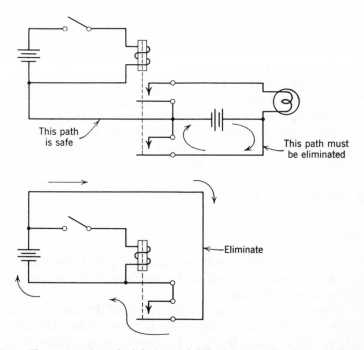

Fig. 7.10   Two examples of violations of Principle 1.   The loops indicated by arrows provide zero resistance paths from one side of the power source to the other.   The path designated as "safe" leads directly from one side of one source to another side of the *other* source.   It is therefore permissible.   (It is also superfluous, as will be discussed in Principle 3.)

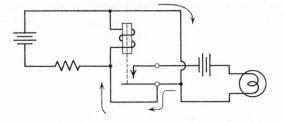

Fig. 7.11 A violation of Principle 2. The path indicated by the arrows provides a direct and permanent path from one side of the relay coil to the other
and, therefore, renders the relay inoperative.

sometimes open and sometimes closed, check all paths under both
states. Remember that *any* one path of zero resistance is a short circuit, even if there are many other paths between *a* and *b* that do contain resistance.

Principle 2

There should be no permanent path of zero resistance between the
two ends of any circuit element. For example, if there is a direct
connection between the two ends of a relay, the relay will be short-
circuited and cannot operate. Figure 7.11 illustrates the sort of error
referred to by this principle. In some circuits, an element is deliberately short-circuited during some phase of the operation of the circuit
as a whole, but there are other phases during which the short circuit is
removed. If it were always present, the short-circuited element could
never perform any function.

Principle 3

Every circuit element should be part of a path from one side of a
power source to the other side of the same source during some part of
the operation of the circuit.

Any element never in a path from one side of the source to the other
cannot have any function in the circuit because current can never flow
through it. The resistor in Fig. 7.12 is superfluous. Since there is no
path from one side of either power source, through the resistor, and
back to the other side of the same power source, current will never flow
through the resistor. Therefore it serves no function and can be
omitted without changing the action of the circuit.

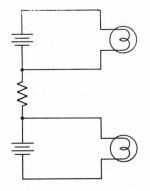

Fig. 7.12 An illustration of Principle 3. The resistor is superfluous. See also the "safe" connection in Fig. 7.10.

The principles listed above, if followed, will eliminate some of the mistakes which prevent a circuit from operating. The following is a list of principles of a different sort. Although it is not logically necessary to employ them, their use generally results in circuits that are simpler to design and construct.

1. If two or more circuit elements require the same kind of power supply (e.g., 115 volts a-c), connect one side of each of them together and to one side of the power supply. Figures 7.13 and 7.14 are examples. This is an extremely useful principle. Whenever you are faced with a circuit problem in which either one or another of a set of circuit elements is to be activated, and each element requires the same voltage, the first connections drawn in the diagram should be these. For example, to draw the diagram for a circuit to light any one of four bulbs, the first step should be as drawn in Fig. 7.14.

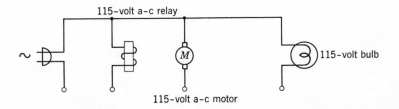

Fig. 7.13 If the circuit to be designed contains a number of elements with identical voltage requirements (115 volts a-c in this example), one side of each may be connected together and to one side of the power source.

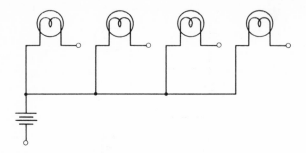

Fig. 7.14 When any one or combination of identical elements (light bulbs in this example) are to be operated, the first step in drawing the circuit is illustrated here.

2. If two or more subcircuits are *nowhere* connected together, it is permissible to make one connection between them anywhere in the circuits. For example, in the diagram of Fig. 7.15, a connection may be made from any point in the circuit labeled 1 to any point in the circuit labeled 2. Such a connection will have no effect on either subcircuit. This principle is useful, for instance, in the case where there are two subcircuits, one of which is supposed to go on when the other is off, and vice versa. The subcircuits 1 and 2 in Fig. 7.16*a* will operate in this way, through the contacts of a DPDT relay. But if the only available relay is a SPDT one (e.g., a sensitive relay), the

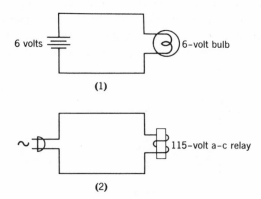

Fig. 7.15 Two completely separate circuits containing elements requiring different power sources. Any point on circuit 1 may be connected to any point on circuit 2 without affecting either circuit.

two circuits may be connected together and to the common contact, as shown in Fig. 7.16b.

3. If two or more subcircuits are nowhere connected together, and if they both require the same kind of power source, a single power source may be used for both.

Label the two sides of one source "+" and "—"; next label the two sides of the other power source "+" and "—" (with alternating current, either side can be called "+"); then connect the "+'s" together and to one side of a single power supply, and the "—'s" together and to the other side of the power supply. Figure 7.17 shows an example of this procedure. If there are several subcircuits to be connected in this way, the circuit diagram can be made easier to follow if the convention illustrated in Fig. 7.18 is followed. Here the points in each subcircuit into which power is to be led are labeled "+" and "—"

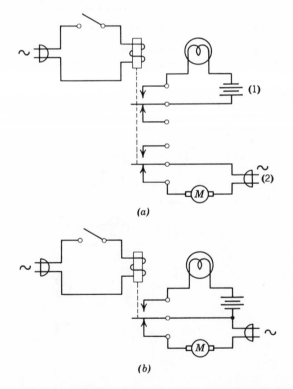

Fig. 7.16 A common application of the principle under discussion and illustrated in Fig. 7.15. The two subcircuits, 1 and 2, are completely separate electrically in Fig. 7.16a. They may therefore be joined at one point, as shown in Fig. 7.16b.

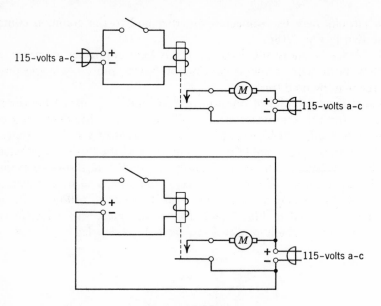

Fig. 7.17 An illustration of the consolidation of separate but identical power supplies when the subcircuits were originally completely separate.

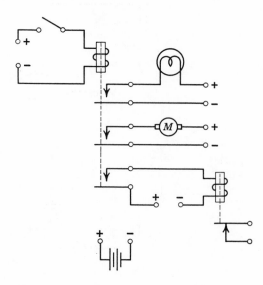

Fig. 7.18 A method for simplifying the circuit diagram when a number of identical sources are consolidated.

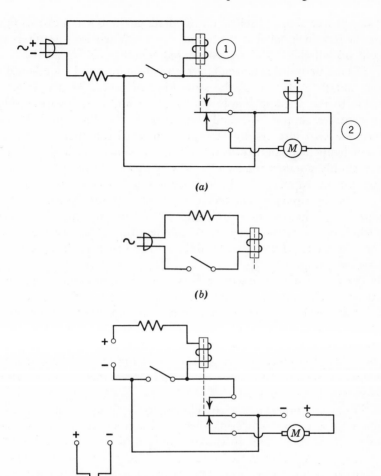

(a)

(b)

(c)

Fig. 7.19 Consolidation of identical sources when the subcircuits were already connected at a point other than one joining the two sources directly. (*a*) The resistor falls between the two sources. (*b*) Rearrangement of subcircuit 1. The resistor is simply moved to the other side of the source. (*c*) Redrawing of the circuit in Fig. 7.19*a*, with the resistor shifted.

and the power supply itself is represented, at the bottom of this figure, with its terminals labeled "+" and "—." When the circuit is connected up, all the "+'s" are connected together, as are all the "—'s."

4. If two or more subcircuits are already connected together at one point, and they all require the same kind of power supply, it *may* be possible to use a single supply for all. To find out, label one side of each separate supply "+" and the other "—." Then find the point where the two circuits are already connected together. If the connection happens to be between "+" in one subcircuit and "+" in the other, simply connect the two "—'s" together and to the "—" side of a single power supply. If the connection is between two "—'s" the "+'s" can be similarly connected together. If the connection is between a "+" in one subcircuit and a "—" in the other, just reverse the labels in one of the circuits, and connect the "+'s" together and the "—'s" together. These cases reduce to the situation described in the preceding paragraph.

If the pre-existing connection between two subcircuits is not at one of these places, then try to change it so that it is. For example, the subcircuits in Fig. 7.19*a* are not joined in any of the ways just described. But the subcircuit 1 can be redrawn as in Fig. 7.19*b* without changing its action, and the remaining connections may then be made to use a single power supply, as shown in Fig. 7.19*c*. It is often but not always possible to change subcircuits in this way, so that a single power supply may be used.

5. Do not connect any two subcircuits together at more than one place, except when connecting them as described in Principles 3 and 4 above. If, at some stage in the designing of a circuit, you would like to connect two subcircuits together, but they are already connected at another point, figure out some way to avoid making the second connection. The most common reason for wanting to connect two circuits together is to make double use of an SPDT contact set. If you face this problem, and the two subcircuits are already connected together somewhere else, the best solution is usually to substitute a DPDT contact set for the SPDT set (e.g., add another relay to the circuit), and thus avoid making the second connection between the two subcircuits.

Problems

1. A subject is presented with a light whose color slowly changes from red through the spectrum to violet. He is to indicate at what times it

appears to be pure yellow, pure green, and pure blue. He does this by momentarily pressing the first of three keys when it is yellow, the second when it is green, and the third when it is blue. The experimenter then reads these times on each of three clocks. The experimenter turns on the light and starts all three clocks by momentarily pressing a button. Design the circuit.

2. Design a circuit to measure choice reaction time in the following way. The experimenter momentarily presses a button which turns on one of two lights and starts the clock. The subject responds by momentarily tapping the appropriate one of two keys. If he presses the correct key, the clock stops. If he presses the wrong one before he presses the correct one, a buzzer turns on and stays on until the experimenter turns it off. The clock always continues to run until the correct response is made.

3. An animal is in a Skinner box that contains two bars. The experimenter has a switch with which he can establish that the animal will be reinforced either for pressing bar A and then bar B, or for pressing bar B and then bar A. The bars are too far apart to be pressed simultaneously. The reinforcer operates once each time its terminals are connected together, and the experimenter resets the apparatus after each reinforcement. Design the circuit.

Chapter 8

Other relays

There are many types of relays other than the simple ones described in the preceding chapter. Some of these will be discussed here. In most cases the functions of the more complex relays may be duplicated by the proper combination of simpler relays. For this reason, it is not essential to be acquainted with a variety of types. However, it is often much more convenient to buy one complex relay than to try to duplicate its action by combining several simpler ones.

MECHANICAL ASPECTS

The physical size of a relay is generally determined by the electrical requirements. For example, if the relay is to switch large currents, its contacts must be big. However, relays of any given electric capacity do come in a range of sizes so that, should it be important for a circuit to be small, it is possible to buy extra small relays.

The relays on your circuit board are exposed, i.e., you can see most of the parts. Many relays, however, are sealed within dustproof and moistureproof cans, with only the terminal posts exposed. The trouble with sealed relays is that, since it is not possible to see and get at the working parts, they are somewhat less adaptable than exposed relays. But there are certain situations in which sealed relays must be used, e.g., if the circuit is to be operated in a very dusty or humid environment. In addition, there are certain types of relays, such as very fast-acting ones, which must be sealed in order to work properly.

Many sealed relays and some that are not sealed are of the plug-in type. This means that the connections are all brought out to the prongs on a plug (Fig. 8.1). To wire such a relay into a circuit, all the connections are made to an appropriate socket and then the relay is simply plugged in. This type of relay is particularly suited for circuits which get a lot of use. Should a relay go bad, it may be replaced very easily.

ELECTRICAL ASPECTS

The coil of any given relay is constructed so that the armature will pull in at some particular voltage and current. Relays of the type used for most switching operations are rated in terms of the voltage necessary for proper operation. For example, the coil of one of the relays on your board is rated at 115 volts a-c. Relays are readily available for use with either a-c or d-c at voltages between about 6 and 220 volts.

Relays that require small amounts of power to operate are usually rated in terms of their resistance and the current necessary to operate them. They are called sensitive relays and generally have a relatively simple contact arrangement, either SPST or SPDT. The sensitive relay on your board is SPDT. These relays are not often used to perform complex switching operations, but only to allow a small amount of power to control a larger one. Figure 8.2 shows some sensitive relays. One of the most sensitive of all relays is depicted in Fig. 8.3. It has an SPDT set of contacts.

Fig. 8.1 A plug-in relay and socket. Connections may be made to the terminals of the socket. (*Courtesy* Helen E. Howell, Berkeley, Calif.)

One of the contacts is mounted on the needle of a sensitive ammeter, and the others are fixed to the frame of the meter. As current passes through the coil of the meter, the needle moves and, at some current value, the contacts close. Usually the contacts are magnetic so that, once they touch, they hold a good contact. It is then necessary to

Fig. 8.2   Assorted   sensitive   relays.   (*Courtesy*   Helen   E.   Howell,   Berkeley, Calif.)

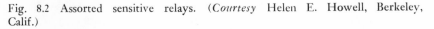

open the contacts by some mechanical device. This type of relay may be made to operate on as little as a few microamperes and less than a millivolt. The meter-type relay is delicate and relatively expensive. When such small amounts of power must control large amounts, it is much more common to use some form of electronic amplification and a less sensitive relay. This frequently turns out to be a cheaper solution. (Many circuits of this type will be discussed in later chapters.)

It is important to realize that there are two different kinds of ratings for any given relay—the coil rating and the contact rating. For example, a relay may have a coil rating of 115 volts a-c and a contact rating of 200 volts at 3 amperes. This means that the relay will close properly on 115 volts a-c, and that the contacts opened and closed by the armature can carry up to 3 amperes and 200 volts without getting too hot. There is no logically necessary relationship between these two types of ratings on any given relay. It does happen, however, that a general relationship exists for practical reasons. If a relay is to have a large contact current rating, it must have large contacts and they must be held together tightly. The contacts must also be relatively far apart when they are open. All these factors necessitate a relatively strong magnetic pull to close the relay, and this in turn requires a relatively high current or voltage rating on the coil of the relay. On the other hand, for a relay to be very sensitive, i.e., to be able to close with a very small amount of power in its coil, the contacts must be very light, and cannot therefore carry large currents.

There is a type of relay that is an exception to this general rule. The mercury-wetted relay can be made very sensitive although the contacts are capable of carrying relatively large amounts of current. The contacts of this type of relay are coated with mercury. When a pair of contacts meet, the pools of mercury on each contact join to form a relatively large contact area. Mercury-wetted relays have another property that is very desirable under some conditions. When the armature of a normal relay is pulled in, or when the lever of a microswitch is pushed, the contacts bounce against each other, and the resulting contact is intermittent for a short time immediately after closure. When mercury-wetted contacts are used, the mercury pool maintains electric contact during the bounce phase, and there is no period of intermittance.

To maintain the mercury in a clean condition, mercury-wetted relays are mounted in sealed containers which are usually filled with an inert gas under pressure. The connections are brought out to a plug at the base of the container. (Most relays can be operated in any position, but mercury-wetted relays only operate properly when used base down.)

Fig. 8.3 A supersensitive relay. The contacts are mounted on a sensitive meter movement. (*Courtesy* Daystrom, Inc.)

SWITCHING OPERATIONS

Latching Relays

The relays described so far operate rather simply, even though combinations of them can perform very complicated logical operations. However, there are several types of relays which operate in a more complicated way and allow the rest of the circuit to be simpler. These relays actually substitute mechanical for electrical logical operations, so that the machinery gets complicated and the circuit gets simpler. For example, look at the relay in Fig. 8.4. This is called a latching relay. It consists of two independent coils, two interlocking armatures, and one set of contacts. When current passes through coil A, the armature A pulls down, closing the contacts. The armature B mechanically catches on armature A and holds it in the closed position even after the current stops flowing in coil A. When current passes through coil B, armature B pulls in, releasing armature A, which returns to its initial position and opens the contacts. In other words, the operation of a latching relay is similar to that of an ordinary relay wired in a holding circuit. Latching relays are more expensive and

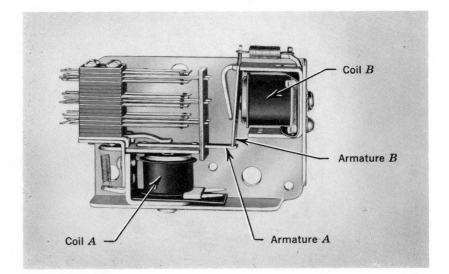

Fig. 8.4 A latching relay. A momentary current through coil A closes the contacts, and through coil B it opens them. (*Courtesy* Guardian Electric Co.)

harder to obtain than ordinary relays, and have only one real advantage over the holding circuit. A latching relay does not require a continuous flow of current to keep it latched. If an apparatus were to be battery-operated, for example, the latching relay might be worth the extra expense because of reduced drain on the battery.

Sequence Relays

There is a class of special relays called sequence relays or ratchet relays, in which successive bursts of current through a coil cause a set of contacts to step through a particular sequence of openings and closings. Generally, when the current through the coil is turned on, the relay cocks, and when the current then goes off, the relay operates and is ready for the next cocking. For example, suppose that the space bar on a typewriter is pulled down by a magnetic coil. When the current goes on, the bar pulls down, cocking the typewriter carriage mechanism. Then, when the current is turned off, the bar is released and the carriage actually shifts over one space. If there were a cam attached to the carriage that closed a pair of contacts on even numbered spaces and opened them on odd numbered spaces, then successive bursts of current through the magnet coil·would produce alternate openings and closings of the contacts.

The relay in Fig. 8.5 is a sequence relay that operates as follows.

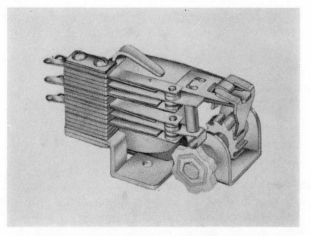

Fig. 8.5 A sequence relay. Successive pulses of current through the coil rotate the camshaft, causing contacts to open and close.

Current through the coil pulls an armature down, and the armature pushes the toothed wheel (which looks like a gear) through a part of a turn. There is a set of cams rigidly attached to the same shaft as the toothed wheel, and the cams open and close the contacts. In the figure, the position of the cam is such that the upper pairs of contacts are closed. When current is turned on through the coil, the armature will advance the toothed wheel one tooth, the cam will rotate through part of a turn, and the contacts will open. When the current through the coil is then turned off, the contacts will remain open but the armature will return to its "ready" position. The next time current flows through the coil, the cam will close the contacts again, and so on. This relay operates when current is turned on and cocks when current is turned off. This is different from the typewriter example discussed above. Relays operating either way are available.

The sequence relay in Fig. 8.5 operates in a way similar to the latching relay, except that the on-off series in the sequence relay is produced by repeated bursts of current through the *same* coil (repeated closures of the same switch), whereas the latching relay operated from two different coils (and switches).

There are occasions when it is very desirable to have successive closings of a single switch produce successive reversals of a contact configuration. One interesting example of this is the binary counting circuit.

PROBLEM. Given a Skinner box with a bar-activated microswitch (pressing the bar closes a microswitch), design a system for reinforcing the animal on any of a number of fixed ratios. For example, the animal may get reinforced for every second press, or every fourth, etc.

Solution. First, we will choose to make available each of the following schedules:
Reinforce on:

> Every press; or
> every second press; or
> every fourth press; or
> every eighth press.

Assume that a device is available which delivers one reinforcement each time it is turned on. The principle to be used in this problem, and for any problem involving binary counting, is that two changes of state in the driving unit are required for each single change of state in the follower. In this case, consider the microswitch as the first driver, in that it will drive an alternating sequence relay. When the switch is closed, the relay contacts will close, but when the switch opens again, the relay contacts stay closed. The next time the switch closes, the contacts open. Thus, the switch must close and open twice for each time the relay contacts close and open once. If this relay is connected so that, in turn, it drives a second sequence relay, then the second relay will operate once for each two operations of the first relay, and thus once for each *four* operations of the switch. This sort of circuit is diagrammed in Fig. 8.6. The sequence of operations of the entire circuit is also shown in this figure. Note that there is a

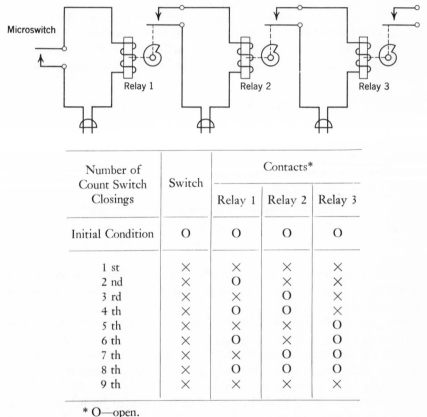

Number of Count Switch Closings	Switch	Contacts*		
		Relay 1	Relay 2	Relay 3
Initial Condition	O	O	O	O
1 st	X	X	X	X
2 nd	X	O	X	X
3 rd	X	X	O	X
4 th	X	O	O	X
5 th	X	X	X	O
6 th	X	O	X	O
7 th	X	X	O	O
8 th	X	O	O	O
9 th	X	X	X	X

* O—open.
X—closed.

Fig. 8.6 A binary counter employing the type of sequence relay in Fig. 8.5. The conditions of contact closure for successive operations of the microswitch are indicated in the table.

unique combination of closed relay contacts for each count from one through eight, and then the sequence repeats. Thus, looking at the relay contacts themselves, it would be possible to say what the count was. This is the principle underlying essentially all of the binary counting systems used in counting and computing equipment.

Figure 8.7 is a circuit diagram showing how this sort of counting circuit can give a solution to the fixed-ratio reinforcement problem under discussion. A standard double-pole relay (relay 0), a reinforcer, and a selector switch have been added to the diagram in Fig. 8.6, and extra pairs of contacts have been added to sequence relays 1 and 2.

The circuit of Fig. 8.7 is designed on the following basis. In order to fulfill the problem requirements, it is necessary to find some particular contact pattern that occurs on each press, another that only occurs on every other press, another every fourth, and another only every eighth press. If you examine the chart in Fig. 8.6, it is evident that:

1. The switch is closed on every bar press.
2. Both the switch and relay-1 contacts are closed on every other press.
3. The switch, relay-1, and relay-2 contacts are *all* closed only on every fourth press.
4. The switch and all three relay contacts are closed only once out of each eight presses.

If a switch could be connected so that the occurrence of any particular one of these four contingencies could be made to deliver a reinforcement, the problem would be solved, and the circuit in Fig. 8.7 will accomplish this.

(Relay 0 serves only to add another pair of contacts to the microswitch, i.e., if that switch were a double-pole one, relay 0 would be unnecessary.)

The circuit operates as follows. First, consider what happens when the selector switch is in the position marked 1:1. Each time the rat presses the bar, the switch closes, thus closing the relay. The relay, in turn, allows current to flow through the reinforcement mechanism, delivering reinforcement at a ratio of one per press. Now let the selector switch be in position 1:2, as it happens to be in the circuit diagram. In this case, current can only flow through the reinforcer if the contacts on *both* relay 0 *and* relay 1 are closed, and from the table it can be seen that this happens every other time the bar is pressed. Similarly, relay 0, relay 1, *and* relay 2 must be closed for reinforce-

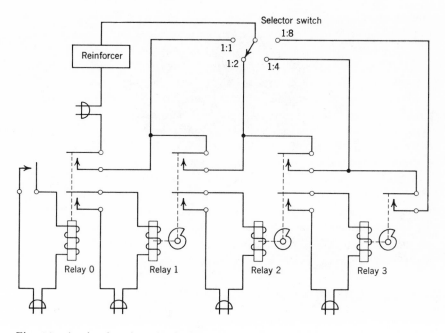

Fig. 8.7 A circuit using the basic counting unit of Fig. 8.6 to allow the re-inforcement of every bar press, every second press, every fourth press, or every eighth press, depending upon the position of the selector switch.

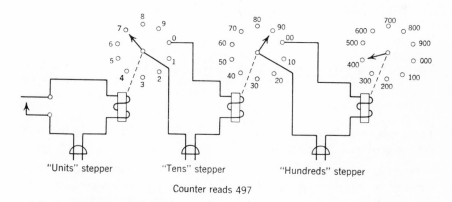

Fig. 8.8 A three-digit decade counter, using three ten-position, continuous-rotation stepping switches.

(a)

(b)

Fig. 8.9 (a) Continuously "round and round" stepping switch. (*Courtesy* Automatic Electric Co.) (b) An add-subtract stepper. (*Courtesy* Guardian Electric Co.)

ment when the selector is in the 1:4 position, and this occurs only once out of each four bar presses.

Suppose, now, that each relay in the counting circuit above went through a sequence of ten positions instead of just two (on and off). A decade counting circuit could then be designed on identical principles, as in Fig. 8.8. Relays like these are essentially electromagnetically controlled selector switches, and are generally called stepping relays, or steppers. Stepping relays may be purchased with as many as 100 steps and 6 decks; that is, 6 mechanically connected rotating arms and 6 sets of 100 contacts. Such a relay would be a 6P100T relay.

Figure 8.9a shows a typical stepping switch (6P26T). Successive pulses through the coil step the arms around, always in the same direction. The stepper in Fig. 8.9b is called an add-subtract stepper. Current through the left-hand coil moves the wheel one step counterclockwise, and current through the right-hand coil one step clockwise. The post mounted on the wheel opens the contacts when the wheel is in one particular position. Add-subtract relays are also constructed with a contact arm mounted on the wheel which moves across a set of stationary contacts, as on the stepper in Fig. 8.9a.

Figure 8.10 shows a stepper that has a built-in resetting mechanism. It operates as follows. As the arm steps forward, it stretches the spring. This spring exerts a force which tends to return the arm to its starting position, but normally a ratchet prevents the arm from doing so. However, when a voltage is applied to the reset coil, the ratchet is pulled back and the arm swings all the way back to its starting position. A circuit using such a resetting relay is shown in Fig. 8.11a.

The circuit in Fig. 8.11a is not completely satisfactory for the fol-

Fig. 8.10 A 3P10T stepping switch with an electrical reset mechanism. (*Courtesy* Helen E. Howell, Berkeley, Calif.)

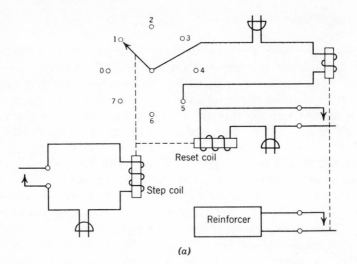

(a)

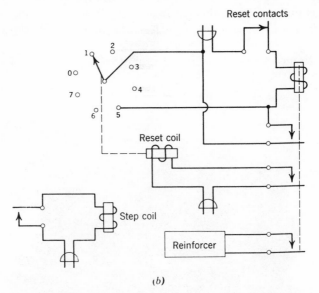

(b)

Fig. 8.11 A circuit using a resetting stepper. The stepper automatically delivers a reinforcement and resets to zero on the fifth closing of the microswitch. (b) The same basic circuit with positive resetting action.

lowing reason. When the arm arrives at position "5," the reset coil will be activated, allowing the arm to begin its travel back to position "0." But as soon at it leaves position "5," current stops flowing through the reset coil, and the ratchet may catch the arm before it gets all the way back to "0." To insure positive resetting, resettable stepping switches usually have an additional set of contacts, such as those labeled "reset contacts" in Fig. 8.10. These contacts are normally closed, but are forced open by the reset contact actuator when the arm is in the "0" position. The circuit in Fig. 8.11*b* illustrates the use of these contacts to obtain positive resetting action. When the arm arrives at position "5," a holding relay is actuated, which holds the resetting coil on until resetting is completed, completion being signalled by the opening of the reset contacts.

In many parts of the country, pinball machines serve as an excellent source of miscellaneous relays. Out-of-date machines or those that no longer work very well can often be purchased for $15 or $20, and the parts they contain are worth at least ten times that amount. For example, consider the unit that indicates the number of free plays earned. The number appearing in the replay window is one of a set of numbers printed on a drum, and the drum is mounted on the axle of a stepping relay. Each time a new replay is won, the relay advances one step, displaying a new number. Each time a game is played, the stepper moves one step backward, subtracting one from the total available replays. Thus the stepper must be an add–subtract stepper. At the owner's pleasure, all replays may be erased. This is done by pressing a switch that resets the stepping relay to zero. Therefore, the relay is an add–subtract, resetting relay. There are other more or less complicated stepping relays in most pinball machines (e.g., to keep score), as well as many standard relays, light bulbs, motors, etc. Usually these elements operate on 24 or 48 volts a-c, and the transformer necessary to obtain this from the 115-volt wall socket can be found somewhere in the pinball machine. (Transformers are discussed in Chapter 10.)

Problems

1. Given a 4P8T and a SP3T stepping relay, a push button, and two bulbs, program a probability guessing stimulus sequence such that successive pressings of the button automatically turn on either one bulb or the other according to a predetermined schedule that is random for 24 presses and then repeats.

2. A pigeon is trained to peck key *A* when a stimulus patch is lit and to peck key *B* when it is dark. The intensity of the patch is changed by changing the resistance in series with the lamp circuit in a stepwise manner. The keys are then connected to the intensity control circuit in such a way that a peck on key *A* makes the patch one step dimmer and a peck on key *B* makes it brighter. The pigeon will then keep the patch at his threshold brightness. [For example, dark adaptation in the pigeon may be measured this way. See D. S. Blough, "A Method for Obtaining Psychophysical Thresholds from the Pigeon," *J. Exp. Anal. Behav.*, 1 (1958), 31–43.] Design the circuit.

3. To maintain the pigeon's performance in the apparatus of Problem 2, he must be reinforced. Add a device to the circuit which automatically turns off the stimulus light on every 20th, 40th, 60th, etc., peck on either key, and then reinforces the pigeon for the next peck if it is on key *B* (the correct response). After the peck (right or wrong), the sequence takes up where it left off. Furthermore, on every 10th, 30th, 50th, etc., peck, the patch is lighted to well above threshold, and the pigeon is reinforced if the next peck is to key *A* (the correct response). Then the sequence resumes again.

4. Design an apparatus to reinforce a rat for double alternation in pressing two bars, i.e., one reinforcement for each *AABB* or *BBAA* sequence. He should not be reinforced for *BABAA*, etc., but *AAAABB* will be reinforced.

Chapter 9

Shock circuits

Electric shock has been widely used to motivate experimental subjects in the behavioral sciences. Two areas of confusion are evident in a great many of the studies in which shock is used. First, there is a lack of understanding of the physical principles which govern the parameters of the shock. Because of this, a number of unwarranted conclusions have been drawn about behavioral principles. Second, and closely related, there are very few studies of the behavioral effects of shock itself. For instance, there are several different sorts of shock that can be administered (e.g., constant current, constant voltage, sine wave, square wave, etc.) and, up to the time of this writing, there has not been a single study that unequivocally evaluates the relative qualities of any of the different kinds of shock.[1] This chapter contains an analysis of the physical characteristics of electric shock and a discussion of techniques for constructing devices which deliver shock.

FUNDAMENTALS OF SHOCK

The box pictured in Fig. 9.1 illustrates a common method of administering shock to animals. The floor of the box consists of a number of parallel metal rods held in place and separated by two strips of insulating material, usually plastic. When a rat stands on such a

[1] There are a few studies which approach this goal. See B. A. Campbell and R. Teghtsoonian, "Electrical and Behavioral Effects of Different Types of Shock Stimuli on the Rat," *J. Comp. Physiol. Psychol.*, **51** (1958), 185–192.

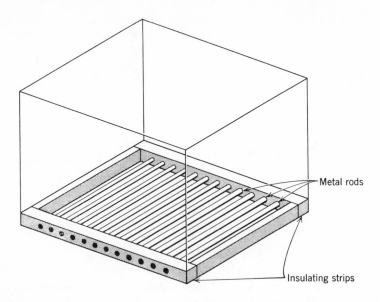

Metal rods

Insulating strips

Fig. 9.1   Apparatus for shocking a rat. The floor is made up of parallel, evenly spaced metal bars, insulated from each other.

floor, it is very likely that his feet will touch several different bars.   If a voltage were applied between each bar and every other one, current would pass through those parts of his anatomy which are bridging the gap between bars.   In the simplest shocking grid (the set of bars is called a grid), the bars are connected together so that a particular voltage appears between each bar and both of its neighbors.   This is accomplished by numbering all of the bars consecutively, and then connecting all of the even ones together and all of the odd ones together.   When the wire from the even-numbered bars is connected to one side of a battery and the wire from the odd-numbered ones to the other side, the battery voltage will appear between every adjacent pair of bars.   This type of connection is shown in Fig. 9.2a.   As it stands, such a shocking system has a number of limitations that will be discussed later.   However, its simplicity makes it useful for discussing certain aspects of electric shock which are fundamental to more complicated systems as well.

To simplify the situation further, assume that the rat happens to be standing with both front paws resting on an odd bar and both hind paws on an even one.   Figure 9.2b is a schematic representation of the electrical aspects of the rat and the shocker.   Current from the battery passes through the junction between a bar and the rat's front feet, through the cornified layers of skin, through the tissues of his legs and trunk, and back out the other set of legs and skin. In a sense, these parts of the rat are all in series with each other so that the same current must flow through all of them. If the total resistance of the path through the rat is 250,000 ohms (a typical value), and if the voltage is 100 volts, then the current flowing through the rat will be:

$$\frac{E}{R} = \frac{100}{0.25 \times 10^6} = 400 \text{ microamperes}$$

An important question is, "How shocking are 400 microamperes?" Or should we ask, "How shocking are 100 volts?" Or, "How shocking is a combination of 100 volts and 400 microamperes?" Consider the voltage question first. Phrased more exactly it is, "How effective to the rat is a 100-volt battery between the grids?" The more dead skin and dirt there are between the bars and his sensitive tissues, the higher is the rat's resistance (the term "rat" now includes the dead skin and dirt). Thus, less current will flow through him.

The circuit in Fig. 9.3 schematizes this situation. As the resistance due to dead skin increases, the voltage across the sensitive tissue, that is, the voltage that actually affects the rat, is reduced. This means that even though the battery happens to show 100 volts between its terminals at all times, the voltage experienced by the rat will be less than 100 volts, and will vary from time to time and from rat to rat. For example, rats usually urinate when they are subjected to the stress

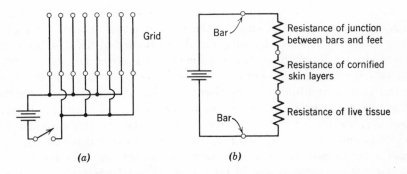

(a)   (b)

Fig. 9.2   (a) A simple circuit for delivering shock voltage to a grid such as the one illustrated in Fig. 9.1. The supply voltage appears between each adjacent pair of rods. This circuit has a number of faults that will be discussed later. (b) Schematic representation of the electrical aspects of the circuit in Fig. 9.2a, when a rat is standing on the grids.

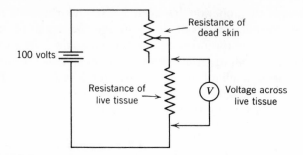

Fig. 9.3 Schematization of the change in shock resulting from changes in the resistance of the animal's dead skin. As the amount of dead skin increases, more of the source voltage is lost across that skin, and less is left to stimulate live tissue.

of electric shock and, since urine is a good conductor of electricity, its absorption by the dead skin can produce radical fluctuations in the voltage affecting the rat, even when the battery voltage is constant.

CONSTANT-VOLTAGE SHOCKER

One thing can be said unequivocally about the shock voltage in the circuit of Fig. 9.2. The voltage between the bars (across the whole animal including his dead skin) is constant. This is in contrast to the current flowing through the animal and the voltage actually affecting him, both of which frequently change in this circuit.

When a rat is being shocked through a circuit such as that in Fig. 9.2, the current through him and the voltage across his sensitive tissues may fluctuate because of changes in the resistance of his skin, but even more drastic fluctuations occur whenever he moves around. Under certain conditions and shocks, a rat will freeze, but in most cases he starts to run or jump. Every time he makes the slightest movement, the pressure exerted on the grids by his feet must change. Consequently, the area of contact between his feet and the bars must change. If he begins to jump up, his feet must push down harder on the bars and a larger area of skin will come in contact with the bars. The larger contact area means, in turn, that the total resistance of the rat to current flow between bars must decrease. These changes in resistance represent very large per cent changes in the total resistance, because the major part of the resistance of a rat on a grid is the resistance of the contacts between his skin and the bars. If an ohmmeter is connected between the bars of a grid on which a rat is walking, the resistance will be found to vary rapidly over at least a 1000% range. In this kind of shock circuit, each change in over-all resistance is accompanied by a directly proportional change in the current running through the rat. The current may fluctuate wildly while the voltage between bars stays constant.

In general, when a battery is connected directly between the grids, the circuit is said to deliver a constant-voltage shock, and it will be referred to as a constant-voltage circuit (recognizing the incorrect implications of that label). The reason for referring to the circuit in this manner will become clear as soon as nonconstant-voltage circuits are discussed.

CONSTANT-CURRENT SHOCKER

The relationship just described can be reversed so that the current stays virtually constant while the voltage fluctuates, if the shocker is connected as shown in Fig. 9.4. This is called a constant-current shocker. Only two things are different in this circuit: The battery voltage has been increased to 1000 volts and a 9-megohm resistor has been put in series with the rat and the battery. Suppose that the rat is standing still and has a resistance of 1 megohm. It can easily be shown by Ohm's law that there will be 100 microamperes flowing through the resistor and the rat, and that a voltage of 900 volts will appear across the resistor and 100 volts across the rat. Thus, so long as the rat is standing still, he is in exactly the same situation as with the constant-voltage shocker of Fig. 9.2. However, if he now should start to jump up and, in so doing, reduce his resistance to, say, 100,000

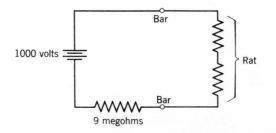

Fig. 9.4 A constant-current shock circuit. Large changes in the rat's resistance result in relatively small changes in the current passing through him.

ohms, the current through him will change from 1000/(1,000,000 +
9,000,000) = 100 microamperes to 1000/(100,000 + 9,000,000) = 110
microamperes. A tenfold change in his resistance will produce only a
10% change in the current flowing through him for the following
reason. The rat's resistance is a small part of the total resistance in
the circuit. Therefore, relatively big changes in his resistance have
only a small effect on the over-all circuit current. This circuit is thus
called a constant-current circuit. Note that, although the current
stays virtually constant through large changes in the rat's resistance,
the voltage across the rat will change drastically. Therefore this circuit is really a constant-current, variable-voltage circuit.

In general, any time the rat's resistance is a very large part of the
total resistance in a shocking circuit, that circuit tends to give a constant voltage and changing current between the grids. When the rat's
resistance constitutes a relatively small proportion of the total circuit
resistance, the circuit will deliver a relatively constant current and a
varying voltage. (Since resistance, voltage, and current are the only
three terms in Ohm's law, the only way to make a shocker that will
hold *both* voltage and current constant is to hold the resistance of the
rat constant too. This can be accomplished by strapping the electrodes directly and very firmly to the animal.)

MATCHED-IMPEDANCE SHOCKER

Several studies to be found in the literature have used a shock circuit
with properties about halfway between the two already discussed.
This circuit, called a matched-impedance circuit, is shown in Fig. 9.5.
Here, a resistance approximately in the range over which the rat's
resistance will fluctuate is connected in series with the battery. As the
animal moves, he undergoes less drastic changes in voltage than in a

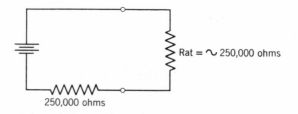

Fig. 9.5 A matched-impedance shock circuit.

constant-current circuit, and less drastic changes in current than in a constant-voltage circuit. On the other hand, neither current nor voltage is held constant. This can be thought of, then, as a sort of compromise circuit. It is called a matched-impedance circuit for a very simple reason. Just as the resistance of a rat or resistor is a measure of its ability to conduct a direct current, impedance is a measure of its ability to pass any kind of current, direct or alternating. In any given object such as a rat or a resistor, the impedance, measured in ohms, is either equal to or greater than the resistance, and can be considered to be made up of resistance plus certain other properties to be discussed later. A matched-impedance circuit is one in which the impedance of the external resistor is roughly matched to the impedance of the rat.

Whereas it is not appropriate to go into great detail here about the physiological and psychological aspects of shock, it should be pointed out that the preceding discussion concerning the unspecifiable electrical aspects of shock is far from complete. Actually, it seems unlikely that the total current passing through or the voltage across a rat is a very good index of anything. Current *density* (amperes per square inch cross-sectional area) through any given portion of the anatomy must be more closely correlated with the physiological effect of shock. With a constant-current circuit, the rat can reduce the current density by gripping the bars tightly to increase contact area and by crouching down to increase his body's cross-sectional area. In this regard, the constant-voltage circuit tends to give a more constant current density than the constant-current circuit.

Considerations of this type, derived from the purely physical properties of shock, have very important correlates in the behavior of the shocked animal. For instance, it would seem likely that a rat in a constant-current shocker would learn to crouch and freeze (because this reduces the current density) as well as not to jump off the grids (because at both the instant of leaving the grid and recontacting it, the areas of contact will be very small and the current density there very great). A rat in a constant-voltage shocker might learn the opposite pattern.

ALTERNATING-CURRENT SHOCK CIRCUITS

The previous discussion was based on shock circuits which use a battery as a voltage source. It is usually better, in practice as well as in theory, to use an a-c shock source.

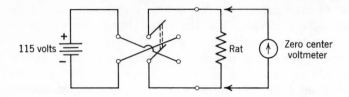

Fig. 9.6 A constant-voltage circuit to deliver an a-c (square-wave) shock. Each time the switch is thrown, the voltage across the rat reverses polarity.

All of the foregoing principles apply to a-c as well as to d-c shocks, and since the properties of a-c circuits have not yet been fully described, d-c circuits were used in the preceding discussion. However, there are certain properties peculiar to a-c circuits which are relevant to shock boxes. Consider the shock circuit in Fig. 9.6. This is similar to the constant-voltage circuit in Fig. 9.2, except that the voltage has been changed and a reversing switch introduced. The animal, in this circuit, would get an a-c shock. Current would flow through him just as in the d-c circuit, except that the direction of current flow would keep reversing itself each time the switch is thrown. Now suppose you were to connect a zero-center voltmeter across the grids in Fig. 9.6.[1] In a voltmeter, when the current flows one way, the pointer moves to the right. When it flows the other way, the pointer moves left. In the usual meter, a leftward movement cannot

[1] A zero-center meter is exactly the same as an ordinary meter except that the resting position of the pointer is in the middle of the scale instead of at the left-hand end.

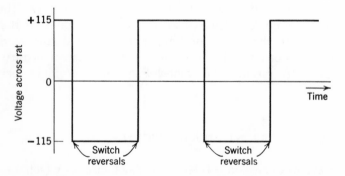

Fig. 9.7 A plot of the shock voltage of the circuit in Fig. 9.6 as a function of time.

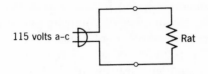

Fig. 9.8 A circuit to deliver a constant-voltage a-c shock (sine wave at 60 cycles per second).

be read, but in a zero-center meter it can.   When the reversing switch is in one position, the meter will read +115, and when it is reversed, the pointer will swing over until it reads —115 volts. A periodic repetition of the switching will result in the temporal voltage pattern shown in Fig. 9.7. The a-c voltage represented by this figure would be described as a square-wave shock of 115-volt amplitude, with a fundamental frequency equal to half the number of reversals per second. Square-wave shocks are used extensively to stimulate nerve tissue in physiological preparations.

   The shock from the circuit in Fig. 9.8 is a sine-wave shock, as represented in Fig. 9.9, because the voltage delivered to wall sockets is sinosoidal.   In almost all parts of the United States, the line power is held to a frequency of 60 cycles per second, and to a voltage of approximately 115 volts. For the sine wave, the term "fundamental frequency" has the same meaning as for the square wave. It is the number of cycles occurring per second. For the sine wave, the "fundamental frequency" is the only frequency, and so the term "fundamental" is usually dropped. The square wave can be said to contain many (theoretically an infinity of) harmonic frequencies in

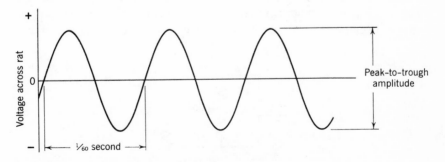

Fig. 9.9 A plot of the shock voltage in Fig. 9.8 as a function of time.

addition to the fundamental, and for this reason the term fundamental is used in describing the number of complete cycles per second.

The simplest measure of voltage of a sine wave is the so-called peak-to-trough amplitude, as indicated at the right in Fig. 9.9. But there is another more common measure of voltage that requires some explanation. If two light bulbs were lit, one by a *square-wave* of 115 volts (230 volts peak-to-trough) and the other by direct current at 115 volts, the two bulbs would be equally bright because the direction of current flow through a light bulb does not affect its brightness. If the direct current were now left across one bulb and a very low frequency sine-wave voltage of 230 volts peak-to-trough put across the other, the one lit by the sine wave would always be either dimmer or, at the very top and bottom of the cycle, equally bright. The average brightness thus would be less for the sine wave than for the direct current or for a square wave of equal peak-to-trough voltage. If the frequency were increased to, say, 60 cycles per second, the changes in voltage would be so rapid that the bulb would not follow them; its brightness would remain fairly constant at a level lower than the brightness of the d-c–powered bulb. To light a bulb with a sine wave and make it just as bright as one lit by 115 volts d-c, the magnitude of the sine wave would have to be increased. It turns out that the necessary peak-to-trough voltage of the sine wave is $\sqrt{2} \times 230 = 324$ volts. The power delivered by a sine wave of 324 volts, peak-to-trough, equals the power of direct current at 115 volts. Since it is generally more useful to specify power than peak-to-trough voltage, a-c voltages are usually rated in terms of their equivalent d-c voltages. Therefore, to say that the wall socket voltage is 115 volts a-c means it will light a bulb with the same brightness as a 115-volt d-c source. Its peak-to-trough voltage is about 324 volts. Whenever the voltage of a sine wave is given, it should be understood to mean the equivalent d-c voltage, not the peak-to-trough voltage. (This equivalent voltage is usually called the rms, or root-mean-square voltage, because it is actually the square root of the average of the

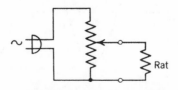

Fig. 9.10   Circuit to deliver a sine-wave shock adjustable from 0 to 115 volts.

square of the instantaneous voltages, integrated over one complete cycle.)

The shock circuit in Fig. 9.8 is a constant-voltage circuit and delivers a 115-volt, 60-cycle shock. For a lower voltage shock, a voltage divider may be added, as shown in Fig. 9.10. This divider works in exactly the same way as it would for a d-c supply. To make the circuit deliver more than 115 volts is not so easy. If it were direct current we could just add some more batteries in series, but the only source of alternating current usually available is the wall socket, at 115 volts. A simple and efficient device that gives higher or lower voltages than 115 volts is called the transformer, which will be discussed in some detail in the next chapter. To make the circuit in Fig. 9.8 into a constant-current shocker, a very high resistance must be added in series with the source and the animal. Such a circuit definitely requires a transformer to obtain higher source voltages.

MISCELLANEOUS CONSIDERATIONS IN
THE DESIGN OF SHOCK BOXES[1]

Grid Construction

When an animal is disturbed, as by shock, he may defecate. The bars of a grid floor must be far enough apart for the feces to fall through. If they do not, they may rest between two bars and short-circuit the shock to the animal. The bars should be of a material that does not corrode readily, because corrosion, helped along by urine, can form a layer that insulates the animal's feet from the bars.

When a rat has been shocked a few times, he tends to stand with his body oriented perpendicular to the direction of the bars. Therefore, if you want him to press a key at the end of the box to turn off the shock, for instance, be sure that the grid bars run across the box, not lengthwise.

Scramblers

In some types of training, a single shock is given in a pulse so short that the animal cannot move very much during the time it is actually on. However, in many applications, the shock is left on for an ap-

[1] Precautions necessary in circuits to shock human subjects will be discussed in Chapter 10.

preciable period, and the animal runs and jumps. In these cases, if the voltage is connected simply between odd and even numbered bars, the rat will soon learn to avoid shock by standing so that his feet are all on odd or on even numbered bars. This difficulty could be avoided if the grids were put so close together that each foot would

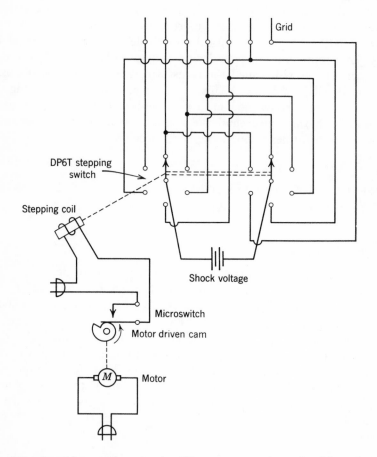

Fig. 9.11 A grid-scrambler circuit. The motor continuously drives the cam, which, in turn, closes the microswitch once each revolution. Each closing of the microswitch advances the DP6T stepping switch one step. The shock voltage thus sweeps from one end of the grid to the other. At any given instant, the voltage appears only between one pair of adjacent bars. Thus, if the rat does not touch two adjacent bars, he will not be shocked. However, this scrambling principle may be extended in such a way that the shock simultaneously sweeps pairs of bars separated by one bar, two bars, etc., by using a stepping switch with more decks (e.g., a 4P6T stepper).

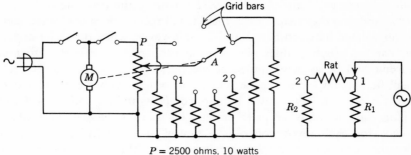

P = 2500 ohms, 10 watts
All other resistors are 100 K ohms

Fig. 9.12 A simple scrambler circuit. The motor drives the contact arm *A* continuously. Suppose the rat is touching bars 1 and 2. When the arm arrives at 1, the circuit is as represented (in a simplified form) in the diagram on the right. The shock voltage appears across the parallel combination of: (*a*) one of the resistors; and (*b*) the rat and another resistor in series. The shock circuit is thus most similar to a matched-impedance circuit. When the contact arm arrives at the bar 2, another shock will be delivered. The rat will be shocked twice for each revolution of the contact arm. (From Wyckoff, L. B. and H. A. Page, *Amer. J. Psychol.*, **67** (1954), 154.)

have to overlap more than one bar, but then the grid would quickly become short circuited by feces. The solution is to introduce the voltage to the grids in a continuously changing pattern, in such a way that the animal cannot avoid shock by assuming any particular position. Devices that do this are called grid scramblers. A fairly simple one is diagramed in Fig. 9.11. In this circuit, each time the stepping switch moves one step, the shock voltage is shifted to a new adjacent pair of bars. The stepper is driven continuously by the cam and microswitch, and the shock sweeps from one end of the grid to the other. The disadvantage of this simple scrambler is that the animal can avoid the shock altogether if he never touches two adjacent bars. A better system is the one diagrammed in Fig. 9.12.[1] The potentiometer *P* serves as an intensity adjustment. The motor *M* drives the contact arm *A* around so that it continuously sweeps the grids, connecting each in turn to the slider arm of the potentiometer. All of the grids are also connected, through resistors, to one end of the potentiometer. In this way, the animal will be shocked at least once for each revolution of the contact arm, no matter what pair of bars he straddles. For example, suppose the rat is touching

[1] From a paper by L. B. Wyckoff and H. A. Page, *Amer. J. Psychol.*, 67, (1954), p. 154.

the bars labeled 1 and 2 in Fig. 9.12.   During the time the slider is at any position other than 1 or 2, the rat will receive no shock, since there is no voltage between bars 1 and 2.   However, when the slider arrives at bar 1 (which it does once during each revolution), the effective circuit will be as diagrammed at the right in Fig. 9.12.   The voltage will be applied across the rat and R_2 in series.   When the slider contacts bar 2, the voltage will be applied across the rat and R_1 in series. Thus, no matter what pairs of bars he touches, he will be shocked twice for each revolution of the motor, at an intensity determined by the setting of the potentiometer and by the size of the resistors (100,000 ohms).   The minimum shock intensity from this circuit is zero (when the slider on the potentiometer is all the way down), and the authors (see footnote, p. 131) state that the maximum value attainable, with the slider all the way up) is a strong shock for a rat.

The scramblers described thus far have used stepping switches and rotating commutator arms to connect the shock between changing sets of grid bars.   A number of scramblers have been developed which employ different means of switching (e.g., gas tubes, transistors, relays), but all of them are based upon the same principle, namely, that the shock voltage must be switched rapidly between different sets of bars.

Chapter 10

Transformers

Figure 10.1 is a drawing of a bar magnet together with a schematic representation of its magnetic field. A magnetic field is a construct having to do with the observable fact that objects in the neighborhood of the bar may be affected by the presence of the bar. Its effect on an object varies depending on where the object is with respect to the bar. This fact is represented by the statement that the strength of the magnetic field varies from place to place around the bar. The lines in Fig. 10.1, called lines of force, are a schematic representation of the spatial distribution of the strength of the field. The closer the lines, the stronger the field. Since this method of representing a magnetic field facilitates the explanation of many phenomena associated with magnetism, it will be used throughout the chapter.

When a steady current is passed through a coil of wire that is wrapped around an iron core, a magnetic field is set up in and around the core. This magnetic field, represented in Fig. 10.2, is identical to the field of a permanent bar magnet; the same method of generating magnetism has already been mentioned in connection with meter movements (see Chapter 1) and relays (see Chapter 6). The magnetic field generated by a steady current is fixed and unchanging even though the electrons ultimately responsible for its maintenance are themselves moving through the coil. However, as soon as the amount of current flowing through the coil is changed in any way, the field changes accordingly. For instance, if the current should suddenly be

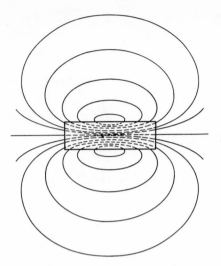

Fig. 10.1 Schematic representation of a bar magnet and its magnetic field. All the lines are actually loops, but some of the loops are too large to be represented on the diagram.

doubled, the field would double in strength, as represented in Fig. 10.3. After doubling the current, there will be twice as many lines of force spread out over a larger volume than before. If one of these hypothetical lines of force were visible while the current were in the process of doubling, it would be seen to move outward. In other

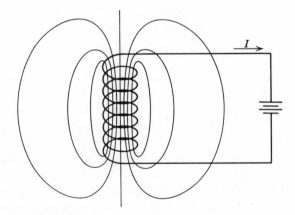

Fig. 10.2 Schematic representation of the magnetic field generated by the passage of current I through a coil of wire.

words, increasing the current through the coil not only adds more lines to the field but also causes the field to expand. Conversely, if the current were reduced, the field would collapse.

Now store that concept for a moment and consider the opposite sort of phenomenon, namely, the effect that a magnetic field has on a coil of wire. If you have a permanent magnet at hand, you can demonstrate certain phenomena very readily. Connect your meter directly across the two ends of the coil on your sensitive relay, and set the meter to its most sensitive scale (e.g., 100 microamperes, 1 volt, etc.). Then put the magnet down next to the relay coils. Some of the lines of force from the magnet will now be passing through the relay coil but you will notice that nothing happens to the meter (see Fig. 10.4). In general, a stationary magnetic field has no effect on a coil of wire. But a moving field does affect the coil. Any time that lines of force move with respect to a coil of wire, they induce a voltage into it. (There is one particular direction of motion of a field with respect to a coil which will not induce a voltage into the coil, but that special case will be ignored for the present discussion.) It is

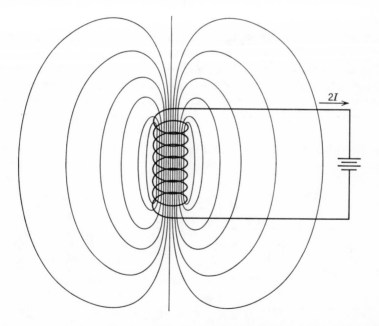

Fig. 10.3   The magnetic field of the coil in Fig. 10.2 when the current through it is doubled. The field is represented as having twice as many lines, distributed over a larger area (volume).

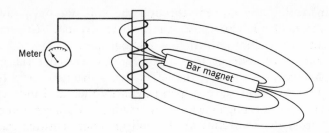

Fig. 10.4 Representation of a bar magnet close to a relay coil. Some of the lines of force intersect the coil. So long as the magnet is stationary with respect to the coil, no current will flow around the loop containing the meter.

convenient to think of this process as one in which each line of magnetic force tends to push some of the free electrons in the wire along in front of it as it moves. You can observe this by moving the magnet rapidly past the relay coil so that its lines of force move through the coil. If you have a reasonably strong magnet and if the meter is set at a sensitive scale, the pointer will jump to the right when the magnet passes in one direction, and to the left when it moves in the opposite direction. The lines of force are pushing electrons one way or the other. Note, though, that the needle reads nonzero only when the field is actually moving.

These two phenomena, the generation of a magnetic field by current flowing in a coil and the induction of current in a coil by a moving magnetic field, are combined in an extensively used device called the transformer. Its principle of operation is fairly simple. Figure 10.5 shows two coils of wire, one connected through a switch to a battery, and the other to a meter. In Fig. 10.5*a*, the switch is open and no

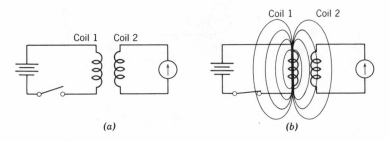

Fig. 10.5 (*a*) A circuit containing two coils of wire, near each other but not connected together electrically. (*b*) Representation of the circuit after the switch has been closed. Some of the lines of force from coil 1 intersect coil 2, but so long as the current through coil 1 is constant, no current will flow through coil 2.

current flows in either circuit.   Figure 10.5*b* shows the state of affairs
when the switch has been closed and current is flowing steadily
through coil 1.   Although the lines of force from coil 1 are passing
through coil 2, no voltage is generated in coil 2 because the lines are
not moving.   However, between the time when no current flows
through coil 1 and when the full current is flowing, that is, between
Figs. 10.5*a* and 10.5*b*, the lines of force must have multiplied and ex-
panded through coil 2 from zero lines and volume to their positions
in Fig. 10.5*b*.   During the time when the field was being built up, a
voltage must have been induced into coil 2.   Similarly, if the switch
were opened again, the field would collapse and, during that short
time, a voltage would be induced into coil 2 as well.   The voltage in
coil 2 would have the opposite polarity in the two cases because the
lines of force would be traveling in opposite directions during the
buildup and collapse of the field.   The buildup and the collapse do
not occur instantaneously but take finite times which depend upon
the characteristics of the circuit.

Now suppose the battery and switch in Fig. 10.5 were replaced by
an a-c source, for instance, the 115-volt a-c wall socket supply, as
diagrammed in Fig. 10.6.   In this case, the current through coil 1
will build up from zero to a maximum, then back through zero again,
etc., repeating this complete cycle 60 times a second.   In turn, the
magnetic field will also build up and collapse over and over again,
continuously generating a changing and reversing voltage in coil 2.
This kind of combination of coils is called a transformer.

For more efficient transfer of power from coil 1 to coil 2, both coils
are typically wound on a single iron core, because such a core tends
to channel the magnetic fields, keeping the lines of force in the close
vicinity of the coils.   The schematic diagram for a transformer, together with photographs of actual transformers, is shown in Fig. 10.7.

If coil 1 consists of the same number of turns of wire as coil 2, the
voltage generated in coil 2 will be the same as that put into coil 1.
However, if there are, say, ten times as many turns on coil 2 as on

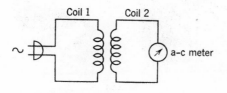

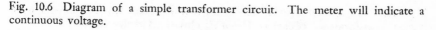

Fig. 10.6 Diagram of a simple transformer circuit. The meter will indicate a
continuous voltage.

coil 1, the lines of force from coil 1 will cut across coil 2 at ten times as many places. Therefore the voltage generated in coil 2 will be ten times as great as the input voltage to coil 1. In general:

$$\frac{V_i}{V_o} = \frac{N_i}{N_o}$$

where V_i = the input voltage
  V_o = the output voltage
  N_i = the number of turns on the input coil
  N_o = the number of turns on the output coil

It is this phenomenon that makes the transformer so useful. For example, suppose that you were designing a circuit to give a rat a strong constant-current shock. For the shock to have a relatively constant current, a large resistance must be in series with the rat, as was explained in Chapter 9. In fact, the resistance must be large

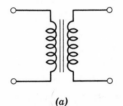

(a)

(b)

Fig. 10.7 (a) Circuit symbol for a transformer, and (b) a photograph of various transformers. (*Courtesy* Helen E. Howell, Berkeley, Calif.)

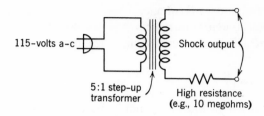

Fig. 10.8   Constant-current a-c shock-delivery circuit.

enough that almost all of the voltage from the source is lost across the resistor, and only about one-tenth of it actually affects the rat. To give the rat a good strong shock, the source voltage must be higher than the 115 volts from the wall.   A 50-volt shock, for example, requires a 500-volt source.   The solution is to put between the wall socket and the shock box a transformer which has about five times as many turns on the output (or secondary) coil as it has on the input (or primary) coil.   The circuit for this shocker is shown in Fig. 10.8.   The transformer is called a step-up transformer.

Electric-eye systems which detect the presence of a rat in an alley require a small source of light such as a flashlight bulb or an automobile taillight bulb.   These bulbs are typically rated at 6 volts. Flashlight batteries could be used to light the bulbs, but they burn out quickly, and storage batteries are inconvenient.   However, a small *step-down* transformer which takes the 115 volts from a wall socket and transforms it to 6 volts is cheap, available, and never wears out. Such a transformer has approximately 20 times as many turns on its input coil as on its output coil.

Note that a transformer is so named because it transforms one alternating voltage into another alternating voltage.   It does not transform direct current into alternating current (that is accomplished by a device called a converter) nor alternating current into direct current (that device is called a rectifier).   A transformer is strictly an a-c device, and as such can be quickly and irreversibly damaged if it is connected across a d-c source.

TRANSFORMER RATINGS

When buying a transformer you should specify:

1. Input (primary) voltage and frequency (usually 115 volts, 60 cycles).

2. Output (secondary) voltage.
3. Output (secondary) current.
4. Other special requirements such as size, etc.

Input (Primary) Voltage

The transformer is most commonly used to provide a convenient source of a-c power at a voltage other than the one provided at the wall socket.[1] There is only one type of transformer used at all frequently in the laboratory that has a rated input voltage or frequency other than 115 volts, 60 cycles. It is called an output transformer and is used in certain electronic circuits which will not be discussed here.

Many transformers found in surplus stores are rated for 400-cycle voltages. They are common because the standard frequency for certain military devices, such as airplanes, is 400 cycles rather than 60 cycles. A 400-cycle transformer will not operate properly on a 60-cycle voltage.

Output (Secondary) Voltage

The output, or secondary voltage, is simply the voltage that the transformer will deliver across its secondary coil terminals when the rated input voltage is applied to its primary coil. If you wish to light a 6-volt bulb from a wall socket, order a transformer with an output voltage of 6 volts.[2]

Many transformers are built to give a variety of output voltages all at the same time. This is sometimes accomplished by winding two or more electrically separate output coils on the same core, as diagrammed in Fig. 10.9a. That arrangement is very common in transformers designed to supply power for electronic devices. Most radios, for instance, require a low voltage, e.g., 6 volts, to light the tubes, and a high voltage, e.g., 300 volts, to drive electrons through the vacuum in the tubes (see Chapter 14).

Multiple-output voltages are also commonly obtained by the method diagrammed in Fig. 10.9b. Connections are made at different places along a single output coil. It has already been pointed out that the

[1] This wall socket voltage is 115 volts, 60 cycles almost everywhere in the United States. While in some geographical areas the line frequency is 50 cps, a transformer built to operate on 60 cps will function just as adequately, except for the most demanding applications, on this lower frequency. Therefore, the input voltage of a transformer will almost always be 115 volts, 60 cps.

[2] The fundamental frequency of the output voltage always equals the input frequency.

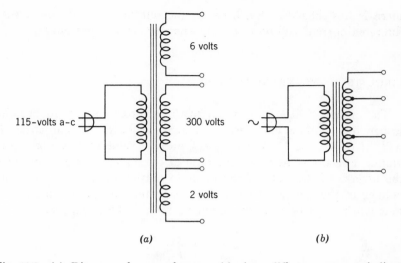

6 volts

115-volts a–c

300 volts

2 volts

(a)   (b)

Fig. 10.9 (a) Diagram of a transformer with three different output windings. (b) Diagram of a transformer with a multiple-tapped output winding.

more turns there are on the secondary winding, the higher the voltage that is generated. It should be evident from Fig. 10.9b that different pairs of terminals have different numbers of turns between them and will, therefore, deliver different voltages. The wires connected along the coil are called taps, and this kind of transformer is said to have a multiple-tapped output winding. The most common tap is one half-way between the two ends of the output coil and such a transformer is said to be center-tapped. Thus, if you want a transformer that will deliver either 6 or 12 volts, ask for a 12-volt-output, center-tapped transformer.

Output Current

Suppose that you wish to light three 6-volt, 5-ampere bulbs in parallel. You must order a transformer that gives a 6-volt output with an output current rating of at least 15 amperes; that is, the output coil must be able to carry 15 amperes without getting too hot. Note that this is a maximum current rating. If a transformer has a 6-volt, 15-ampere output rating, it will always put out about 6 volts, but it will not necessarily deliver 15 amperes at all times. If there is nothing connected between the two terminals of the output coil, it will not deliver any current at all (6 volts/infinite ohms = 0 ampere). But if there is less than 0.4 ohm between the output terminals, more than the rated current will flow, and the transformer will get too hot.

CIRCUITS USING TRANSFORMERS

The circuit in Fig. 10.10 will light three automobile headlight bulbs in parallel. If these bulbs draw 5 amperes each, the current labeled I_2 will, of course, be 15 amperes a-c. But the value of I_1 is not so obvious. For any transformer the ratio of the input to output current is the inverse of the ratio of the input to output voltage. If the input voltage of the transformer is twice the output voltage, the input current will always be half the output current. This is expressed as

$$\frac{V_{input}}{V_{output}} = \frac{I_{output}}{I_{input}}$$

Note that this equation can also be expressed as

$$V_{input} \times I_{input} = V_{output} \times I_{output}$$

(i.e.)

$$\text{Input watts} = \text{output watts}$$

In other words, if a certain amount of power is coming out of a transformer, the same amount will be going in. This makes sense as long as the transformer itself does not use up much power. Most transformers operate so efficiently that errors introduced by using these equations are negligible. In the example in Fig. 10.10, we are given the output current (15 amperes), the output voltage (6 volts), and the input voltage (115 volts). Therefore

$$I_{input} = \frac{15 \times 6}{115} = 0.78 \text{ ampere}$$

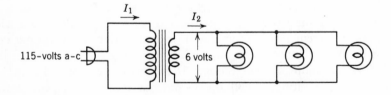

Fig. 10.10   Circuit to light three automobile headlight bulbs in parallel. I_1 is the input current and I_2 the output current of the transformer.

To extend this treatment, consider what happens when there is no connection (an infinite resistance) between the two output terminals of the transformer. The output voltage will still be 6 volts, but now the output current is zero. The output power is zero watts, and therefore the input power must also be zero watts. Since the input voltage is not zero, the input current must be zero. In other words, according to this equation, a transformer plugged into the wall will not draw any current in its primary as long as nothing is connected across its secondary. This conclusion looks peculiar but is true for all practical purposes.

ESTIMATING THE RATINGS OF AN UNKNOWN TRANSFORMER

Transformers which have no ratings engraved on them can usually be found in the dark corners of the laboratory. This section will describe several ways in which you may start to classify them.

First of all, if what you think might be a transformer has only two wires coming out of it, it is a choke rather than a transformer. A choke looks like a transformer but it consists of only a single coil of wire on an iron core.

If there are either three of four terminals on the unknown transformer and they are labeled with letters such as b, p, or g, it is an output transformer and should not be used except in certain electronic applications which will not be discussed here. But if the transformer has at least four terminals or wires, and if they are not labeled with the letters, b, p, or g, it may be usable. The easiest way to determine its output voltage is to apply 115 volts, 60 cycles per second, to the primary coil and measure the voltages resulting in the secondary or secondaries. On some transformers the primary is labeled "primary," or "input," or "115 volts a-c," and then this procedure is straightforward, but usually there are no such markings and you have to guess which wires connect to the input coil. When there are only four wires or terminals and none is labeled, the four must be divided into two pairs, one pair from the input and the other from the output coil. If the pairing is not obvious from the geography of the transformer, it can be determined simply by using an ohmmeter to find out which pairs of wires are connected together. Now examine the leads themselves. If one pair consists of fairly heavy wires, it is very likely that the unit is a step-down transformer and that the heavy pair are the secondary leads. If one pair of terminals is mounted on a large ceramic holder, that pair is probably the output of a very-high-voltage transformer (e.g., 5000 volts or more). If neither is true, either coil can be used as the primary and the other as the secondary. In one case you will have a step-up transformer, and in the other a step-down transformer. To find out the ratio of input to output voltage, one pair of terminals may be connected across the 115-volt wall voltage, and the voltage between the others measured with an a-c voltmeter. However, since it is possible that the application of 115 volts to one of the coils will damage it, a safer procedure is to increase the input voltage gradually from zero to 115 volts, stopping if the transformer begins to heat up.

If there are five wires on an unknown transformer, it is probable that the fifth wire is a center tap on the output coil. If so, an ohm-meter will indicate that there is one pair and one trio of connected wires. The output voltages (two of them) can then be measured by applying a known a-c voltage across the pair and measuring the voltages between pairs of the three remaining wires.

When there are more than five wires or terminals on a transformer, the job becomes a lot more difficult. In general, the best procedure is to find out with an ohmmeter which wires are connected to each other, and then try to reconstruct the circuit diagram of the trans-former from this information. Suppose you find a transformer with eight wires coming out of its casing, and an ohmmeter indicates that there are one pair and two groups of three. Because primaries rarely have center taps, the pair is very likely the primary. Then examine the wires themselves. If in one of the groups of three, two of the wires are thick, the chances are very good that the group of three is a low-voltage output coil with a center tap (probably 6 volts), and that the other group of three is a high-voltage output coil with a center tap (e.g., 300 volts).

It is very difficult for an unpracticed worker to judge the output-current rating of an unknown transformer. The only real way to determine this is to let the transformer draw some current and see if it gets hot. This is done by putting the rated voltage across the input terminals and connecting a variable resistor across the output. Then gradually increase the current by decreasing the resistance until the transformer either gets hot or is delivering the required current. A good criterion for "hot" is this: If you can hold your hand against the transformer, it is not overheating. If you have to pull your hand away, the transformer is overloaded. Any transformer running near its rated load will be hot, but it should not be so hot that you cannot hold your hand against it.

ADJUSTABLE-VOLTAGE TRANSFORMERS

One of the most useful gadgets around a laboratory is the adjustable voltage transformer, often referred to as "Variac." (Variac is a trade name for a particular, widely sold brand of adjustable voltage transformer.) The customary input voltage to this type of transformer is 115 volts, 60 cycles, and the output can be adjusted continuously from zero to 115 or zero to 140 volts by turning a knob on the top. Figure 10.11*a* shows a circuit diagram for a 0- to 115-volt adjustable transformer, and a 0- to 140-volt adjustable transformer is presented in the circuit diagram of Fig. 10.11*b*. The device in Fig. 10.11*a* resembles a potentiometer connected as a voltage divider. But the similarity is somewhat misleading, as can be seen from the fact that a potentiometer hooked up as shown in Fig. 10.11*b* would deliver a maximum of only 115 volts. The theory of operation of this sort of transformer is too complicated to be discussed herein. At any given setting of the slider arm, it acts like a normal, 2-coil transformer except that there is a direct electric connection between the input and the output. This connection is sometimes important, as will be pointed out in the next section. Adjustable voltage transformers are very convenient for changing the intensity of light bulbs, the speed of motors, etc. They are particularly useful for testing devices the ratings of which are unknown. For example, suppose that you need a relay and you find one in the stockpile, but the coil voltage required to make it operate is unknown. Connect it across the output of an adjustable-voltage transformer and gradually increase the voltage from zero until it closes firmly. Then read the required voltage with a voltmeter. (If the relay never closes firmly but just buzzes, it is a d-c relay.)

The same procedure can be applied to other devices such as un-

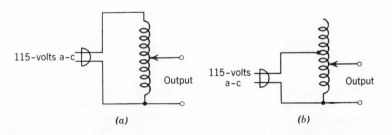

Fig. 10.11   (*a*) Diagram of a transformer whose output voltage is adjustable from 0 to 115 volts.   (*b*) Diagram of a 0 to 140-volt adjustable voltage transformer.

labeled motors or transformers: increase the applied voltage gradually until the devices operate properly.

ISOLATION TRANSFORMERS

There is a class of transformers called isolation transformers which usually have the same number of turns of wire on the primary as on

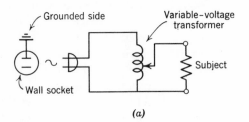

(a)

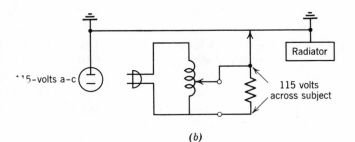

(b)

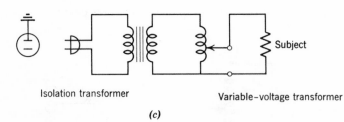

(c)

Fig. 10.12   (a) Circuit to shock subjects. This circuit should not be used because of the serious shock hazard. (b) Diagram of the actual circuit when a subject, being shocked by the circuit in Fig. 10.12a touches any grounded object. The full wall-socket voltage appears across the subject. (c) A safe circuit for shocking human subjects. The isolation transformer eliminates the shock hazard of the circuit in Fig. 10.12a.

the secondary, so that they neither step up nor step down the input voltage. They are used when it is desired to isolate a circuit electrically from the source of power. For example, suppose that you constructed the very simple device shown in Fig. 10.12*a* to deliver a weak electric shock to a human subject. One side of the wall socket is already connected to "ground," that is, to the earth itself, and to the water pipes, radiator, etc. This side of the socket is so labeled in the diagram of Fig. 10.12*a*. Now suppose that the subject reaches over and touches some metal object that is in contact with a radiator. He will be completing the circuit shown in Fig. 10.12*b*, and will no longer be a useful subject. This possibility can be eliminated by placing an isolation transformer between the adjustable voltage transformer and the wall socket, as in Fig. 10.12*c*.

CONSTANT VOLTAGE TRANSFORMERS

The voltage at the wall socket is usually said to be 115 volts. Actually, that voltage varies widely from time to time. It is a common experience to see the room lights dim when the refrigerator goes on. The refrigerator motor, when it first turns on, draws a large current which flows through the wires leading into the house and to the wall socket. The increased current running through the resistance of those wires causes an increased voltage drop in the wires, and less voltage is left to heat the lights. In and around the laboratory, and all along the circuit that includes the power station and the laboratory, devices turn on and off repeatedly, so that it is not unusual for the voltage at the wall to vary from 90 to 130 volts during the day. (The voltage can be higher than 115 because, to overcome the average voltage loss in the wires, the power company delivers more than 115 volts to the system. If everyone but you should suddenly turn off everything electrical, all of your light bulbs would burn out.) For many devices, such changes in voltage do not matter very much (e.g., fan motors, relays), but several types of apparatus are very sensitive to voltage changes and must be protected from them. All laboratory apparatus in which the intensity of a light bulb is important fall into this category because relatively small changes in line voltage will produce large changes in any lamp's brightness. For example, variations in the line voltage can be a source of great variance in tachistoscopic studies.

Devices which take variable a-c inputs and deliver constant-voltage a-c outputs are called voltage regulators or voltage stabilizers and may be ordered at any electronics supply store. There are a number of different types of voltage regulators, some considerably more costly than others. The cheapest, and one which meets most requirements, is called a constant-voltage transformer. It has no moving parts and is essentially a standard transformer built around a special core. The molecules of metal in any transformer core are involved in the transfer of energy from the input to the output coil. In a constant-voltage transformer, all of the core molecules are brought into action when the instantaneous input voltage is, say, 90 volts. The coils are wound so that the output voltage is 115 volts under this condition. Any further increase in the input voltage cannot affect the output voltage appreciably because all of the core molecules are already involved (the core is said to be saturated). This transformer will, therefore, give almost constant output voltage for input voltages ranging from 90 to some higher voltage where the system begins to break down. Typically, the upper limit is approximately 130 volts. Transformers of this type are built with various output-current capacities from about $\frac{1}{10}$ ampere up to 10 or 20 amperes. The rating is usually stated in units, called volt-amperes, which are very closely related to watts. If you want 115 volts at about 4 amperes, buy a 500-volt-ampere unit. (For a-c circuits, power—in watts—is sometimes different from the simple product of volts times amperes. However, this difference can be ignored for all of the applications discussed in this book.)

The constant-voltage transformers described above have several defects which may be of consequence in certain applications. First, they only hold the voltage stable to about 1% of its nominal level. For the rare situation in which something better is needed, a more expensive unit must be bought. Second, these transformers usually hum and, because of this, should not be used when absolute quiet is needed. A third defect is that, since the core saturates in the normal range of input voltages, the output wave form is a flat-topped wave that approaches the shape of a square wave. For the rare occasions when a very low harmonic content is required of the supply voltage, regulators which give pure sine-wave outputs can be purchased.

Voltage regulators are not to be confused with the very common piece of electronic equipment called a regulated power supply. The term "power supply," when it is applied to a single unit of equipment, usually refers to a unit that supplies d-c power. A regulated, or stabilized, power supply unit is one that delivers a constant *d-c* output voltage independent of changes in the line voltage. (See Chapter 15 for a discussion of d-c power supplies.)

Chapter 11

Motors

Electric motors range in size from ones much smaller than the toy motor mounted on your circuit board to motors that pull railroad trains. There is a complex and highly developed technology associated with the large motors used in industry, but most of it is not relevant to the small motors used in behavior research. Useful laboratory motors usually generate less than 1 horsepower, and are called fractional horsepower motors. Their use does not require a very profound understanding of the basic principles of motor action, and in this chapter, such principles will only be touched upon. Behavioral research workers are primarily concerned with the motors' speed characteristics, and these will be the main topic of this chapter.

There are only a few considerations which need to be taken into account when choosing an electric motor. The most important ones are the force it will exert, its speed of rotation, and the constancy or adjustability of its speed.

TORQUE

The force that a motor will exert is usually stated in terms of torque, a word that may need some explanation. If a device is to lift an object weighing 1 pound, it must exert more than 1 pound of force. The machine in Fig. 11.1a will do this. It is simply a weight, weighing a little more than 1 pound, on a string that runs over a pulley. The device in Fig. 11.1b will also lift a 1-pound object. However, because of the well-known laws of the lever, it is not really correct to give the

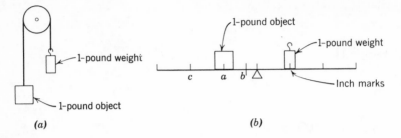

(a)   *(b)*

Fig. 11.1   (*a*) A simple machine to lift a 1-pound object.   (*b*) Another machine to lift a 1-pound object.   The bar, marked off in inches, pivots about its center.   The device exerts a torque of 1 pound-inch.

machine in Fig. 11.1*b* a rating of 1 pound of force.   It exerts 1 pound of force at the place labeled *a* in the figure, but exerts 3 pounds at *b*, and ½ pound at *c*.   It would be more completely specified if it were given a rating such as "3 pounds at one third inch."   Torque is the term that applies to this sort of combination of force and distance. The torque of the device in Fig. 11.1*b* is 1 pound-inch.   This rating means that the device will exert 1 pound of force at 1 inch, ½ pound at 2 inches, etc.   In general, the product of the force and the distance equals 1 pound-inch.   The mode of movement of this lever is one of rotation around a pivotal point.   Any device, such as an electric motor, that has a rotational mode of movement can be most concisely rated in terms of its torque.   For example, the motor needed to lift the weight in Fig. 11.2 must be one rated at at least 10 ounce-inches.

A motor rating that is related to torque is horsepower.   Horsepower is directly proportional to the product of torque and speed.   (A 1-horsepower motor will lift a 550-pound weight 1 foot per second.)

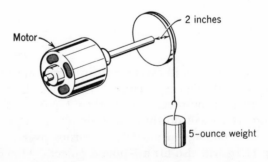

Fig. 11.2   A motor and pulley to lift a weight.   In order that the weight be lifted, the motor must exert a torque of more than 10 ounce-inches.

Most laboratory motors deliver ⅕ horsepower or less, and 1-horse-power electric motors are fairly large. (Vacuum cleaner motors range from about ¾ to 1½ horsepower.)

SPEED CHARACTERISTICS

Electric motors can be classified into three types, according to their speed characteristics. For the purposes of this discussion, the types will be called (1) moderately constant, not very adjustable speed, (2) adjustable speed, and (3) absolutely constant speed.

Moderately Adjustable, Not Very Constant Speed Motors

Most of the motors used in laboratory equipment run on alternating current at relatively fixed speeds. A typical speed is 1700 revolutions per minute. By using built-in gear boxes, the output shafts of many such motors are made to turn at slower rates.

As long as this type of motor is not severely overloaded, it will run at a speed reasonably close to its rated rpm. (The rated speed is usually stamped on the nameplate.) However, changes in the torque needed to turn the load, and changes in the line voltage, will result in changes in the speed. For this reason such motors should not be used when speed control is critical. Neither should they be used when it is necessary to adjust the speed of rotation. Reducing the input voltage will slow this kind of motor down, but it will also greatly reduce its torque. As a consequence, if the voltage is cut in half, the motor will either run at a very erratic speed or stop altogether. If the label on a motor does not indicate that it belongs to either of the two categories to be discussed below, it probably belongs to this first category.

Adjustable-Speed Motors

Frequently an experiment requires a motor the speed of which is adjustable and only moderately constant once its level has been set. There is one type of motor that fulfills this requirement very well. It is variously called a series motor, a universal motor, or a sewing machine motor. If any of those terms is stamped on the nameplate of an unknown motor, or if the nameplate simply says a-c/d-c, it is a series motor. The speed of a series motor may be easily adjusted over a ten-to-one range by running the motor from the output of an adjustable voltage transformer.   When controlled in this way, the motor will deliver a substantial amount of torque at all speeds.

When a series motor is connected across a source of power, the amount of current it draws is inversely related to its speed of rotation. For example, if a large load is suddenly added to the shaft, slowing it down, the motor will draw a correspondingly large current.   If the source of power contains an appreciable internal resistance, this increase in current will cause an increased voltage drop across the resistance, and less voltage will be available to run the motor.   The torque will consequently be reduced.   Since the internal resistance of an adjustable voltage transformer is quite small, it offers a good means of controlling the speed of a series motor.   However, if a series resistance or a potentiometer is used to control the voltage to the motor, the motor will lose torque and its speed will become unstable when it is reduced.

Series motors typically turn at relatively high speeds (5000 to 10,000 rpm) when run at rated voltage, but they may be purchased with built in gear boxes which reduce the maximum rated output speeds to almost any lower value.

Constant-Speed Motors

There are many applications in which the speed of a motor must be absolutely constant, e.g., when a motor is used to time a sequence of stimuli.   In these cases, the motor needed is called a synchronous motor.   A synchronous motor will run at exactly the speed for which it is rated over a very wide range of applied loads and voltages.   Almost all electric clocks, for example, are driven by synchronous motors. In such a motor, the armature is driven by what amounts to a rotating magnetic field, and the rate of rotation of the field depends only upon the physical structure of the motor and upon the *frequency* of the voltage that is driving it.   So long as the line voltage alternates at 60 cycles per second, a synchronous motor will run at a constant speed (except with very great loads or very low voltages, when it will simply stop).   Whereas the line voltage may vary from time to time, the line frequency is controlled with extreme accuracy at the power station.

Synchronous motors almost always run at some even submultiple of 3600 rpm (60 revolutions per second).   Probably the most common speed for the armature is 1800 rpm, but other armature speeds are available.   Gear boxes built into synchronous motors produce output speeds all the way down to 1 revolution per year.

At any given horsepower or torque, synchronous motors are some-

Fig. 11.3   Various synchronous motors.   (*Courtesy* Helen E. Howell, Berkeley, Calif.)

what bigger and more expensive than the other types.   In the laboratory, they usually fall into one of two groups; large, high-torque motors, for doing real work (e.g., pulling paper through a kymograph), and small, low-torque motors, for timing purposes (e.g., turning a cam that operates a switch to shock a brain every 30 seconds). Figure 11.3 is a photograph of some of these motors.

MISCELLANEOUS TYPES OF MOTORS

Reversible Motors

Most electric motors discussed so far will turn in only one direction, but there are special types whose direction of rotation can be readily reversed.   Reversible motors of the first type (moderately constant speed, not very adjustable) are simply called reversible motors.   Typically, four wires of different colors emerge from the casing.   When two of them are connected together and the other two are connected across the power supply, the motor will run in one direction and, when a different combination is connected, the motor will reverse. The particular combinations are ideosyncratic to individual motors, and such motors always come with instructions on how to connect them up.

Reversible synchronous motors are also available but they are less common. They usually consist of two different motors connected to one output shaft, one a clockwise and the other a counterclockwise driver. The direction of rotation of the shaft depends upon which driver has voltage applied to it.

The direction of rotation of standard series motors cannot be reversed. When a motor is needed whose speed is adjustable and whose direction of rotation is reversible, still a different kind of motor is available. The field of this kind of motor is supplied by a set of permanent magnets instead of the electromagnetic field present in the motors discussed previously. It is called a permanent-magnet motor. The one on your circuit board is of this type. Reversing the direction of current flow through a permanent magnet motor reverses the direction of rotation, and lowering the voltage reduces the speed. Permanent-magnet motors run on direct current only, and, except for the very small ones that will not do much work, they draw too much current to be powered by dry-cell batteries. Therefore, they are inconvenient to use unless a source of direct current is available in your laboratory.

Governor-Controlled Motors

Ordinarily, the speed of a series motor varies with small changes in the line voltage or the load. However, some series motors are manufactured with built-in governors to maintain a constant speed. The basic principles underlying the operation of these governors will be discussed in Chapter 17. It will be sufficient now to say that three types of governor-controlled series motors are available, one with a fixed speed, another whose speed can be varied by an adjustment of the governor when the motor is turned off, and a third type in which the governor can be adjusted while the motor is actually running.

SUMMARY OF SPEED CHARACTERISTICS

The following is a list of the kinds of motors which fit specific requirements:

1. For very constant speed on a-c power:
   a. Synchronous.
   b. Governor-controlled series.
2. For constant speed on direct current:
   a. Governor-controlled series.
3. For adjustable speed on alternating current:
   a. Series (universal, sewing-machine).
   b. Series with adjustable governor (for constant speed at each setting).
4. For adjustable speed on direct current:
   a. Series.
   b. Series with adjustable governor.
   c. Permanent magnet.
5. For reversible direction of rotation on alternating current:
   a. Reversible alternating current.
   b. Reversible synchronous (for very constant speed).
6. For reversible direction on direct current.
   a. Permanent magnet.

MISCELLANEOUS INFORMATION

There are some additional details concerning these motors which, though of less general relevance, are still worth noting.

High Starting Torque

Series motors have one outstanding characteristic that has not been mentioned. For a fixed input voltage, their output torque is inversely related to their speed. In other words, the series motor exerts its greatest torque when it is first turned on and is just starting up. This is not the case for the other motors that have been discussed. Should you need a motor that starts up quickly under a heavy load and does not need a push to get it going, use a series motor.

Sparking

When an electric motor runs, electric currents circulate in its armature. In most a-c motors, there is no direct electric connection between the armature and the power supply; current is electromagnetically induced into the armature. (For this reason, such motors are called induction motors.)   But in d-c and a-c/d-c (series) motors, the armature current is brought in through a set of moving contacts called the brushes and commutator.   As the armature turns, these contacts are rapidly made and broken, and sparks tend to jump at each break.   You can see these sparks if you look at the spinning shaft of your toy motor in a darkened room.   The sparks act as small radio broadcasting stations, and play havoc with any sensitive electronic apparatus that may be operating nearby.   For this reason, d-c and a-c/d-c motors should not be used near bioelectric recording equipment.

Chapter 12

Electrical transients

Any *change* in the amount of current flowing through a circuit is called a transient. The use of the transient properties of alternating current for transferring power in transformers has already been discussed in Chapter 10. Circuits using transients to perform timing operations will be analyzed extensively in Chapter 13. This chapter will discuss the use of transients in experimental situations where steady states are irrelevant, and only changes in state are of interest.

THE SENSING OF TRANSIENTS

The discussion will center around a specific laboratory problem—the registration of the activity of an animal. This problem is a common one, and is representative of problems which involve the sensing of transients. It has a great number of solutions, and several pertinent ones will be explained. To state the problem more specifically, suppose we wish to measure the diurnal variations in the activity of an animal confined to a living cage.

When the animal moves around, he exerts forces on the cage. Probably the easiest way to sense the animal's movement would be to suspend the cage on springs and detect the movement of the cage. In the old days, your assistant would have set about to smoke a kymograph drum and to rig up a system of levers, strings, and sealing wax to scratch a crooked line in the smoke. Next he would have varnished the record to preserve it, and after it had dried he would have spent

157

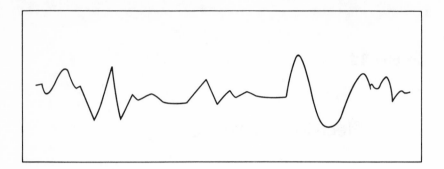

Fig. 12.1 A record of an animal's activity as it might appear on a smoked kymograph drum.

many painful hours measuring the characteristics of the crookedness of the line. In selecting what to measure, he would have followed very specific instructions based on decisions that you had made previously. Now these instructions are crucial, and their choice and phrasing involve some very subtle considerations. For example, in order to get a rough measure of gross activity, he might have been told to count all the times the record reverses directions (see Fig. 12.1), or to count the number of times that the trace abruptly changes its angle. This sort of instruction can be qualified more and more to meet specific objectives. The reason this is being discussed in a book on electric apparatus is that any piece of apparatus designed to replace your assistant must embody the same instructions that would have been given to him. The nature of these instructions and of the sensing system itself determine the structure of the apparatus. Conversely, practical considerations about the structure of the apparatus often influence the nature of the instructions.

Inductive Sensing

The apparatus to be designed is supposed to measure activity, and activity consists of *changes* in the animal's posture or position, independent of the posture or position itself. If the cage were suspended by a spring, changes around the resting level would indicate the animal's movements.

First a device will be designed to follow the instruction, "Count the number of times the cage moves faster than some threshold rate." This instruction suggests the use of some electric device that responds

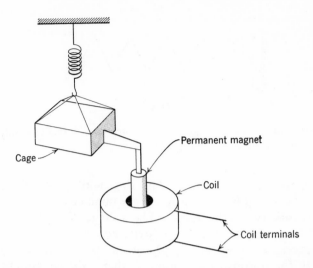

Fig. 12.2 An electric device for registering activity. The cage is suspended by a spring. As the animal moves, the cage moves up and down, driving the magnet in and out of the coil. A voltage will therefore be generated between the coil terminals whenever the animal moves.

only to transients. A very simple one is shown in Fig. 12.2. Here a permanent magnet fastened rigidly to the cage moves in and out of a coil of wire when the cage is moved. A voltage proportional to the velocity of the cage will be generated between the terminals of the coil. At zero velocity, there will be zero voltage, etc. This magnet-coil combination is a simple and very effective sensor of movement. If a very sensitive relay were connected across the coil and an electromagnetic counter were operated from the relay contacts, as in Fig. 12.3, a count would be registered each time the animal moved at a velocity greater

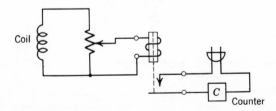

Fig. 12.3 Circuit to count the number of times the movement of the cage exceeds some threshold velocity.

Fig. 12.4 Plot of a type of cage motion which would result in only a single count when driving the circuit in Fig. 12.3.

than some threshold velocity.[1] The threshold speed will be determined by the strength of the magnet, the number of turns on the coil, and the sensitivity of the relay. The voltage divider in the circuit of Fig. 12.3 serves as an over-all sensitivity control.

In practice, the circuit in Fig. 12.3 would require an extremely sensitive relay for reasonable operation, so that a simple amplifier should probably be interposed between the sensing coil and the relay coil. This sort of amplifier will be discussed in Chapter 14. Its inclusion in the circuit does not change the basic principles of operation of this activity sensor.

The circuit in Fig. 12.3 might not always follow the intended instructions. For example, it would probably give only one count for a motion such as that shown in Fig. 12.4, even though the movement changed direction several times. Although the direction of current

[1] An ordinary, nonelectromagnetic counter is a set of wheels with digits on them geared together in such a way that every time a lever is pushed, the total count increases by one. An electromagnetic counter is just one of these connected so that the lever is pushed by electromagnetism instead of by hand.

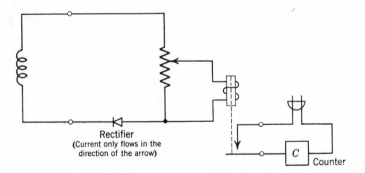

Fig. 12.5 A circuit to register a count each time the cage exceeds a threshold velocity in one direction.

in Fig. 12.4 reverses on each cycle and the current magnitude thus goes through zero for an instant at each reversal, the inertia of the relay and counter would probably be sufficient to prevent the relay from ever opening. Electromagnetic counters are built so that they register one count for each make *and* break of current through their coils. If current is continuous, the counter does not continuously advance (counters function very much like stepping relays). Therefore, the motion in Fig. 12.4 would only register one count.

The circuit in Fig. 12.5 avoids this difficulty. The magnet coil is

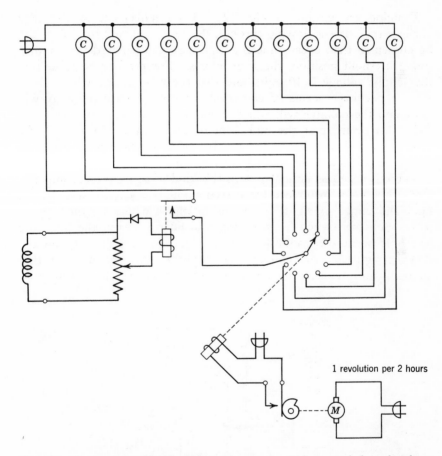

Fig. 12.6 A circuit to record total activity over a 24-hour period, each 2-hour subperiod being stored on a separate counter. The motor makes one rotation every 2 hours. On each rotation, the cam closes and opens a switch. The stepping switch (SP12T) is thus advanced one position every 2 hours.

connected to the relay through a rectifier. A rectifier is a device which passes current easily in one direction but shows a high resistance to current flow in the opposite direction. Therefore, in Fig. 12.5, the relay operates only on motion in one direction.

Just for closure, the circuit in Fig. 12.6 is included. This circuit will automatically record activity over a 24-hour period, storing the sum of all activity in each successive 2-hour period on a separate counter.

Transformers as Transient Sensors

Examine the circuit in Fig. 12.7. Each movement of the cage changes the current flowing through the relay coil, and the values can be chosen so that, every time the cage moves downward farther than some threshold position, the relay closes. For example, suppose that the supply voltage is 10 volts, and that the relay is one which closes when the voltage across its coil reaches 5 volts. Then the relay will close and the counter will add a count whenever the cage moves the slider downward past the mid-point of the resistor. In general, the total count will equal the total number of times the slider passed this threshold position while moving downward.

There is a serious difficulty with this kind of activity recording system. The count produced by a fixed amount of activity will depend upon the animal's weight. Consider an animal whose weight happens to be such that, when he is at rest, the slider is just at the threshold level. If he now engages in activity which bounces the cage up and down irregularly, the counter will register every bounce. If that animal is now replaced by one that is lighter, so that the resting posi-

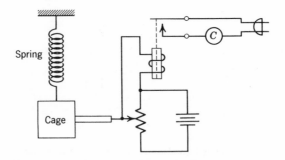

Fig. 12.7 Circuit to register a count each time the cage moves downward past some threshold position.

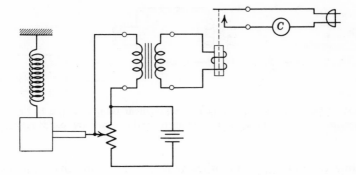

Fig. 12.8 Circuit to register a count each time the velocity of the cage exceeds some threshold velocity.

tion of the slider is above the threshold level, when he moves, some of the bounces will not be big enough to move the slider beyond the threshold position, and they will not register. Thus the same amount of actual activity will result in a smaller count. For the same reason, any change in a single animal's weight, such as would result from eating or urinating, would be indistinguishable from a change in his activity.

This defect can be remedied by putting, between the voltage divider and the relay, a device that senses only electric transients, such as the transformer in Fig. 12.8. The transformer functions in the same way in this circuit as when connected in the usual way. Any current flowing through the primary coil sets up a magnetic field in the region of the secondary coil. As long as the primary current is steady, there is no movement of the field with respect to the secondary coil, and no voltage is induced into it. But every change in the input current induces a voltage in the secondary. The greater the rate of change of current in the primary, the greater the amplitude of the output voltage. For these reasons, the circuit in Fig. 12.8 will register a count each time the animal moves faster than some threshold rate, just as the circuit in Fig. 12.3 did. In this case too, it is usually more practical to insert a simple amplifier between the transformer and the relay. Otherwise an extremely sensitive relay is needed.

Another common situation in which a circuit must discriminate between transients and steady states is the one in which the making and/or breaking of a circuit is to be sensed. For example, in Skinner boxes, usually one and only one reinforcement is given for each bar press. If the animal sits on the bar, the reinforcement should not

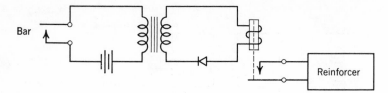

Fig. 12.9 Circuit to deliver a single reinforcement each time the bar is pressed. The rectifier prevents the reinforcer from operating when the bar is released.

continue to pour out. In other words, the circuit that controls the reinforcement should operate only when the response circuit is changing from off to on. There are numerous ways to accomplish this, and the one best suited to any given problem depends on other related apparatus elements. One circuit that will work is shown in Fig. 12.9. Here, each time the bar is pressed, the amount of current flowing through the primary of the transformer increases from zero to some finite value. A magnetic field is thus built up and, while it is building, it generates enough voltage in the secondary to close the relay. As soon as the current in the primary reaches equilibrium, the voltage in the secondary again drops to zero and the relay opens. Therefore, even if the bar is held down for a long time, the relay stays closed for only a short time. When the bar is released, the magnetic field in the transformer collapses, generating another pulse of voltage in the secondary, and this pulse might also be expected to deliver a reinforcement. However, the current generated in the secondary of the transformer flows in opposite directions for the making and the breaking of the primary circuit. Therefore the rectifier, when connected as in Fig. 12.9, will prevent the relay from closing when the bar is released.

Capacitative Sensing

Any electric current can be considered as made up of two components, a steady or d-c one and a changing or a-c one. Such components are clear in the voltage pattern shown in Fig. 12.10, where a battery is connected in series with the wall-socket voltage. An animal sitting in an activity cage and twitching might generate a similar wave form. In the preceding discussion, the transformer has been described as a transient sensing device. But it is also possible, and in some ways more useful, to consider the transformer as a device that transmits the a-c components of a signal while blocking the d-c component.

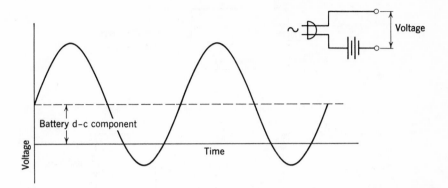

Fig. 12.10 Plot of voltage vs. time for a battery and the a-c wall source in series.

Exactly the same thing can be done with an altogether different circuit element—the capacitor (condenser, *archaic*). A capacitor consists of two sheets of a conductive material separated by a good insulator. The sketch in Fig. 12.11 shows a crude but functional capacitor. Assume that the capacitor is electrically neutral, that is, there are neither too few nor too many electrons on the plates or the glass. Now suppose that the two terminals of the capacitor are connected to the terminals of a battery, as shown in Fig. 12.12a. The negative terminal of the battery has an excess of electrons and the

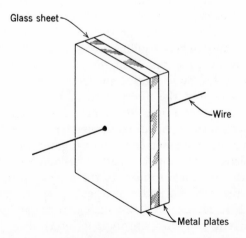

Fig. 12.11 A crude capacitor, consisting of two metal plates separated by a sheet of glass.

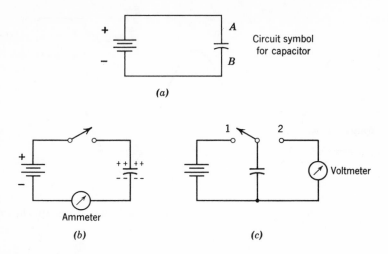

Fig. 12.12 (*a*) Circuit diagram of a capacitor connected across a battery. (*b*) The distribution of charges on the plates of a capacitor after it has been connected across a battery. The meter in the circuit is a fast, sensitive ammeter. It will show a momentary deflection when the switch is first closed. (*c*) Circuit to indicate the discharging of a capacitor. When the switch is in position 1, the capacitor is charged. When it is first thrown to position 2, the voltmeter will read a voltage (actually the battery voltage), and if the switch is held in position 2, the meter reading will gradually approach zero.

positive has too few. Since each of the plates was originally neutral, some of the electrons from plate *A* will migrate to the "+" terminal and some of the electrons from the "−" terminal will move up to the plate *B* of the capacitor. Because the glass is a good insulator, they will stop there and, when equilibrium is reached, no more current will flow. The charges will then be distributed as shown in Fig. 12.12*b*. If a very fast and sensitive ammeter were connected to record the current as shown in the figure, it would register a short pulse of current when the connections were first made, and then no more. Now the capacitor may be disconnected from the battery and, as long as the two leads are not connected together, the charge will remain on the plates. As soon as a path is provided for the excess electrons on the negative plate to flow to the positive plate, a current will flow through the path until the charges are again neutralized. The voltmeter in Fig. 12.12*c* provides such a path, and it will indicate a voltage (current will flow through its coil) that decreases as the charge dissipates. You can see this phenomenon easily by using the equipment on your board. Your capacitors are of a type (to be described on page 192), that work properly only when the impressed voltage is of the correct polarity.   Connect one of them across the 22½ volts of your battery, making sure that the end of the capacitor marked "+" is connected to the "+" terminal of the battery and the "—" to the negative terminal.   (Each of the wires sticking out of the end of the capacitor is connected to one of the plates.)   Now set your meter to read at least 22½ volts d-c, disconnect the capacitor from the battery, and connect it between the meter leads.   The meter will read something less than 22½ volts, and the reading will gradually drop as the current running through the meter equalizes the charges on the two plates of the capacitor.

Now connect the circuit in Fig. 12.13.   When the last connection is made, you may see the meter needle twitch as the current charging the capacitor passes through the meter.   However, after a short time, the voltage produced by the charges on the plates of the capacitor just balances the voltage of the battery, and current ceases to flow.   (If your meter continues to read something other than zero and you have connected up the circuit properly, your capacitor is faulty.) If you now disconnect the lead to the negative side of the battery and touch it to some other battery terminal, changing the voltage across the capacitor, the meter needle should jump again.   In general, the needle will read a value other than zero only when the input voltage is changing, and for a very short interval after it has changed. Furthermore, the direction in which the needle moves does not depend on the absolute voltage level but only on whether the voltage has increased or decreased.   The capacitor thus behaves very much like the transformer described earlier in this chapter.   It transmits changes in input voltage but passes no current when the input is steady.   In other words, a capacitor also transmits the a-c component of an input voltage but blocks the d-c component.

The circuit in Fig. 12.14 performs exactly the same function as the

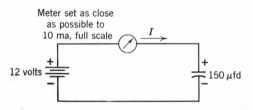

Fig. 12.13   Circuit to demonstrate the current flow I during the charging of a capacitor.

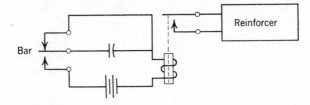

Fig. 12.14   Circuit to deliver a single reinforcement each time the bar is pressed. When the switch is in its normal position, the capacitor is discharged. Upon pressing the bar, the capacitor will charge up through the relay coil, causing the armature to pull in momentarily. As soon as the capacitor is charged, current will stop flowing through the coil, and the relay will open. When the bar is released, the capacitor is discharged, and the circuit is returned to its initial condition.

transformer circuit in Fig. 12.9.   Each time the bar is depressed, the reinforcement mechanism operates, but it will not operate again until the bar is released and then depressed again.   This is the general way in which a capacitor is used to detect changes in voltage.   The particular values of circuit parameters (e.g., the size of the capacitor) which optimize circuit performance obviously depend upon the particular intended function of the circuit.   In many cases, the experienced designer just guesses at some values, tries them out, and then plays with them until things work reasonably well.   This approach requires some understanding of the properties of charging and discharging capacitors, which will be discussed in detail in the following chapter.   But it should be emphasized that expert circuit designers very often arrive at specific circuit values through crude trial-and-error procedures, because such procedures are often more efficient on the whole than trying to go through a set of elaborate computations.

Chapter **13**

Time delay circuits

The term "timer," or "timing circuit," is commonly used in two different ways. It can refer either to a piece of apparatus which measures the amount of time elapsing between events (e.g., a stop watch) or to something which actually controls the time interval between events (e.g., the timer on an electric oven). This chapter will discuss only timers of the second sort.

MOTOR-DRIVEN TIMERS

A variety of motor-driven timers is available at any electronic suppliers. These timers consist basically of a set of contacts mechanically opened and closed, according to some predetermined schedule, by the action of a constant-speed motor (usually a synchronous motor). Some units, such as the darkroom timer shown in Fig. 13.1, go through just one cycle and then have to be reset. The timer in this figure is designed specifically for turning on and off the lamp in an enlarger, but it can be used in many other applications as well. The timer is plugged into the wall, the gadget to be timed is plugged into the socket on the side of the timer, and the desired time interval is set on the dial. Then when the switch in the upper right corner is turned to "on," two things happen: (1) the wall-socket voltage is connected to the timer socket (so that the enlarger lights), and (2), the timer motor starts to run, driving the pointer toward zero. When the pointer reaches zero, the voltage is disconnected from the timer socket (the enlarger goes off). The switch at the upper left reverses the condition of

Fig. 13.1   Darkroom timer.   (*Courtesy* Dimco-Gray Co.)

the contacts connected to the timer socket, so that the voltage goes *off* while the timer is running and turns on when the pointer reaches zero.

The timer in Fig. 13.2 is also an enlarger timer with an action very similar to the one just described.   However, it is constructed to reset itself automatically.   The pointer is set to the desired interval and the button is pushed.   This connects the voltage to the timer socket and starts the motor running.   When the pointer gets to zero, the voltage will turn off just as in the timer described above.   But this timer will then continue through one more step, during which the pointer reverses itself and runs back to the position where it was originally set. To get another cycle, the button is simply pressed once again.   Timers such as this one, which reset automatically by mechanical means, usually complete the resetting operation and are ready to be restarted within 1 or 2 seconds, regardless of the duration of the interval actually produced by the timer.   (Relay capacitor timers, such as will be discussed later in this chapter, can be made to reset instantaneously.)

As an example of the use of this timer in behavioral research, suppose that someone were interested in the question of whether or not darkness is a positive reinforcer for a nocturnal animal, say a cat.   A cat is put into a lighted cage and the conditions are to be arranged such that, every time the cat makes some response, the light will turn off for 10 seconds, then go back on again.   If the experimenter simply plugged the light into the socket of a resetting timer and turned the

Fig. 13.2 Darkroom timer with an automatic resetting mechanism. (*Courtesy* Industrial Timer Corp.)

switch to the "off during the cycle" mode, his only problem would be to train the cat to make the response of pushing the button on the timer. Since this is not a very easy response for a cat, there is a better solution. The push button is a single-pole, single-throw switch that is normally open, and which closes momentarily when the button is pushed. All the experimenter has to do is take apart the timer, connect two wires, one to each of the push button contacts, and bring the wires out of the timer casing. Now any time these two wires are con-

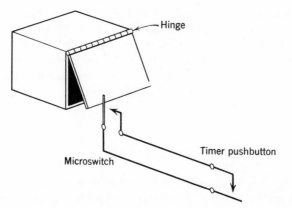

Fig. 13.3 Schematized diagram to permit a cat to operate an automatically resetting timer.

Fig. 13.4 A motor-driven repeat-cycle timer. The synchronous motor continuously drives the cam shaft, and the cams drive microswitches. (*Courtesy* Herbach & Raderman Co.)

nected together, the timer will go through a complete cycle.[1]   In this way, a response more suitable to a cat's behavior repertory can be made to turn off the light.   For example, the end of the cage may be hinged and set up to close a normally open, single-pole, single-throw microswitch, as in Fig. 13.3.

Another common type of motor-driven timer runs continuously, repeating some predetermined cycle over and over.   The timer shown in Fig. 13.4 is typical.   A set of cams is driven by a synchronous motor, and each of the cams presses on a microswitch.   As the motor shaft turns, the cams operate their microswitches in a sequence that can be changed by adjusting the positions of the cams with respect to the motor shaft.   Similarly, the length of time that each microswitch is on or off can be changed by changing the shape of its cam.   These timers can be bought with almost any number of cams and microswitches, and with motor speeds ranging from about 2 revolutions per second up to 1 revolution per year.   They are useful when a series of events should occur in some fixed time sequence, and the duration of each cycle is known in advance.

MISCELLANEOUS TIME DELAY RELAYS

For timing that is accurate and reliable to a few percent, at low or moderate cost, motor-driven timers are probably the most suitable.

[1] On the timer shown in Fig. 13.2, the push-button contacts are internally connected to the socket labeled "remote start."

But for applications in which the interval need not be maintained that accurately, there are other timers that are cheaper. One of these is shown in Fig. 13.5. This timer consists of a heating coil and two contacts, one of which is mounted on the end of a bimetallic bar. When current is passed through the coil, it heats up the bimetallic bar, causing it to bend. If the unit is normally open, when the bar gets hot and bends far enough, the contacts close and then stay closed as long as current continues through the coil. The time between the onset of coil current and the closing of the contacts is determined primarily by the physical characteristics of the bar and the coil as well as by the voltage across the coil. A normally closed unit behaves in the same way except that the contacts are closed at first, and open when the bar bends far enough. These time-delay units are relatively cheap and are available with delays ranging from about 1 second to 30 seconds. However, both their age and the room temperature affect the time interval, so they should not be used where the reliability of the interval is critical.

As long as current continues to flow through the heater coil of a thermal time-delay relay, the contacts will remain in the same condition (i.e., closed in a normally open relay, open in a normally closed relay). When the current is turned off, the bimetallic bar cools and the contacts return to their "normal" condition. The cooling process is slower than the initial heating. This kind of relay, therefore, cannot be used for operations which must be restarted soon after the first cycle is completed.

Timers using the viscosity of fluids to achieve a time delay are also available. They are somewhat more consistent than the heater type, and many of them can be set to give a range of intervals by adjusting

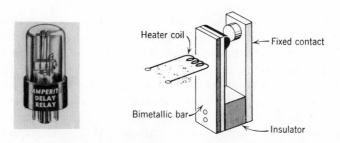

Fig. 13.5 Heater-type time-delay relay. The one in the sketch is normally open. When current passes through the coil, the bimetallic bar bends until the contacts touch. (*Courtesy* Amperite Co., Inc.)

the diameter of an aperture through which a fluid flows. These timers are also more expensive than the heater type.

It is sometimes necessary in the design of circuits to include a short delay the duration of which need not be adjusted, e.g., to ensure that one event occurs before another. This is accomplished in some commercial time-delay relays in the following way. A slug of copper is built into the body of an otherwise standard relay in such a position that some of the magnetic field of the relay coil passes through it. When a voltage is first impressed across the relay coil and the magnetic field begins to build up, it generates a current in the slug which, in turn, tends to oppose the magnetic field of the coil. This interaction results in a slower buildup of the net magnetic field. In this way, the time between the application of voltage to the relay coil and the closure of its contacts can be increased from the normal time (a few milliseconds) to as much as one-half second. Such a relay is called a "slow-make" relay. By placing the copper slug in a different position, the collapse of the field that occurs when power is removed from the relay coil may be slowed down. That kind of relay closes rapidly when power is applied, but the contacts remain closed for a longer period than normal when the power is removed. It is therefore called a "slow-break" relay.

Since it is not really the purpose of this book to catalogue available electric devices but rather to discuss the uses of basic principles in the design of electric apparatus, the preceding discussion is not very extensive. Furthermore, for many of the situations in which timing is required, you can build your own time-delay unit by applying some of the principles already discussed.

RELAY-CAPACITOR TIMERS

By putting together simple combinations of capacitors, resistors, batteries, and relays, it is possible to build time-delay circuits which will be sufficiently versatile and accurate to fill many of the needs that arise in behavior research. You will recall from Chapter 12 that, when a capacitor is connected across a voltage source, charges build up on the two plates of the capacitor, and when the capacitor is fully charged, the voltage due to those charges is equal in magnitude and opposite in polarity to the source voltage. When the capacitor is then disconnected from the source and the two plates are connected to each other through some conductive path, current will flow until the plates are discharged. The solid line in Fig. 13.6 is a plot of the

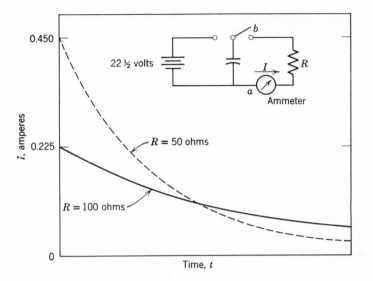

Fig. 13.6 Plot of the current flowing out of the capacitor in the inset circuit diagram. Initially, the capacitor is fully charged by the battery. The origin of the plot represents the instant when the switch is first thrown to the *b* position. (Before the switch is thrown, the current *I* is obviously zero.) The solid curve holds when the resistance through which the capacitor is discharging is 100 ohms, and the dashed curve is for a 50-ohm resistance.

current flowing out of a capacitor as a function of time when there is a path *ab*, from one plate to the other, containing a resistance *R* and an ammeter. The curve is an exponential decay curve that approaches zero asymtotically. Consider the state of the capacitor after it has been connected across a 22½-volt battery for a long time, then disconnected from the battery but not yet connected to the meter. There is an excess of electrons on the negative plate relative to the positive plate, and such a relation defines the fact that there is a voltage between the plates. Just before the capacitor was disconnected from the battery, the circuit was in equilibrium and no current was flowing. This means that the voltage between the plates of the capacitor was just big enough to balance the voltage of the battery itself; that is, there was enough charge on the plates of the capacitor to produce a voltage just equal in magnitude and opposite in direction to the battery voltage. When the battery is removed, and from that time until a path is provided for current to flow between the plates, the voltage across the capacitor will be 22½ volts. Therefore, at the instant when the path *ab* in Fig. 13.6 is first connected across the capacitor, the current flowing will be:

$$I = \frac{E}{R}$$

$$= \frac{22\frac{1}{2}}{100}$$

$$= 0.225 \text{ ampere}$$

This is the value of the current at $t = 0$, the first point on the solid curve of Fig. 13.6. As time passes, the fact that current is flowing means that the difference in electron densities between the two plates is being reduced. Therefore the voltage between plates is being reduced, which, in turn, means that the current will be smaller. This is the condition for an exponential decay.

Now consider what would happen if the resistance in the path were to be cut in half, to 50 ohms. The initial voltage would still be the same and the initial current would be twice as great. Therefore, the charge would dissipate more quickly and the curve should be steeper.

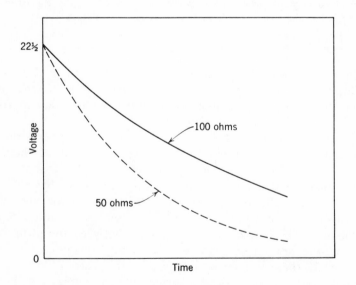

Fig. 13.7 Plots of the voltage between points *a* and *b* in the circuit of Fig. 13.6, as a function of the time after the switch is thrown to the *b* position. Again, the solid curve is for the 100-ohm and the dashed curve for the 50-ohm discharging path.

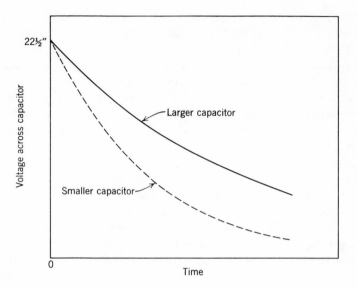

22½″

Voltage across capacitor

Larger capacitor

Smaller capacitor

0

Time

Fig. 13.8 Plots of the voltage across the capacitor in the circuit of Fig. 13.6, as a function of time after the switch is thrown to position *b*, for two capacitors of different sizes.

The dashed curve in Fig. 13.6 is a plot of the 50-ohm condition. Similarly, the solid and dashed curves in Fig. 13.7 represent the *voltage* across the capacitor as a function of time for the 100- and the 50-ohm conditions respectively.   The steepness of these curves clearly depends upon the rate at which electrons can flow from one plate to the other, i.e., the resistance of the circuit.   But the steepness also depends upon the amount of charge that the capacitor has in the fully charged condition.   In other words, if two capacitors are initially charged to the same voltage, and both are then discharged through 100-ohm resistors, the one that was constructed to soak up the bigger charge in the first place will be longer in losing its charge because it has more to lose. For example, if the plates of one capacitor have twice the area of the plates of the other, the larger one will hold twice as great a charge when they are both fully charged to the same voltage.   If they are now discharged through equal resistances, the voltage across the larger one will decay more slowly.   The curves in Fig. 13.8 represent the voltage-decay characteristics of these two circuits.

One might expect that, if the larger capacitor had more charge on it at $t = 0$, it would show a higher voltage than the other at $t = 0$, but the Fig. 13.8 shows that the voltages across the two are equal at

$t = 0$. The voltage that appears across a capacitor after it has been fully charged, but before it has been discharged at all ($t = 0$), always equals exactly the voltage of the source that did the charging. This is true by definition, because a fully charged capacitor is at equilibrium with the charging source. The voltage across a capacitor is a measure of what might be considered the charge *density* as contrasted to the total charge. Charging a capacitor to a given voltage level produces a particular charge density, but the actual total amount of charge in the capacitor will depend on some of the physical characteristics of the capacitor itself.

The term used to indicate the relative amount of charge that a capacitor contains when it is fully charged to a given voltage is "capacitance," measured in units called farads or, much more commonly, microfarads (one-millionth of a farad). The capacitance of a capacitor depends principally upon the size and closeness of its plates. Plates that are larger and closer together give greater capacitance.

The curves in Figs. 13.7 and 13.8 look similar and are, in fact, identical. A decrease in the resistance of the discharging circuit has exactly the same effect on the time characteristics of the discharge as an increase in the capacitance of the capacitor. There is a simple way of describing the time characteristics. These curves and all voltage- or current-vs.-time curves for simple capacitative circuits have the same shape, that of an exponential rise or decay. This is the classic growth curve extremely prevalent in physical and biological systems. The curve starts at some level and asymptotically approaches some other level. The characteristics of any simple exponential curve may be concisely described by stating the "time constant" of the curve, that is, the time it takes for the curve to get from its starting level to a level $(1/e) \times$ (the asymptotic level), where e is the base of the natural logarithms, 2.7. Since 1/2.7 is reasonably close to $\frac{1}{3}$, the time constant of any such curve is the time it takes for whatever value is being plotted to get about two-thirds of the way from where it starts to where it will end up. The shape of exponentials is such that the starting level can be taken as any level at all, and the above statement is still true. For example, in the curve of Fig. 13.9, the time constant is 10 seconds. It takes 10 seconds for the curve to get from 100 volts to approximately 33 volts (actually $1/2.7 \times 100 = 37$ volts). It also takes 10 seconds to get from 33 volts to 11 volts, from 11 to 3.7, etc. It takes 10 seconds to get from 80 volts to 27 volts, etc.

The curve in Fig. 13.9 is a plot of the voltage across a capacitor as it discharges through a resistor. It is a very convenient fact, and one that should be retained by anyone interested in building electric

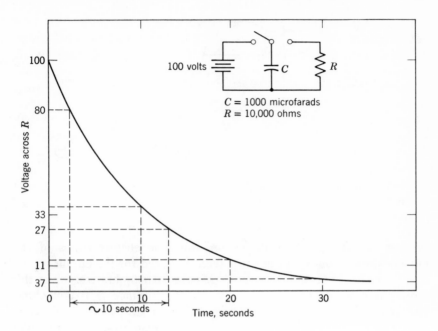

Fig. 13.9 The time course of discharge of the capacitor in the inset circuit. The discharging circuit has a time constant of 10 seconds.

apparatus, that the time constant in seconds for this or any capacitative discharge curve equals the product of the resistance through which the capacitor is discharging (measured in ohms) and the capacitance of the capacitor (measured in farads).

$$\text{Time constant (seconds)} = R \text{ (ohms)} \times C \text{ (farads)}$$

For example, in this circuit,

$$\text{Time constant} = 10{,}000 \text{ ohms} \times 1000 \text{ microfarads}$$

$$= 10^4 \times 10^3 \times 10^{-6}$$

$$= 10 \text{ seconds}$$

Now let us reconsider the problem discussed earlier in this chapter, that of turning off a light for 10 seconds after a cat closes a switch. The 10-second time interval can be determined by the travel of a motor shaft, as with the dark-room timer, or by the time it takes a bar to heat up or fluid to pass through an orifice. But it can also be established by a purely electrical phenomenon—the discharging of a ca-

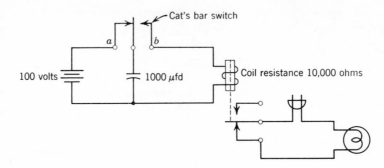

Fig. 13.10 Circuit to turn off a light for 10 seconds when the bar is pressed and held down.

pacitor. In the previous discussion, the time characteristics of the current flowing out of a capacitor were analyzed for the circuit repro-duced in Fig. 13.9. Now suppose that the 10,000-ohm resistor in this circuit is replaced by a relay whose coil resistance is 10,000 ohms, and which opens when the voltage across it drops below 33 volts (see Fig. 13.10). In this case, since the voltage-vs.-time curve will be the same as it was before (it is determined only by the capacitance and the resistance), the relay will pull in when the switch is first thrown into the *b* position, and stay in for about 10 seconds, i.e., until the voltage across it falls below 33 volts. Therefore, if the cat's lamp is connected up as in Fig. 13.10, the lamp will go off for 10 seconds when the cat presses the bar. As soon as the cat releases the bar, shifting the switch back to the *a* position, the capacitor will be recharged and the circuit will be ready for another cycle. (This circuit only gives a full 10-second interval if the cat holds the bar down for at least 10 seconds. Circuits for momentary bar presses will be discussed later.)

To get a feeling for how this circuit operates, connect up the circuit in Fig. 13.11 on your board, taking care to connect the ca-pacitor with the correct polarity.

There is a resistor in this circuit in the loop through which the ca-pacitor is recharged. If the resistance of that path were very low, a very high current would flow at the first instant that the switch is thrown to the recharging position, and the switch contacts might be damaged. The 30-ohm resistor limits the current to a reasonable value but still allows the capacitor to charge up very quickly.

If your circuit is working properly, when you press the micro-switch and hold it down, the light should go on for a short time and then go off again. The time interval marked off by such a circuit can be computed, at least roughly, from the electrical parameters of the circuit. First of all, the time constant is easy to compute. It is just the product of the capacitance of the capacitor and the resistance of the relay coil. If the resistance of the relay coil in the circuit of Fig. 13.11 is 10,000 ohms, the time constant is:

$$150 \times 10^{-6} \text{ (farads)} \times 10,000 \text{ ohms} = 150 \times 10^{-2} = 1.5 \text{ seconds}$$

This means that the voltage will drop about two-thirds of the way from its maximum value (the battery voltage) to 0 in 1.5 seconds. Since the battery voltage is 22½ volts, the voltage across the relay will be ⅓ × 22½ = about 7 volts, 1.5 seconds after the switch is thrown. Another 1½ seconds after that, the voltage will be about 2 volts (⅓ × 7 = about 2). If the relay is one that opens when the voltage falls to 5 volts, the light will stay on for something between 1½ and 2 seconds.

The interval marked off by this circuit may be changed by causing the voltage to drop to 5 volts more or less rapidly. One procedure is simply to change the charging voltage. This does not change the time constant of the circuit, but, since it changes the initial voltage, the time to reach 5 volts is changed accordingly.

The other means of adjusting the timing of this circuit involves changing the time constant itself. Since the time constant equals the product of the capacitance and the resistance, either of these may be increased or decreased to get a corresponding increase or decrease

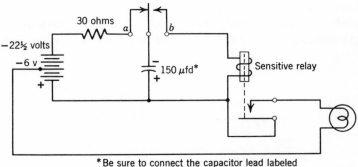

*Be sure to connect the capacitor lead labeled
"+" to the "+" side of the battery

Fig. 13.11 Circuit, to be constructed on your board, to turn on a light for a short time after the switch is thrown to *b* and held there. The duration of the light depends upon the properties of your sensitive relay.

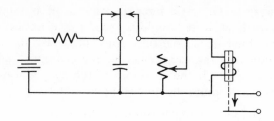

Fig. 13.12   A timing circuit with a continuously adjustable duration.

in the time to reach 5 volts. For example, if the capacitance is doubled, say, by connecting a second equal capacitor in parallel with the one that is already there, the time will be approximately doubled. If the net resistance through which the capacitor discharges is cut in half by connecting a resistance equal to the resistance of the relay coil in parallel with the relay coil, the time interval will be cut in half. This last means of adjusting the timing is usually the most convenient, and may be done as shown in Fig. 13.12, to give a continuous adjustment from zero up to some maximum time interval.

For a relay with a given sensitivity, for instance, one that opens at 5 volts, the higher the resistance of the relay the greater the time constant and the time interval. However, it does *not* follow that adding a resistance in series with the relay coil, as shown in Fig. 13.13, will increase the time the relay is closed. An addition of resistance equal to the relay coil resistance, for example, will indeed double the time constant of the circuit, and the voltage across the *capacitor* will take twice as long to reach 5 volts, but it is the voltage across the *relay* that matters and, since the relay and the series resistor have equal resistances, the voltage across the relay will be 5 volts when the

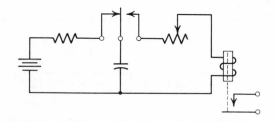

Fig. 13.13   Timing circuit with a resistance in series with the relay. Increasing the value of this resistance *reduces* the time interval somewhat.

voltage across the capacitor is *10 volts,* not 5.   The capacitor voltage will actually reach 10 volts with the series resistor in less time than it would reach 5 volts without the resistor.   Thus, adding resistance in series with the relay coil is just another way of *reducing* the time interval.

Now examine the circuit in Fig. 13.14. Here, the capacitor is connected in series with the relay coil and the battery. When the switch is in the *a* position, the capacitor is completely discharged. At the instant that the switch is thrown into the *b* position, a current will flow through the battery and relay to charge up the plates of the capacitor. The charging of a capacitor follows exactly the same laws as does discharging, so that the curve in Fig. 13.14 is again an exponential whose time constant equals the capacitance of the capacitor multiplied by the resistance of the path through which the capacitor is charging. Therefore, the relay in Fig. 13.14 will close when the switch is thrown to *b*, and stay closed until the charging current drops below whatever level is necessary to hold the relay closed. The action of this circuit may be conveniently diagrammed as shown in Fig. 13.15, and the duration of the relay closure may be determined

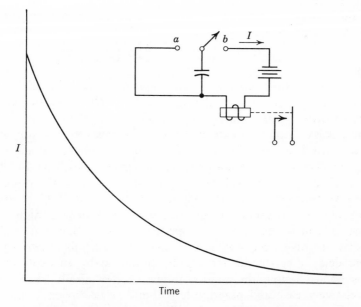

Fig. 13.14 Another circuit that performs the same function as those already discussed, along with a plot of the relay-coil current as a function of time.

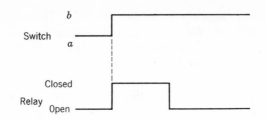

Fig. 13.15   A schematic representation of the timing action of the circuits shown in Figs. 13.11 and 13.14.

from the time constant of the circuit and the relay characteristics exactly as in the circuit of Fig. 13.10.

Most relays that are reasonably priced and suited for the sorts of timing purposes discussed in this chapter have two special characteristics that are important.   First, the actual time required for closing is usually on the order of several milliseconds, so that it is not a good idea to try to build a relay timer for intervals much shorter than 25 to 50 milliseconds unless a special-purpose relay is used.   Second, the highest coil resistance readily available in relays is about 10,000 ohms.   Since it is also practical to buy capacitors with values up to 5000 microfarads or so, simple relay-capacitor timers may conveniently have time constants of up to

$$10^4 \times 5 \times 10^3 \times 10^{-6} = 50 \text{ seconds}$$

For a given time constant and a given relay, the higher the applied voltage, the longer the time delay.   (It takes the voltage longer to drop to the relay's opening level if it starts higher.)   But the time delay cannot be extended too far in this way because, at the time the switch is first closed, the full voltage is impressed across the relay, and since relays are not generally designed to withstand voltages very much greater than the voltage required for normal closing, the starting voltage cannot be too high.   As a rough rule of thumb, it is probably safe to use a voltage source about 6 times as high as the voltage at which the relay just opens or closes.   Since the voltage drops two-thirds of the way in one time constant, this means that the longest delay that should actually be produced by this sort of circuit is about double the time constant of the circuit.   In general, it is relatively easy and practicable to build relay-capacitor timers to operate over the range of about 50 milliseconds to 100 seconds.

The two timing circuits already discussed operate as diagrammed in

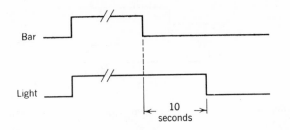

Fig. 13.16 Diagram of a timing program in which a bulb remains lighted for 10 seconds after a bar has been released.

Fig. 13.15 when, for example, a light is to stay on for the first 10 seconds of a steady bar press. This circuit is sometimes called a step-to-pulse converter, because the input is a step and the output a pulse of fixed duration. This kind of converter is a useful building block in many more complex circuits, as will be illustrated later.

Now consider a slightly different problem, that of causing the light to go on when a bar is pressed and go off 10 seconds after the bar is released, as shown in Fig. 13.16. This requires that the relay controlling the light stay closed after the switch is opened. Therefore some form of holding circuit is suggested, but the holding circuit must open itself after 10 seconds. The easiest way to make a holding circuit turn itself off is diagrammed in Fig. 13.17. The action of this circuit is as follows. Before the bar is pressed, no current can flow anywhere because the open bar switch blocks the only path through the power source. As soon as the bar is pressed, current will flow through the relay coil, and the relay will close. The closing

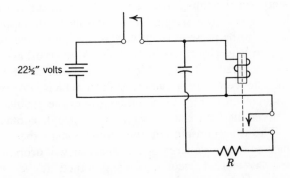

Fig. 13.17 Circuit to perform the timing operation diagrammed in Fig. 13.16.

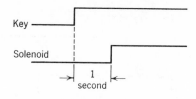

Fig. 13.18   Diagram of a timing program in which a solenoid operates one second after a key is pressed.

of the relay connects the capacitor and the relay coil in parallel across the battery, and the capacitor will charge up through resistance R. (The resistance R here, again, serves to limit the otherwise very high current flow at the instant when the relay is first closed. Its value should be low, e.g., 30 ohms, so that it will permit the capacitor to charge up rapidly.) The relay will clearly stay closed as long as the bar is held down. At the instant the bar is released, the battery will be disconnected from the relay coil, but the capacitor will still be connected across the coil. Since the capacitor was connected across the 22½-volt battery until the last instant before the bar was released, the capacitor itself will deliver a potential of 22½ volts. Therefore, at the first instant after the bar has been released, there will still be 22½ volts across the relay coil and the armature will remain pulled down. The capacitor will then discharge through the relay coil, and the relay will finally open when the discharging current falls below the value necessary to hold it closed. This time interval may be calculated as were the others mentioned above. Build this circuit on your board. It is an important and useful one.

A different timing requirement is one in which a delay is to be introduced between the time a response is made and the reinforcement is delivered. To take the simplest case of this kind, suppose that a human subject is to be presented with a flash of light 1 second after he presses a key, and he is instructed to hold down the key until after the flash has occurred. The problem is diagrammed in Fig. 13.18, the flash being delivered by a camera shutter which is operated by a solenoid. The circuit in Fig. 13.19 almost solves the problem. When the subject closes his key, the relay closes (through contact 1 and a capacitor). The time constant of the loop through the relay coil is chosen so that the current charging the capacitor will drop low enough to open the relay after 1 second, as diagrammed in the upper right of Fig. 13.19. The solenoid is connected in series with contact

3 (on the relay) and contact 2 (on the key), so that it will operate only when both contact pairs are closed. When the key is first pressed, both of those contacts are closed, but contact 3 immediately opens (when the relay closes) and then stays open for 1 second. At the end of that time, contact 3 closes again and the solenoid will be activated. The current through the solenoid can, therefore, be diagrammed as shown in the inset to Fig. 13.19. The duration of the first short pulse of current depends upon how long it takes the relay to close (and contact 3 to open) after the key has been pressed. If the relay is fast enough and the solenoid slow enough, that first pulse will not operate the shutter and only one flash will be delivered, but there is a chance that the pulse will actually trigger the shutter and two flashes will be delivered. Although it may be possible to find a fast relay and a slow solenoid to put into the circuit, it is better to change the circuit itself so that the pulse cannot occur.

The pulse cannot occur in the circuit of Fig. 13.20. The pulse in the circuit of Fig. 13.19 occurs because contact 3 will not open until after contact 2 has closed. The circuit in Fig. 13.20 causes contact 3 to open before contact 2 closes. When the subject closes his key, relay *A* closes, and stays closed for 1 second. The solenoid is again connected in series through contacts 2 and 3, so that both must be closed for the shutter to be triggered. When the relay closes, it opens contact 3, and that contact then stays open for 1 second, as in the preceding circuit. But in Fig. 13.20, contact 2 will not close until after contact 3 has already closed. Contact 2 is initially open. Then, when relay *A* operates, it first opens contact 3 and *then* closes

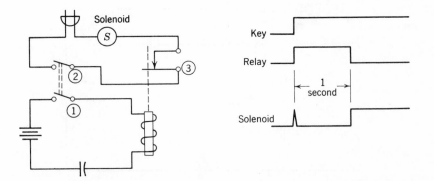

Fig. 13.19 A circuit which almost performs the timing operation in Fig. 13.18. The actual timing sequence is as diagrammed at the right in this figure.

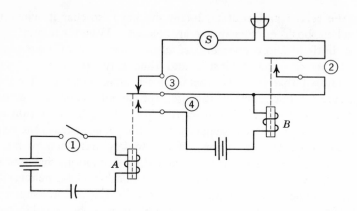

Fig. 13.20   A circuit to eliminate the first short current pulse of the circuit shown in Fig. 13.19.   However, the current through the solenoid in this circuit will stay on for only a very short time.

contact 4, operating relay B.   When relay B operates, it, in turn, closes contact 2.   Now when relay A opens, after 1 second, contact 3 will close, and since contact 2 is also closed, current will pass through the solenoid.   However, this circuit is not quite complete because, when relay A opens, it will also allow relay B to open, so the time during

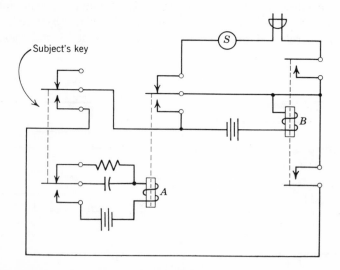

Fig. 13.21   A circuit which correctly performs the timing operation of Fig. 13.18. Releasing the subject's key turns off relay B and discharges the capacitor.

which contacts 2 and 3 are both closed will be very short.   This problem is remedied in the circuit of Fig. 13.21.   Here relay B is made to
hold itself closed even after relay A has opened.   The holding circuit
is broken when the subject releases his key, and the circuit is restored
to its initial state.

The circuit in Fig. 13.22 performs the same function as that in Fig.
13.21, and is much simpler to construct.   It operates in the following
way.   When the key is first closed, current will flow through R to the
capacitor and the relay.   If the capacitor is initially completely discharged, it will act as a path of zero resistance (a short circuit) when
the key is first closed.   Therefore no current will flow through the
relay at that first instant.   However, as the charge builds up on the
plates of the capacitor, a larger and larger proportion of the current
will flow through the relay until, when the capacitor is fully charged,
it will act as a path of infinite resistance, and the current through the
relay will simply equal the voltage of the battery divided by the sum
of the resistances of R and the relay.   Thus the current through the
relay will gradually increase from zero to some final value, and the
time it takes to reach a level great enough to close the relay will depend
upon the time constant of the circuit.

The action of this circuit may be conceived of in a somewhat different, but equivalent, way.   When the key is first closed, the charge

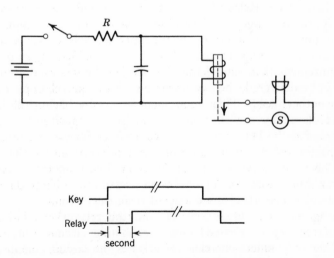

Fig. 13.22   A circuit to perform the timing operation diagrammed in Fig. 13.18.
A more complete timing diagram is included in this figure.

in the capacitor is zero and the voltage generated in it and impressed across the relay is also zero.   However, as time passes, the capacitor builds up a charge, and the resulting voltage across the relay gradually approaches some final level.   When the voltage is great enough, the relay will close.

Note, in the diagram for the timing in this circuit, that the relay does not *open* until after the key has been opened.   This is because, after the key opens, the capacitor will discharge through the relay, holding it closed until the discharge current falls below the relay's threshold.

The calculation of the time constant for this circuit is not as simple as for the circuits discussed above, and it is not really worth going through.   Trial-and-error procedures should be used for selecting the components for any particular time delay in this circuit.

The circuits in Figs. 13.21 and 13.22 only operate properly if the subject holds his key closed until the stimulus has been delivered.   If he just taps the key, nothing happens.   However, it is often necessary that the stimulus be delivered 1 second after a key has been pressed, regardless of the duration of the press (e.g., it is hard to instruct a pigeon to hold down his key until the reinforcement is delivered). This timing requirement and a circuit which will satisfy it are shown in Fig. 13.23.   The requirement that the circuit continue to perform and operate the shutter even after the key has been released (should the subject give a very short press) suggests that some sort of holding circuit is needed.   Relay *A* is therefore connected basically as a holding relay, the holding circuit passing through a normally closed pair of contacts on a second relay *B*, whose function will be explained later. The circuit containing the coil of relay *A* is modified slightly to satisfy the requirement that, should the key be held down steadily, only one flash will be delivered; the key must be released and then pressed again to get another flash.   This requirement is met by having the holding relay *A* closed by the current that charges a capacitor C_1.   In this way, pressing the key can only have an effect for a short time while the capacitor is charging up (and the time constant of this circuit should be very short so that the charging time is short).   Any time after that, but before the key has been released to discharge the capacitor, the key is essentially disconnected from the circuit.

Pressing the key closes relay *A*, and the relay then holds closed (even if the key is released) until the holding circuit is broken.   A second set of contacts on relay *A* activates the circuit containing the coil of relay *B*.   This relay is connected up in such a way that it will close 1 second after its circuit is activated, as did the relay in Fig. 13.22.

When B finally closes, it fires the shutter and, at the same time, opens the circuit that was holding relay A closed. Relay A will now open, even if the key is still held closed, because the fact that the capacitor is charged up has made the key ineffective. When relay A opens, capacitor C_2 will begin to discharge through relay B, and relay B will soon open. As soon as the key is released, the capacitor C_1 will discharge and the circuit is back to its initial condition, ready to repeat its operation. (That statement is not quite true. Relay B will remain closed for a short time after A has opened, while capacitor C_2 discharges through it. Therefore, if the subject presses the key again before B has opened, B will remain closed, and he will not get another flash.)

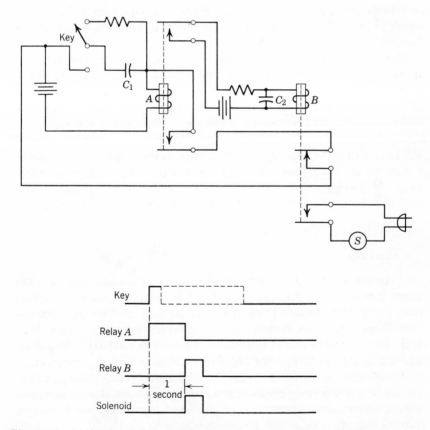

Fig. 13.23   A circuit to fire a solenoid 1 second after the closure of a key, regardless of how long the key is held down.

SOME IMPORTANT DETAILS ABOUT CAPACITOR-RELAY
TIMING CIRCUIT COMPONENTS

Rated Voltages and Currents for Relays

The coils of most relays are rated in terms of the a-c or d-c voltage
necessary for *firm* closing. For d-c relays so rated (e.g., 24 volts
d-c), this means that the relay will actually pull closed at a voltage
somewhat lower than the rated one (e.g., 18 volts d-c), and will not be
injured by steady impressed voltages of somewhat higher values. The
precise value for relay closure must be determined for each relay individually, and the voltage above which the relay will become too hot
also depends on the idiosyncrasies of the particular relay. Alternating-
current relays may also be used in timing circuits with a d-c power
supply, but in this case the rated a-c voltage is much greater than the
d-c voltage actually required for closing.

When the current or voltage through a relay coil is gradually increased from zero, the relay will pull closed at some particular level.
If the same relay is already closed, and the coil current is gradually
decreased, it will not open until the current drops to a level somewhat
lower than the level required for closing. The closing and the opening threshold levels are different because a given current in the coil
will have a stronger magnetic effect on the armature when the armature
is close to the core (when the relay is closed) than when it is farther
away. Although a few relays are rated for both opening and closing
currents, the levels must be determined individually for most relays.

Capacitors

There are a number of different kinds of capacitors, made by different processes and particularly suited for different purposes. However, for general applications, they may be divided into two types—
electrolytic and nonelectrolytic. Electrolytic capacitors have relatively large capacitances [1 microfarad (MFD) to 5000 MFD or more],
whereas nonelectrolytic ones run from fractions of micromicrofarads
(MMFD) up to a few hundred MFD. For a given capacitance, an electrolytic is considerably smaller and usually cheaper than a nonelectrolytic capacitor. However, electrolytic capacitors have certain
features that are undesirable in some applications.

Electrolytic capacitors are made by a process in which a very thin oxide layer is formed between two sheets of metal foil. The foil is then rolled up into a cylinder and the cylinder is covered by a paper or metal tube. Two wires, one attached to each sheet, extend from the ends of the tube. The oxide layer acts as a rectifier, showing a high resistance to current flow in one direction and a low resistance in the other. If a voltage of one polarity is applied to such a capacitor, it will behave as if it contained two plates insulated from each other; that is, very little current will flow and it will exhibit a large capacitance. When the polarity is reversed, a large current will flow, the capacitor heats up, and may even explode. Therefore, electrolytic capacitors can only be used in d-c circuits and the polarity markings on the body of the capacitor must be carefully followed. The terminal marked "+" must be connected in such a way that it is always positive or neutral with respect to the negative terminal. This feature of electrolytic capacitors usually does not interfere with their use in timing circuits as long as the polarity markings are followed.

A much more severe limitation in the use of electrolytic capacitors for timing circuits is that their capacitance is not very stable. The thickness of the insulating film sometimes varies with the applied voltage because this film is actually formed by the passage of current from one plate to the other. A capacitor rated at 2000 MFD, 15 volts, may well show a capacitance of 5000 MFD if the impressed voltage is only 6 volts; and this capacitance value will not necessarily be stable from time to time even when the applied voltage is constant. If the duration of a timed interval is critical, nonelectrolytic capacitors should be used, even though they are bulkier and more expensive. The stability of any electrolytic-capacitor timing circuit depends very much upon the particular capacitors and the particular time interval to be used. But as a rough rule of thumb, 5% variations in time interval may be expected from day to day, and steady drifts may be expected over long periods of time.

One more feature of electrolytic capacitors that is sometimes relevant to timing applications is the fact that they leak. That is, if a charge is placed on the plates of an electrolytic capacitor and then the capacitor is disconnected from the circuit, the charge will gradually dissipate because electrons will pass through the oxide film inside the capacitor. Ordinary nonelectrolytic capacitors leak more slowly, and there are certain specially constructed ones (e.g., "Glassmike") which will hold a charge for days without appreciable leakage. These very low-leakage capacitors do not have large capacitance. A large number of them may be connected in parallel to produce the equivalent of a single, high-capacitance unit, but the procedure is expensive. When a problem seems to require a large capacitance with low leakage, it is wise to search for some other timing principle.

Problems

1. Design a model of a neurone such that, when a steady voltage is impressed across the input, the output is a series of flashes of a pilot light bulb. The frequency of flashes should be a function of the input voltage, but the amplitude and duration of each flash should be relatively independent of input voltage.

2. Design a model of a synapse that has elements of spatial and temporal summation. The synapse should have two inputs, each of which is a stage such as the one in Problem 1. The output of the synapse should be a series of flashes whose frequency is proportional to the rate of total input impulses (i.e., total input pulses per second).

3. An experiment is designed to study the properties of competition between two teams of three members each. All six players have reaction-time keys. When the experimenter momentarily taps his key, a light goes on and stays on for 3 seconds. All players press their keys as soon as the light goes on, and hold them down until they are told to release them. Three seconds after the light first went on, the teams are automatically instructed as to which won in the following way. If the total reaction time (the sum of three times) of team A was shorter, bulb A lights. If team B's total time was shorter, bulb B lights. Design the circuit. (You do not need clocks.)

Chapter **14**

Amplifiers

This chapter is intended as an introduction to electronic circuits. The basic principles of operation of electron tube and transistor amplifiers will be discussed but the actual design and construction of electronic instruments will be left for some of the more advanced texts listed at the end of this chapter.

The basic action of most of the electronic circuits used in behavioral research is one of amplification. That is, an electrical signal of low voltage and/or amperage is put in and the output is a more powerful signal, correlated in some way with the input. Such amplification is performed not by a process analogous to magnification, but by allowing a low power input to control the larger power of the output, just as the small effort required to open a valve may produce large changes in the amount of power coming out of a water pipe. (The electron tube is called a valve in England.)

ELECTRON TUBES

Diodes

The diode is the simplest electron tube. It is often used as a rectifier, that is, a device for changing alternating current into direct current, but recent advances in technology have produced other, non-electronic rectifiers which are smaller, more efficient, and sometimes cheaper than the electron diode. Diodes will be discussed here prin-

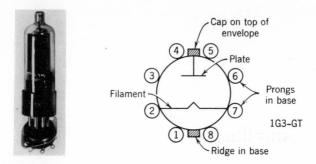

Fig. 14.1   Photograph of a typical diode and its schematic diagram.   (*Courtesy* of Helen E. Howell, Berkeley, Calif.)

cipally because they provide an easy approach to the explanation of the more complicated tubes.

Figure 14.1 shows a photograph of a typical electron diode and a schematic diagram of its parts.   The base of the tube is usually made out of some form of plastic material in which prongs are imbedded. A chamber, called the envelope, most often made of glass but sometimes of metal, is cemented into the base.   Wires running from the parts inside the envelope are brought out and soldered to the prongs. Therefore, when the tube is plugged into a tube socket, as in the figure, the terminals on the bottom of the socket provide convenient connections to the internal tube parts.

After the elements of the tube are put together, the envelope is evacuated to a high vacuum and sealed off.   Inside the envelope are the two basic elements, a source of electrons and a collector.   The source can be either of two sorts.   The simplest is a filament of tungsten wire coated with various chemicals.   When a current is passed through the filament, it heats up and glows, heating the chemical coating on its surface.   The chemicals are so constituted that large numbers of electrons are boiled off when they are hot.   Thus the coated filament acts as a source of free electrons when current is passed through it.

The other type of electron source is very similar.   It consists of a metal surface coated with the same kind of electron-emitting chemicals.   The metal is wrapped around an uncoated tungsten filament and is heated when current is passed through the filament.   The metal surface is often connected to the filament right inside the tube, as indicated in the tube diagram in Fig. 14.2.   The source of electrons is called the cathode because it is usually connected to the negative side of a supply voltage, as will be explained later.

The other important element in the electron diode is the electron collector.   It is a relatively large piece of metal (or sometimes carbon) that surrounds the cathode, and is called the plate, or more rarely, the anode.

Suppose that a diode were connected as in the circuit in Fig. 14.3. One source, labeled "C," provides the power to heat the cathode, and electrons will boil off into the surrounding space.   A second source, labeled B, makes the plate positive with respect to the cathode.   The electrons that have been freed from the cathode will therefore be attracted toward the plate, and current will flow around the loop indicated by the arrows in the figure.   This current is called the plate current.   (The current heating the cathode is called the filament or heater current.)   The voltmeter connected across a resistor in the plate circuit will thus register a voltage proportional to the rate at which electrons pass from the cathode to the plate.

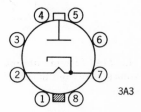

Fig. 14.2   Diagram of diode containing a heated cathode that is internally connected to the filament.

If a diode is connected as in Fig. 14.3, it will exhibit certain properties.   First, it may be obvious that the greater the filament current, the greater will be the plate current, because electrons will boil off and be available at a greater rate.   There are several limits to this statement, however.   Below a critical filament temperature, no electrons at all will be given off.   And above some temperature, the filament will melt.   Between those limits, the rate of electron emission is a very nonlinear function of filament voltage.   For these reasons, the filament

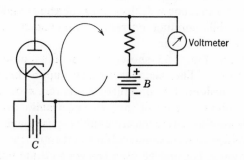

Fig. 14.3   A circuit to drive a diode.

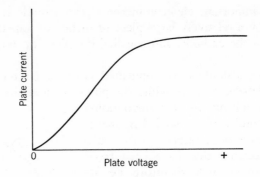

Fig. 14.4 Plot of the plate current of a generalized diode as a function of the voltage between the cathode and plate.

voltage in a vacuum tube is almost always held constant, and is not used as a means of varying the plate current.

For a fixed filament voltage, the plate current will vary with the voltage between the filament and the plate, as in Fig. 14.4. At low plate voltages, electrons are boiled off the cathode more rapidly than they are drawn to the plate, and they tend to accumulate in a cloud around the cathode. This cloud is called the space charge. As the plate voltage increases, more and more of the electrons in the space charge are drawn to the plate. Therefore, the plate current increases and the size of the space charge decreases. At high plate voltages the electrons are drawn to the plate at the same rate as they are freed from the cathode. Thus the space charge disappears, and further increases in the plate voltage do not increase the plate current appreciably.

The preceding discussion applies to the case when the plate voltage is increased from zero to a high positive one, relative to the cathode. When the plate is made negative with respect to the filament, it should be obvious that no current will flow, and the tube is said to be cut off; that is, a diode will conduct current in only one direction, and can therefore be used as a rectifier.

The diagram in Fig. 14.5 shows the use of a diode in rectifying alternating current. The filament battery simply heats the filament and should be considered as completely separate from the rest of the circuit. Since points A and B are the two sides of a 115-volt a-c source, A will be alternately positive and negative with respect to B. When A is positive, electrons will flow through the tube and the resistor, but when A is negative with respect to B, no current will flow. And since, when current does flow, its magnitude will be related

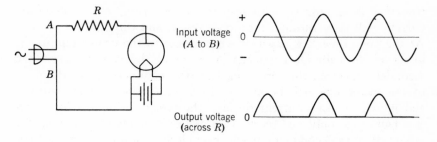

Fig. 14.5   A half-wave rectifier circuit, using a single diode. The input and output voltages are plotted at the right of this figure as a function of time.

monotonically to the magnitude of the voltage (as in Fig. 14.4), the current through the resistor will change in time, as shown in Fig. 14.5. The input voltage is alternating in polarity, and the output voltage and current are pulsating direct current.   This circuit is called a half-wave rectifier, because only half of the input wave appears in the output.

The circuit in Fig. 14.6 is a little more complicated but used much more extensively.   It is called a full-wave rectifier circuit, and its action is as follows.   The output winding of the transformer has a center tap which is connected to the cathodes of two separate diodes. (The cathodes may be heated by a second output winding on the transformer, as in this diagram.)   When the upper end of the secondary winding A is positive with respect to the lower end B, it is also

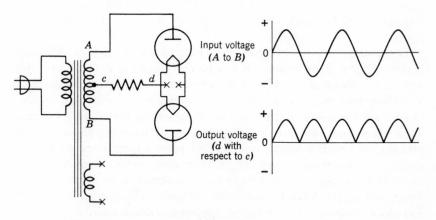

Fig. 14.6   A full-wave rectifier circuit, using two diodes.

true that *A* is positive with respect to the center tap. Therefore, current will flow through the upper diode, and through the resistor. At the same time *B* is negative with respect to the center tap, so the lower diode will not conduct. As soon as the voltage across the secondary reverses, the top diode will stop conducting, but the plate of the lower one will become positive with respect to its cathode, and it will conduct current through the resistor. Thus, whereas on any half-cycle only one of the two diodes is conducting, one or the other will always conduct current through the resistor, and the current will always pass through the resistor in the *same direction* (from *c* to *d*). The voltage and current through the resistor will be as in the diagram. It is said to be full-wave rectified power.

When a current passes through a coil of wire, a magnetic field is generated around the coil, and any change in current causes the field to move, thus inducing a current into any nearby coil. This effect was discussed at length in Chapter 10, as it relates to the inducing of a current into the secondary coil of a transformer. However, the changing magnetic field also tends to induce a current into the coil which is generating the field in the first place, and the induced current is always opposite in polarity to the "primary" current, that is, the current that is setting up the field in the first place. Therefore the net current actually passing through the coil will always be less than it would have been if the magnetic field were not moving. In other words, a coil will conduct more current when a d-c voltage is placed across it than it will with an equivalent a-c voltage. (The property of a coil of wire which gives it greater conductance for direct current than alternating current is called inductance.) Thus, when a voltage is impressed across a coil which has both a-c and d-c components, the coil will tend to block the a-c component more than the d-c component.

The voltage across the resistor in Fig. 14.6 is always of the same polarity, but it is pulsating. It can be considered as the sum of a d-c and an a-c component. If a capacitor is connected across the resistor, it will tend to short-circuit the a-c components while leaving the d-c unaffected for some of the reasons discussed in preceding chapters. Thus both capacitors and coils discriminate between a-c and d-c components, and their effects may be combined in what is called a filter circuit, as illustrated at the output of the full-wave rectifier in Fig. 14.7. The output of such a filter has a smoother wave form than the input, and as the filter is made more effective (e.g., by adding more and more components), the output approaches direct current.

The filtering characteristics of various combinations of capacitors, inductances (called chokes), and resistances are too complicated to be discussed here. In general, however, it is important to understand what is meant by the term "filtered" as applied to the output of a power supply. (The development of a loud hum is a trouble that commonly develops in radios and phonographs. The hum is at a frequency of 60 cycles per second, and is caused by the malfunctioning of one or more of the filtering capacitors in the power supply of the amplifier. When a filter capacitor stops working, the voltages to the rest of the radio contain more "60-cycle ripple" than they should, and this results in a 60-cycle modulation of the audio output.)

Full-wave rectifier circuits are so very common as sources of d-c power for electronic apparatus that manufacturers supply special

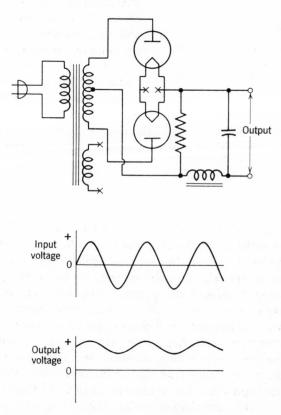

Fig. 14.7 A full-wave rectifier circuit with a filter section. This particular combination of elements does not act as a very good filter, but is shown merely to illustrate general filtering principles.

vacuum tubes which contain two diodes within one envelope to save space. Since the two cathodes are always connected together in such a circuit, it is electrically the same thing to use a single cathode and two separate plates. However, for clarity in circuit diagramming, the single cathode in this case is represented as if it were two. Figure 14.8 shows the circuit symbol for this sort of tube. The fact that the two diodes are in the same element is indicated by the extension and dotting of the line representing the envelope.

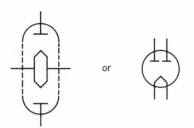

Fig. 14.8 Two forms of circuit symbol for a single tube that contains one cathode and two plates.

If you examine an actual diode like the one in Fig. 14.1, you may see what looks like another element sticking out to the side of the others. It is also likely that there will be a metallic discoloration of the inside of the envelope near this element. The element is called a "getter." When the tube is being manufactured, the getter is coated with a burnable compound, and after evacuation of the envelope, the coating is ignited to burn out the last bit of oxygen. When the tube is being used, the getter serves no function.

Triodes

The curve in Fig. 14.9 is a simplified plot of the spatial gradient of voltage between the cathode and plate of a conducting diode when the plate voltage is 100 volts. (In an actual diode, the curve dips down below the horizontal axis near the cathode because of the presence of the space charge, but for these purposes, the curve can be considered as always above zero.) If a surface that is transparent to electrons were introduced at the position labeled G, and if it were given a voltage of 20 volts negative with respect to the cathode, it would exactly cancel the positive plate voltage between the cathode and G. Then electrons leaving the cathode would not be attracted to the plate, and the current through the tube would be cut off. If the surface were moved closer to the cathode, say to G', then it would require only 10 volts, negative with respect to the cathode, to cut off the current to the plate. Now consider the circuit in Fig. 14.10, where the resistance of R is very great compared with the resistance that the diode (without

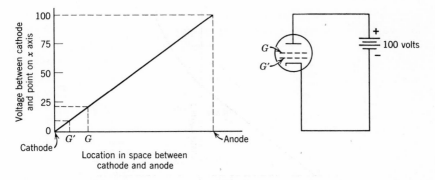

Fig. 14.9 A simplified plot of the voltage gradient between the cathode and plate of a diode when the total cathode-to-plate voltage is 100 volts.

the transparent surface) shows to current flow. When the tube is conducting, almost all of the 100 volts will appear across the resistor, by Ohm's law. If the surface is then introduced at G' and is given a voltage of 10 volts, negative with respect to the cathode, the current through the tube and the resistor will be cut off, so the voltage across the resistor will drop to zero.   (It is as if the resistance of the tube had been increased to infinity. The entire plate voltage will appear across the tube.)   Thus, the voltage across the resistor has been changed from almost 100 volts to zero by the addition of only 10 volts to the surface at G'. Such a setup can then be said to have amplified the input voltage (the voltage between the cathode and the surface) by a factor of ten, considering the voltage across the resistor as the output voltage. The closer the surface to the cathode, the smaller the required cutoff voltage, and the greater the amplification factor.

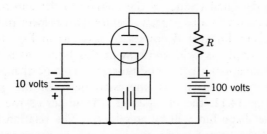

Fig. 14.10 A simple triode circuit, in which the 10 volts between the cathode and grid essentially cancel out the 100 volts between the cathode and plate, resulting in a plate current of zero ampere. The dashed line within the tube envelope represents the grid of the triode.

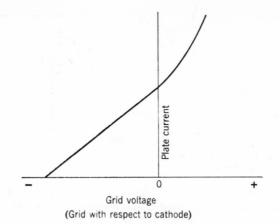

Fig. 14.11 A simplified curve of plate current as a function of grid voltage for a typical triode with a fixed plate voltage. As the grid is made more negative with respect to the cathode, the plate current is reduced.

This sort of amplification is accomplished by inserting a fine wire screen in the position G', directly between the cathode and the plate and much closer to the cathode than to the plate. Such a screen acts essentially as a surface that is transparent to electrons, because most of them travel right through the gaps between wires. But the electric field set up by the screen is fairly uniform, that is, it does not have gaps. It is true, in a real tube, that some of the electrons actually strike the grid, but their number is very small. This kind of tube, containing three basic elements, is called a triode. The screen is called a grid, and when it is designed to operate in the manner just described, it is called a control grid.

For a well-designed triode, as the voltage to the control grid is increased from zero to more negative values with respect to the cathode, the plate current linearly decreases to zero, as in Fig. 14.11. (The plate voltage supply is held constant in this figure, as it usually is in actual electronic apparatus.) Therefore, if a voltage changing between zero and 10 volts negative is impressed between the grid and the cathode in Fig. 14.12, the changes in voltage across the resistor will have the same shape but will be amplified. The relationship between the input and the output of the amplifier may be represented as shown in Fig. 14.13a. The curve plotted is the same as that in Fig. 14.11. The output voltage corresponding to any particular input voltage (between cathode and grid) may be found simply by finding the input voltage on the horizontal axis, projecting this up to the curve, and then reading off the corresponding output voltage (plate current multiplied by R).   Since the output voltage will, in this circuit, change almost instantaneously when the input voltage changes, this procedure may be used to determine the shape of the output wave corresponding to any given input wave, as illustrated in Fig. 14.13.   If the input voltage changes abruptly as in Fig. 14.13a, the output voltage will change proportionally.   That is, so long as the part of the curve being used is linear, the output wave will have the same shape as the input but will be amplified.

This is further illustrated in Fig. 14.13b.   Here a sine wave is impressed across the input, and a sine wave will appear at the output. You may actually go through the construction of the output sine wave to prove that it is as represented here, but a logical argument may be sufficient to explain the correctness of the plot.   From Fig. 14.13a it should be clear that any size of input step will be magnified by the same factor at the output.   In other words, the shape of the wave containing two unequal steps is faithfully reproduced at the output.   If the sine wave input of Fig. 14.13b is considered to be a set of very small steps of differing amplitude, it therefore follows that the output will be a set of larger steps of the same relative sizes as those in the input.   Thus the output will also be a sine wave.   In fact, any wave form at all will be faithfully reproduced at the output as long as the tube is operating on the linear part of its curve.   (This statement holds for the hypothetical amplifier diagrammed in Fig.

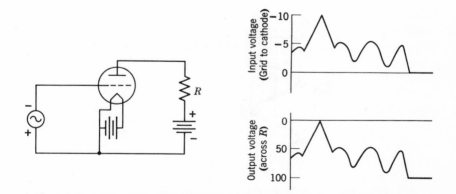

Fig. 14.12   A simple triode amplifier.   As long as the input (grid) voltage is always on the linear portion of the curve in Fig. 14.11, the output voltage will be an undistorted but amplified replica of the input voltage.

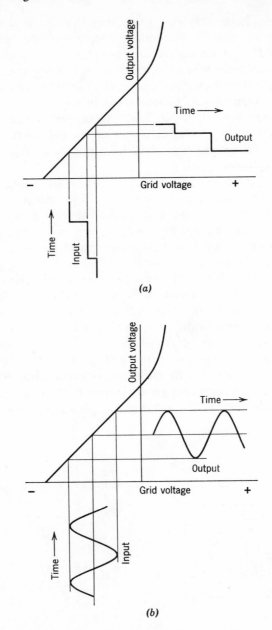

Fig. 14.13 (a) Graphical method for determining the shape of an output wave that results from the input wave at the lower left. The input here consists of two steps of different amplitudes. (b) A sine-wave input and its corresponding sine wave output.

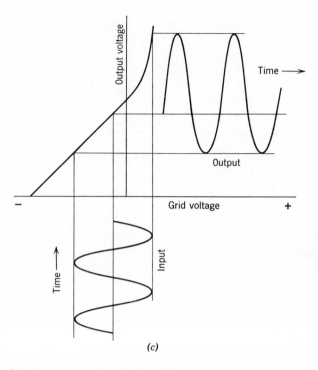

(c)

Fig. 14.13   (c) A representation of the distortion that can occur when a vacuum tube is operated on the nonlinear part of its characteristic curve. A pure sine wave is fed in, but the output wave is not pure.

14.12.   However, for any real amplifier, a number of properties must be included in the true circuit diagram which limit its capabilities for undistorted reproduction.   Some of these properties will be discussed later in this chapter.)

Figure 14.13c illustrates how the input wave form may be distorted by the amplifier if the input voltage causes the tube to operate beyond the linear portion of its grid-voltage–vs.–plate-current curve.

The circuit drawn in Fig. 14.12 is almost usable as an amplifier. When a so-called grid resistor is added, as in Fig. 14.14, the circuit will work.   The grid resistor is necessary because, if the few electrons that actually do strike the wires of the grid have no path over which to flow back to the cathode, the grid will gradually become more and more negative even with a constant input voltage, and the amplifier will soon cut off completely.

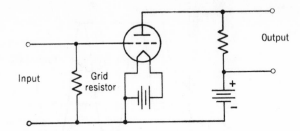

Fig. 14.14 A grid resistor added to the triode amplifier of Fig. 14.12 to prevent the buildup of electrons on the grid.

Should the input to the amplifier in Fig. 14.14 drive the grid positive with respect to the plate, the output would become nonlinear. In order to amplify signals of either polarity linearly, a d-c voltage, called the grid-bias voltage, is usually added to the circuit, as shown in Fig. 14.15. This voltage sums with the input voltage. Therefore, the grid will remain negative, even when the input voltage is positive, as long as the input voltage is not greater than the grid-bias voltage.

Multigrid Tubes

Other grids are added to many vacuum tubes to satisfy special requirements, and the tubes are named accordingly (e.g., a pentode has a filament, a plate, and three grids). The details of these tubes will not be discussed here, except to say that most of them are simply modifications of triodes to perform specialized functions, and they behave according to the same underlying principles.

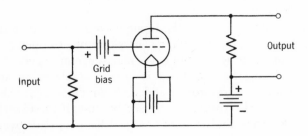

Fig. 14.15 A grid-bias voltage added to the triode amplifier to insure that the triode will operate on the linear part of its curve regardless of the polarity of the input voltage.

Nomenclature and Symbols

Vacuum tubes are identified by a set of numbers and letters.   Should a designer want to find the exact characteristics of a given tube, he would look it up, according to its numbers and letters, in what is called a tube manual.   However, for our purposes, it is sufficient to know only very roughly what the numbers themselves indicate.   A very common tube is labeled 6L6, another 117Z5.   The 6 and the 117 are the only parts of those labels that really mean anything by themselves. The 6L6 requires a filament voltage of 6 volts and the 117Z5 a filament voltage of 117 volts.   The letters GT after the above kind of designation (e.g., 50L6-GT) refer to the kind of envelope that contains the tube elements.   The only difference between a 50L6 and a 50L6-GT is that one is smaller than the other and the GT has a glass envelope instead of the standard metal one.   In all but the most specialized equipment, a bad tube of either kind may be replaced by the other as long as there is room for it.

The symbols commonly used for various vacuum tubes are shown in Fig. 14.16.   The small, numbered circles refer to the pins on the

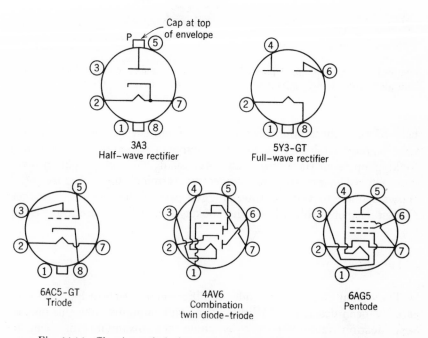

Fig. 14.16   Circuit symbols for a selection of different vacuum tubes.

Fig. 14.17   A tube plugged part of the way into its socket in a typical piece of laboratory equipment.   (*Courtesy* Helen E. Howell, Berkeley, Calif.)

base of the tube as the tube is viewed from the bottom.   When the tube is plugged into a socket, the numbers also refer to the socket looking up from the bottom, and are usually embossed right into the base material next to their respective terminal lugs.   Figure 14.17 shows a standard vacuum tube plugged part of the way into a socket. Circuit elements soldered to the socket terminal lugs are also visible.

AMPLIFIERS

The action of a simple triode amplifier such as that in Fig. 14.15 has already been described.   With a single tube amplifier like this one, an amplification factor of $\times 80$ is about the maximum that can be achieved.   However, if a second stage of amplification, just like the

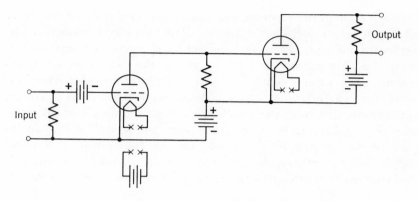

Fig. 14.18   A two-stage, direct-coupled triode amplifier.

first, is simply connected so that its input is the output of the first
stage, then the over-all amplification will be the product of the amplification that occurs in each stage considered alone.   Thus, the circuit
in Fig. 14.18 may have an amplification of as much as 6400.

The circuit in Fig. 14.18 is in no way affected if the two filaments
are connected in parallel across a single power supply, and this is true
for most of the circuits that involve electron tubes, as long as the
tubes all run at the same filament voltage.   However, if the parallel
filament connections were all drawn in, they would add needless confusion.   Therefore the convention used in Figure 14.18, terminating the
filament leads in x's and showing elsewhere the connection of the x's,
is customary in almost all electronic circuit diagrams.

However, for this particular type of amplifier, the plate-voltage
supplies cannot be connected in parallel.   A separate supply is drawn

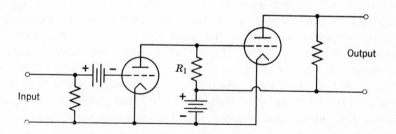

Fig. 14.19   The circuit for a two-stage, direct-coupled triode amplifier in which
a single plate-voltage supply is used.   The circuit will *not* operate correctly for
reasons explained in the text.

for each stage in this diagram, and it is a logical necessity of the circuit itself that two supplies are required. The two may be connected together at one end, but there is no way making the circuit work by using the same supply for both stages. If the two plates were connected across a single supply, as in Fig. 14.19, the amplifier would not work for the following reason. When there is no current flowing through the first tube, there will be no voltage drop across the resistance R_1. Therefore the grid of the second tube will be very highly positive with respect to its cathode, i.e., the full voltage of the plate supply will be between the grid and cathode. Thus the second tube will conduct very strongly and the amplifier will not work as it should.[1]

Capacitance-Coupled Amplifiers

The sort of amplifier discussed so far is called a direct-coupled amplifier because the input is connected directly to the first stage, and the first stage is directly connected to the second. For a number of reasons, most of which are too complex to go into here, multistage, direct-coupled amplifiers are very unstable unless a lot of special circuit gimmicks are added. In addition, such amplifiers require a fairly complicated power supply or a lot of batteries, at least one for each stage of amplification, for the reasons discussed in the preceding section. Many of these problems are solved when the input and/or the stages are connected through capacitors, as shown in Fig. 14.20. This amplifier is said to be capacitance-coupled. Because a capacitor acts as an extremely high impedance to direct current, virtually all of the steady voltage from the plate supply appears across the capacitor, and the grid of the second tube is not strongly positive with respect to its cathode. Thus a single-plate power supply may be used. However, for the same reason, only *changes* in the output voltage of the first stage will be impressed upon the second stage grid and appear amplified in the output. In general, the output of a capacitance-coupled amplifier is a sort of first derivative of the input because of the action of the capacitor. Thus a square-wave input will appear at the output as a set of spikes, and a sine wave as a sine wave (see Fig. 14.20). For a great many purposes, in any audio oscillator or hi-fi amplifier, for example, only changes in the input voltage need be amplified, and capacitance-coupled amplifiers are almost always used in

---

[1] It is possible to drive a multistage, direct-coupled amplifier from a single plate-voltage supply, but only with the use of additional tubes and circuitry which act to isolate the various stages from each other. Such circuits are beyond the scope of this book.

those devices. Most electroencephalographic and nerve-potential amplifiers are also of this type.

Figures 14.21*b* and 14.21*c* show the output of a capacitance-coupled amplifier when the input is the square wave in Fig. 14.21*a*. For the output in Fig. 14.21*b*, the coupling capacitor has a very small capacitance. Thus it charges up and discharges very rapidly, and the output consists of very short spikes. When the capacitance of the coupling capacitor is increased, it takes longer to charge and discharge, and the output looks more like that of Fig. 14.21*c*. Similarly, if a very-low-frequency sine wave is across the input, a small, coupling capacitor will charge up almost as fast as the input to it (it will show a high impedance), and the output voltage will be smaller than if the sine wave had a higher frequency or if the amplifier had a larger coupling capacitance. In general, any capacitance-coupled amplifier will have a frequency-response curve that shows zero output for a zero frequency input and an increasing output as the frequency increases. Furthermore, the increase in output as a function of the frequency of the input wave will depend upon the value of the coupling capacitance, as shown in Fig. 14.22.

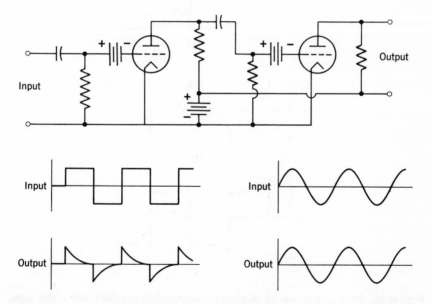

Fig. 14.20 A two-stage, capacitance-coupled amplifier. Its outputs are plotted for a square-wave and a sine-wave input. The square wave is badly distorted by the coupling capacitance but the sine wave is not.

The curves in Fig. 14.22 drop again at very high frequencies.   There are a number of reasons for this which are beyond the scope of this book.   However, in general, the following happens.   Inside each tube, the grid and cathode and the grid and plate are really capacitors with very low capacitances (they are a pair of conductors separated by an insulating medium).   All of the wiring of the circuit itself also has capacitance.   As long as the frequency of the input is not too high (e.g., 100,000 cycles per second (cps)), these capacitances have little effect, but when the frequency is really high, they begin to offer relatively low-impedance paths for current to flow, and the circuit acts as if miscellaneous low resistances were put in at undesirable places.

The frequency-response curve of an ideal, *direct-coupled* amplifier would be horizontal from zero to an infinite frequency.   For such an amplifier, the output wave could be a perfect, undistorted replica of the input wave for any kind of signal.   The frequency response curve

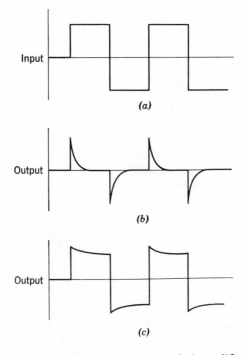

Fig. 14.21   Output patterns of a capacitance-coupled amplifier when the input is a square wave.   (*a*) The input wave.   (*b*) The output when the coupling capacitor has a small capacitance.   (*c*) The output when the coupling capacitor has a large capacitance.

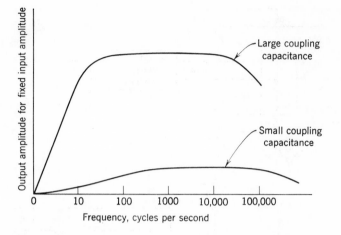

Fig. 14.22 Frequency response curves of a capacitance-coupled amplifier for two different values of coupling capacitance.

for any real amplifier indicates the extent to which the output is distorted.   If the input is a pure sine wave of any frequency, the output will also be a sine wave of the same frequency, but the amplitude of the output will depend upon the frequency according to the frequency-response curve.   (There are causes of distortion not reflected in the frequency-response curve, but they will be ignored in this discussion.)   If the input is any complex wave, it may be considered as the sum of a set of sine waves of various frequencies and amplitudes (Fourier's theorem), and the frequency-response curve indicates how each of these sine components will be attenuated by the amplifier. Thus, a capacitance-coupled amplifier will distort the input wave form by amplifying the low-frequency components of any input wave much less than the high-frequency components.

Chopper Amplifiers

Often a slowly changing or steady voltage must be amplified by a large factor, as for example when the psychogalvanic skin response is to be recorded. A multistage, direct-coupled amplifier would serve the purpose, but because such amplifiers must be very carefully designed if they are to be stable, they are relatively expensive.   Capacitance-coupled amplifiers are cheaper, but since they cannot amplify low frequencies with the same gain as higher ones, any input signal which contains low-frequency or d-c components will be distorted

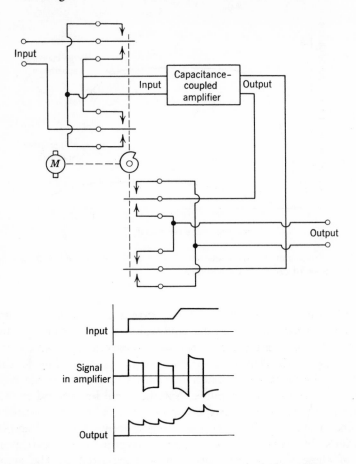

Fig. 14.23 Semischematic diagram of a chopper amplifier. The motor continuously drives the cam. Each rotation of the cam reverses the contact configuration at the input and the output of a capacitance-coupled amplifier. The input and output contact assemblies are connected to act as reversing switches.

during amplification. Amplification of low-frequency signals (including direct current) is therefore sometimes accomplished by a special device called a chopper or breaker amplifier. A chopper amplifier takes a small, steady voltage or a slowly changing one and converts it to a proportional alternating voltage. This a-c signal is fed to a very-high-gain, capacitance-coupled amplifier, and then converted back to a proportional d-c signal at the output of the amplifier. These conversions are sometimes performed by a mechanical chopper, as shown in Fig. 14.23. Here the d-c input is fed to a reversing switch which is mechanically driven back and forth. Thus, a d-c input signal is converted to a square wave whose peak-to-trough amplitude is twice the input-voltage level, and whose frequency equals the frequency at which the switch is driven. The square wave is amplified by the capacitance-coupled amplifier, and then fed into another set of contacts that are mechanically connected to the contacts which convert the input. The output contacts are connected so that during the times the input voltage is normal, the output voltage is normal, but when the input voltage is reversed, the output of the amplifier is reversed, too. Therefore the output of the entire unit is a steady voltage proportional to the input voltage. (It is chopped at the input and "unchopped" at the output.)

The chopping action introduces noise into the output of breaker amplifiers at frequencies near the chopping frequency and higher, so such amplifiers are not suitable for amplifying signals whose frequency sometimes approaches the chopping frequency. It is thus desirable to chop the input at a high rate, and in some chopper amplifiers the mechanical switching has been replaced by a set of electronic switches which chop at rates of 10,000 cps or more.

Push-Pull and Grid-Ground Connections

Most sensitive amplifiers, both direct- and capacitance-coupled, are designed for what is known as push-pull amplification. The basic circuit for this kind of amplification is shown in Fig. 14.24. The input voltage is impressed across a pair of grid resistors and two triodes con-

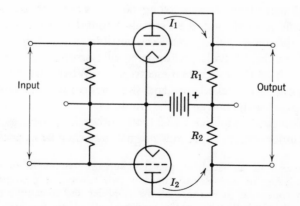

Fig. 14.24 A one-stage triode amplifier with a push-pull input and output.

nected in opposition. When the upper input terminal is positive with respect to the lower one, the upper triode passes more current through the output resistor R_1, and the lower triode less through R_2. Therefore, a difference in voltage appears across the output terminals that is proportional to the input signal. There are several fairly complicated reasons why push-pull circuits are advantageous, and two of them will be mentioned very briefly here. It is often convenient to amplify the algebraic difference between two voltages. The push-pull circuit automatically does this when each of the two voltages is connected between one of the input terminals and the center, ground terminal,[1] as in Fig. 14.25a. Suppose, for example, that the occurrence of a stimulus is to be marked directly on a record of a psychogalvanic skin response (PGR). The PGR itself is fed between one of the input terminals and ground, and a pulse at the occurrence of the stimulus is fed between the other terminal and ground. The pulse appears on the record added to the PGR.

Because the push-pull circuit amplifies the algebraic difference between the two input voltages when they are connected as shown in Fig. 14.25a, this kind of circuit may be used to reduce unwanted voltages relative to the desired ones. Any two equal voltages that appear with the same polarity at the same time on both sides of the input will cancel each other out, while differences are amplified. One all too common trouble in electronic apparatus is what is called 60-cycle pickup. The power lines, lighting circuits, etc., that surround most laboratories actually broadcast fairly strong signals at 60 cps, and any sensitive amplifier will pick these signals out of the air and add them to the voltage that is supposed to be amplified. For example, if an amplifier is connected to the brain to record brain waves, the record will often show a strong 60-cps wave. When a push-pull input circuit is used, and the central—ground—terminal is also connected to the animal, it is sometimes possible to find a location on the animal where the 60-cycle pickup is equally strong between that location and each of the other two electrodes. When this is the case, the 60-cps pickup is cancelled out, and the uncontaminated brain wave is all that appears at the output of the amplifier.

Most biological amplifiers, and many other amplifiers as well, have push-pull input stages. The input signal may then be connected either

---

[1] The terminal of an amplifier that is internally connected to the cathode of the first tube (or cathodes of the first two tubes in a push-pull input) is usually also connected to the case of the amplifier and sometimes to the earth itself (through a third wire in the power cord). This terminal is therefore called the grounded terminal, or simply, "ground."

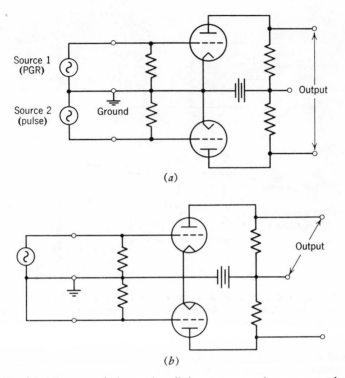

Fig. 14.25 (*a*) The use of the push-pull input to superimpose a marker on a PGR recording. (*b*) Circuit of a push-pull amplifier used with a grid-ground input and output.

from one side to the other, as shown in Figs. 14.24 and 14.25*a*, or the signal may be connected between one of the grids and the ground, the other grid being connected directly to the ground, as shown in Fig. 14.25*b*. The first of these input connections is called a push-pull input and the second (Fig. 14.25*b*) a grid-ground input.

Input Impedance

Consider the measuring of the voltage across a cell membrane. Say that the actual voltage generated is 50 microvolts. The circuit in Fig. 14.26*a* represents a suitable amplifier and a voltmeter. (Actually more than one stage of amplification would be needed, but the addition of other stages to this figure would just complicate things without changing anything basic.) Before the membrane is connected to the

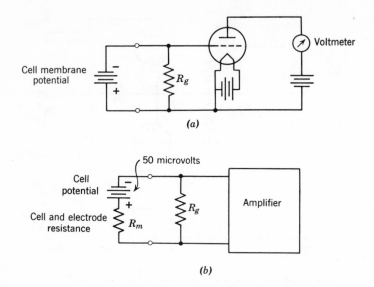

(a)

(b)

Fig. 14.26 (a) Circuit using a direct-coupled triode amplifier to measure a cell membrane potential. (b) Semischematic diagram of the actual circuit when the membrane potential is being measured. Some of the potential to be measured is lost across the internal resistance of the cell and electrodes.

amplifier, there is a finite resistance between the two amplifier input terminals, consisting of the grid-to-cathode resistance of the tube in parallel with the grid resistor R_g. The actual grid-to-cathode resistance of vacuum tubes is so very great that it may be considered infinite for these purposes (and for all but a very few special amplifier circuits). Therefore, the resistance that will be connected from one end of the cell membrane to the other will approximately equal the resistance of R_g. But the cell membrane and the electrodes themselves also have resistance, which may be diagrammed as shown in Fig. 14.26b. The current that will flow when the amplifier is connected to the membrane equals $50 \times 10^{-6}/R_g + R_m$. The voltage that the amplifier will "see" is the voltage between the grid and cathode of its first stage, and this is the voltage across R_g. Therefore, if R_g happens to be equal to R_m, for example, the amplifier will see only 25 microvolts. In general, as R_g increases relative to the internal resistance of the source and electrodes, the proportion of source voltage that the amplifier will see increases. In addition, as the resistance of the entire input loop increases, the current drawn from the source decreases. If the source happens to be something like a cell, the less current drawn from it, the more normally it will behave. For these reasons, the resistance between the input terminals of an amplifier is important to know, and, at least for biological amplifiers, a large input resistance is desirable. However, it cannot be made infinitely large because at very high values of R_g (e.g., 40 megohms), the resistances of things such as the insulation between the pins in the base of the tube become comparable to R_g, and the voltage between the grid and cathode is reduced.

The term "resistance" has been used in this discussion so far because it is a familiar concept. Actually the more general term "impedance" should be substituted for resistance. The impedance between the input terminals of an amplifier is called the input impedance. For any input signal whose frequency is not too high (say, up to a few thousand cycles per second), the input impedance of a direct-coupled amplifier essentially equals the resistance of the resistor connected between the grid and cathode of the first tube. For higher frequency signals and for capacitance-coupled amplifiers, the calculation or measurement of the input impedance is beyond the scope of this discussion.

Output Impedance

Any instrument that is driven by an amplifier (e.g., a meter, relay, etc.) must draw a certain amount of current from the output of the amplifier, and that current must also pass through part of the output stage of the amplifier. The greater the impedance of that part of the amplifier, the more voltage will be lost across it, and the less will be available to drive the meter or relay. The impedance inside the amplifier through which the output current must pass is called the output impedance, and it is exactly analogous to the internal impedance of any power source, such as a battery or a living cell. As a general rule, the lower the output impedance, the better.[1]

Most loudspeakers have fairly low impedances and draw relatively large amounts of current at low voltages, but most vacuum tubes have the opposite property, that is, they pass small currents at high voltages. Therefore vacuum tubes are not very suitable for directly driving loudspeakers. However, the characteristics of tubes and loudspeakers may be matched by placing a transformer between them, as in Fig. 14.27.

[1] It is also true that, for maximum transfer of *power* from the amplifier to the load, the output impedance should equal the load impedance. In cases where power is at a premium (for example, when a loudspeaker is to be driven loudly), a speaker should be chosen whose impedance is approximately the same as the output impedance of the amplifier. A detailed discussion of this point is beyond the scope of this book.

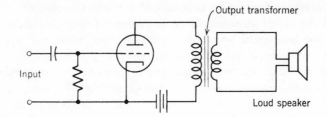

Fig. 14.27 A one-stage amplifier designed to drive a loudspeaker. The output is transformer-coupled.

The (step-down) transformer is called an output transformer and is used in virtually all vacuum tube amplifiers that are designed to drive loudspeakers. As a rule the secondaries of such transformers have several taps, so that the amplifier may be fitted to speakers with different impedances.

Caution: When the output of an amplifier is transformer-coupled, the amplifier must never be turned on unless the loudspeaker or equivalent resistance is connected across the output terminals. If there is no load (e.g., one of the loudspeaker wires is disconnected), very large voltages may be induced into the output stage of the amplifier, damaging the transformer or output tubes or both.

TRANSISTOR CIRCUITS

When a small signal must be amplified by a very large factor or when the output signal must be an undistorted replica of the input, it is best to buy a commercial amplifier. But there are many occasions when less exacting amplification is required, and for these situations an adequate and cheap transistor amplifier may be easily built.

The fundamental principles of operation of transistors will not be discussed here. They are too complicated and, in many ways, not well enough understood to be worth presenting in this book. What will be discussed is the design and construction of a one-transistor amplifier to be used where a small signal must reliably operate a relay.

Consider, as an example, a situation in which a rat must cross a charged grid to get to food, and the number of times he gets shocked during a 24-hour period is to be counted. Assume that the shock is a constant-current d-c shock of 1 milliampere. If a very sensitive relay, one that closes with a current of less than 1 milliampere, were connected in series with the rat, and the relay were to operate a counter, as in Fig. 14.28a, the counter would register the number of shocks. But relays that sensitive are expensive and hard to find.   If an amplifier were introduced, such as the vacuum-tube amplifier in Fig. 14.28b, the signal could be amplified sufficiently to operate a less expensive and more available relay.   Although a vacuum-tube amplifier could be built to perform this function, the characteristics of transistors make them particularly suited to this application, and a transistor amplifier would be easier and cheaper to build.

Figure 14.29 is a photograph of several different types of transistors. All have three principle elements, an emitter, a base, and a collector. These elements may be considered as analogous to the three elements of a triode vacuum tube.   The emitter corresponds to the cathode, the base to the grid, and the collector to the plate.   The emitter emits charges which are collected by the collector after having been controlled in density by the base.

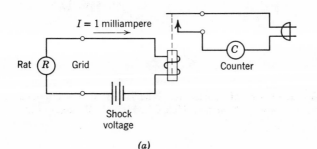

(a)

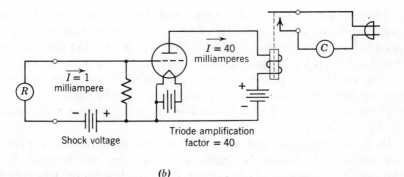

(b)

Fig. 14.28   (a) Simple circuit to count the number of times a rat gets shocked. This circuit requires a very sensitive relay.   (b) A circuit containing a triode amplifier stage, allowing the use of a less sensitive relay.

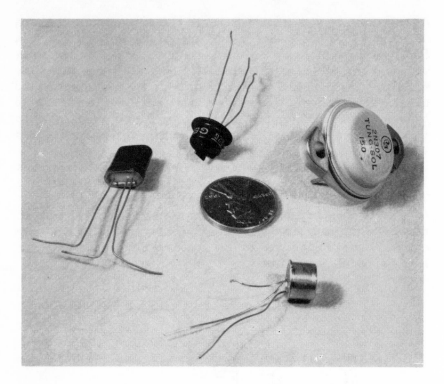

Fig. 14.29 An assortment of transistors. The largest one is designed to control large amounts of power. (*Courtesy* Helen E. Howell, Berkeley, Calif.)

The circuit in Fig. 14.30 shows one form of a basic transistor amplifier, to be discussed in this chapter. When the voltage E_c is applied between the emitter and the collector, current will flow through that loop. This current is called the collector current. If the base is then made more positive with respect to the emitter, the collector current will increase, in a way analogous to the increase in plate current when the grid of a triode is made more positive with respect to the cathode.

In a vacuum tube, the resistance of the path from the grid to the cathode is extremely high, and virtually no current flows through it. However, the resistance from the base to the emitter of a transistor is relatively low (the actual value depends upon the particular transistor), so the voltage between the base and emitter will cause an appreciable current to flow in that loop.

For a typical transistor, a change of 1 milliampere in the base current will produce a corresponding change of about 40 milliamperes in
the collector current.   (Common transistors range in amplification
factors from about 20 to about 100.)   If the transistor is connected
into the shock circuit, as in Fig. 14.30, the 1 milliampere that flows
through the rat and the base-emitter circuit will change the current
through the relay coil by 40 milliamperes.   In this way, the transistor
eliminates the need for a very sensitive and expensive relay.

The two principle classifications of transistors are the *p-n-p* and the
n-p-n.   These letters refer to the physical structures of the transistors
themselves.   The two types perform in exactly the same way except
that all the voltages impressed on a *p-n-p* must have the opposite
polarity from those on an *n-p-n*.   In the above examples, the polarities
are correct for the *n-p-n* transistor.   This one was chosen for discussion because the voltages have the same polarities as the corresponding
vacuum-tube amplifier voltages.   However, many of the transistors
most useful for behavioral work are only made with the *p-n-p* construction; thus, for the rest of this discussion, *p-n-p* will be used, and
the polarities will be opposite from those in Fig. 14.30.

Figure 14.31 is a diagram of an amplifier circuit that will work
satisfactorily in the shock-detection problem and in any others for
which the current-amplification requirements are similar.   When the
rat is touching the grids, the shock box drives a 1-milliampere direct
current through the base-to-emitter circuit of the transistor, making
the base negative with respect to the emitter.   This base-to-emitter
current change produces a corresponding change of about 40 milliamperes in the emitter-collector circuit, which contains the relay coil.
The 50,000-ohm variable resistance serves as a bias control.   When the
slider is all the way to the left, the base is virtually disconnected from

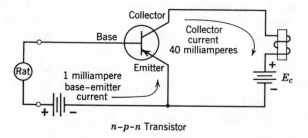

n–p–n Transistor

Fig. 14.30 A circuit to count the number of times a rat gets shocked, using
an insensitive relay and a transistor amplifier.

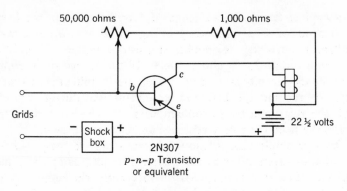

Fig. 14.31 A single-stage, direct-coupled transistor amplifier that will operate satisfactorily in measuring the number of times a rat is shocked, and in a great many other situations in which a small current must be amplified to drive a relay.

the negative side of the battery (because, for this transistor, the base to emitter resistance is considerably lower than 50,000 ohms). When the slider is all the way to the right, the base is almost the full 22½ volts negative with respect to the emitter. The 1000-ohm fixed resistor prevents the base from going so far negative that the collector current rating is exceeded. The variable resistor may thus be set so that, when there is no shock, the relay has some current flowing through it, but not enough to hold it closed. Then the actual change in collector current need only be big enough to change the relay from open to closed rather than all the way from zero current to closed.

The particular transistor in Fig. 14.31 is a cheap and versatile one at the time of this writing. However, transistor technology is progressing at such a remarkable rate that it may be considered a collector's item by the time this chapter is printed. The transistor in this circuit is one of a class called power transistors, because they are capable of controlling a large amount of power without overheating. (The actual power requirements of the circuit in Fig. 14.31 are well below the maximum ratings of the transistor.) Other types, such as audio-amplifier transistors, are no cheaper and are much more easily damaged by circuit misconnections. For applications in which the output of the amplifier is to control a relay, power transistors are preferable.

Transistors are extremely reliable devices, and are not damaged by fairly severe mechanical shocks (e.g., dropping on the floor). In reliability, size, basic circuit complexity, and efficiency, transistors are superior to vacuum tubes. At their present stage of development, they are inferior to vacuum tubes for two reasons that are revelant to typical behavioral applications. The first important disadvantage of transistors relative to vacuum tubes depends upon the fact that the interelement resistances of transistors are very much lower than the corresponding resistances for vacuum tubes. Because of these relatively low resistances, the input and output elements and all the stages of a multistage amplifier interact with each other, making the quantitative design of multielement circuits very difficult. In almost all vacuum-tube amplifiers, for example, the current that flows in the plate circuit of one stage has virtually no effect on the functioning of the preceding stage (unless feedback is deliberately introduced), and each stage can be designed and understood more or less by itself. But changing the value of a resistor anywhere in a multistage transistor circuit changes the functioning of almost everything else in the entire circuit.

The second principle disadvantage of transistors is that they are very sensitive to heat. When soldering a circuit, great care must be taken that the transistors are not made hot. Sometimes a transistor can be firmly connected into a circuit without soldering anything directly to its leads. For example, some transistors fit into sockets, as illustrated in Fig. 14.32a. Solderless connections may be made to power transistors as in Fig. 14.32b. The clips in this photograph are obtained by smashing a tube socket designed to fit a miniature vacuum tube. If wires must be soldered directly to the transistor leads, a pair of pliers or some other heat sink should be clamped between the body of the transistor and the place on the lead where it is to be soldered.

Once the circuit is operating, a transistor's sensitivity to heat is manifested in the fact that its parameters (e.g., amplification factor, base-emitter resistance, etc.) change with its temperature. Therefore any transistor circuit that must be really stable in its characteristics must be carefully designed with special stabilizing circuitry. (Circuits to operate relays need only be designed so that the change in output current is normally well above the minimum necessary to close the relay.)

There are many books and booklets on the design of transistor circuits for a variety of applications. Because of the very rapid development of transistor technology, it is not worthwhile to list special references here, but excellent booklets may be purchased at any electronics supply store.

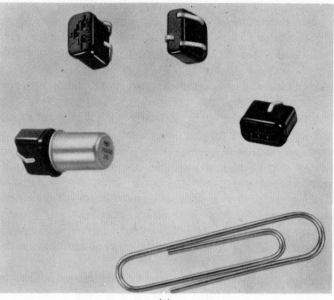

(a)

(b)

Fig. 14.32 (a) Transistor sockets. (*Courtesy* Cinch Mfg. Co.) (b) A method of connecting power transistors into a circuit. The clips are obtained by smashing a miniature tube socket, as shown in this figure. (*Courtesy* of Helen E. Howell, Berkeley, Calif.)

SELECTED REFERENCES ON ELECTRONICS

The Radio Amateur's Handbook, and its workbook, *A Course in Radio Fundamentals,* published by The American Radio Relay League, are available at electronic supply houses. Much of the content of these books is not relevant to behavioral research, but they include reasonably good treatments of basic electronics.

Paperback editions on various special topics in electronics from the *Electronic Technology* series, published by Rider, are available at many electronic supply houses, as well as some bookstores.

P. E. K. Donaldson, *Electronic Apparatus for Biological Research, 1958.* Butterworths Scientific Publications, London, 1958, and Academic Press, New York.

I. C. Whitfield, *An Introduction to Electronics for Physiological Workers,* 2nd ed., 1959, Macmillan and Co., Ltd., London, and St. Martin's Press, New York.

Chapter 15

Some useful electronic apparatus

THE CATHODE-RAY OSCILLOSCOPE

The cathode-ray oscilloscope is easily the most versatile piece of electronic equipment to be found in a behavior laboratory. It may be used directly to measure steady or fluctuating voltages of any level from about 200 microvolts to 1000 volts as well as very short or moderately long time intervals (about 1 microsecond to 50 seconds), to investigate the relationships between two simultaneous signals, to trouble-shoot other electronic apparatus, to provide a visual stimulus that changes in almost any desired way at any time, and even to display moving reversible figures. These are just a few of the functions that may be performed directly and simply with any good, standard laboratory oscilloscope.

This discussion will be based on the assumption that you have an oscilloscope available to experiment with. The oscilloscope should have a direct-coupled vertical amplifier whose gain is calibrated. Also be sure to borrow the oscilloscope instruction manual. Although oscilloscopes can be damaged by mechanical shocks, there is almost no way to damage them electrically (except for one instance which will be explained later). Therefore, anyone who has an oscilloscope available should not hesitate to loan it to you while you learn how to operate it. Do not use an oscilloscope unless it is in its cabinet (there are dangerous voltages within the circuits, but when it is in its cabinet, none of them appear at the front panel). Also avoid any oscilloscope that does not have a plastic or thick glass plate protecting the face of the cathode-ray tube itself. The tube is large and evacuated to a high vacuum.   A scratch or blow anywhere on its envelope may cause it to implode.

The Cathode-Ray Tube and Controls

The cathode-ray tube is the subunit within the oscilloscope that converts electric signals into a corresponding visual display.   This tube is diagrammed in Fig. 15.1.   In the small end is a unit, called the electron gun, consisting of a filament, grids, and plates.   Electrons boiled off the filament (or heated cathode) are shaped by the electrostatic field of the grids and plates into a narrow stream moving toward the face of the tube.   The inside of the face is coated with a substance, called the phosphor, which gives off light when struck by electrons.   The stream of electrons from the electron gun strikes this phosphor layer, and a spot of light is generated which is visible through the glass face of the tube.   Usually the phosphor and the surrounding regions on the inside of the tube are coated with a metallic layer which is positive with respect to the cathode, completing the circuit.

Somewhere on the front panel of the oscilloscope, there is a knob labeled "intensity" or "brightness."   This knob controls the density of the electron beam and the brightness of the spot.   If an intense beam of electrons strikes the phosphor in one small region for a period of time, the phosphor may burn and become discolored.   Therefore, always make sure that, if the spot is stationary on the screen, it is not turned up to a high intensity.   Now turn on the power switch of the oscilloscope.   This switch may be a toggle switch, or it may be

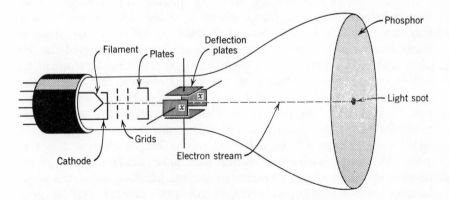

Fig. 15.1   Semischematic diagram of a cathode-ray tube.

combined with some other knob on the front panel (e.g., the intensity control).   After a minute or two of warmup time, the bright spot should be visible on the face of the cathode-ray tube.   If there is no spot, try turning up the intensity control.   If this does not work, the spot may be falling somewhere off the screen.   There are two control knobs labeled "horizontal (or x)," and "vertical (or y) position."   Turn these knobs until the spot appears.   Remember that as soon as it does, the brightness control should be turned down to a moderate level.   If none of these procedures bring anything to the screen, or if a line is present instead of a point, you may have to adjust a different set of controls, called the sweep controls, to be explained later.   There is a knob somewhere on the panel which is labeled "horizontal (or x) amplifier gain."   This control should be set to some low value (e.g., 20 volts per centimeter).   If the spot still will not appear, or if it is still a line, look for a control labeled "triggering" or "sweep mode" and set it to a position labeled "horizontal (or x) amplifier."   If, after all these adjustments are made, you still cannot produce a single stationary spot on the screen, ask the owner to help you.

The intensity control changes the voltages within the electron gun to change the intensity of the electron beam that strikes the screen. The control labeled "focus" changes the relative voltages between elements in the gun to change the diameter of the electron beam as it strikes the screen.   Turn the focus control and observe its effect on the spot.   Usually the intensity and focus control interact somewhat, so that the spot must be refocused when the intensity is changed.

As the electrons inside the cathode-ray tube stream from the gun to the screen, they pass between two pairs of plates, as indicated in Fig. 15.1.   These plates are called deflection plates.   If a voltage is connected between the two plates labeled x in Fig. 15.1, in such a way that the left plate is positive with respect to the right one, then, as each electron passes between the plates, it is attracted toward the left plate and repelled from the right one.   If the voltage between plates is very great, the electrons may actually strike the left one, but as long as that voltage is low relative to the voltage pulling the electrons toward the screen, the path of each electron will simply be deflected toward the left, but each one will still strike the screen.   Thus the spot on the screen will be deflected to the left, as illustrated in Fig. 15.2.   When the horizontal-position control on the front panel of the oscilloscope is turned, it changes the voltage between these two plates in the cathode-ray tube, so that, by turning this control, you can position the spot horizontally on the screen.   The plates are called hori-

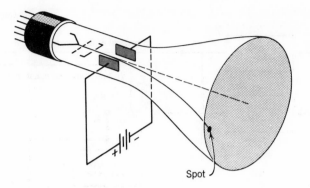

Fig. 15.2. Sketch of the spot deflection produced by a voltage applied between the horizontal deflection plates of a cathode-ray tube.

zontal deflection plates. (Note that the plates themselves are in vertical planes, but they are named according to the direction in which they deflect the spot.) The cathode-ray tube also contains a second pair of plates which operate in exactly the same way, except that they are in horizontal planes and therefore deflect the spot vertically. The vertical-position control adjusts the voltage between these two vertical deflection plates.

Sweep Generator and Controls

Figure 15.3 is a block diagram of the units within the cabinet of a standard oscilloscope. The cathode-ray tube and controls were discussed in the preceding section. The unit labeled "sweep generator" will be discussed now.

The sweep generator is an electronic device which generates a sawtooth wave form. The output voltage of this device is as plotted in Fig. 15.4a, and the pattern is repeated each time the sweep generator is triggered. The output of the sweep generator may be connected (through an amplifier) to the horizontal deflection plates by means of a switch on the front panel of the oscilloscope. Now suppose that the spot is positioned at the left side of the screen and the connected sweep generator is triggered. The voltage between the horizontal deflection plates will slowly and linearly increase from zero to some maximum value and then drop to zero again. The spot will therefore move across the screen smoothly until voltage drops to zero, at which point it will jump back to its initial position. In a properly designed

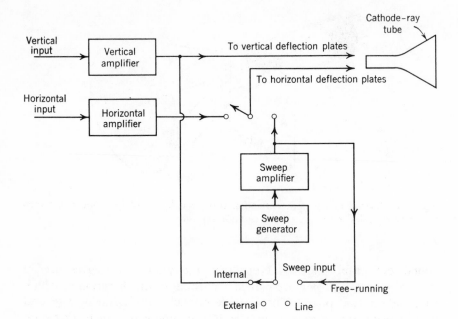

Fig. 15.3 Block diagram of the principal control elements within a cathode-ray oscilloscope.

cathode-ray tube, the deflection of the spot is a linear function of the voltage between the deflection plates. Therefore, as long as the output of the sweep generator is linear, the spot will move linearly across the screen.

On the front panel of the oscilloscope there is a cluster of controls related to the sweep generator. One of these controls may be switched to a position labeled "free-running." (The control itself is probably labeled "sweep mode.") When this control is set to free-running, the sweep generator is automatically triggered every time its output voltage drops to zero. In other words, its output will be a series of saw-teeth, as illustrated in Fig. 15.4b. Set the control to the free-running position, and observe that the spot is now in continuous motion. (You may also have to change another switch in the same cluster to a position labeled "sweep.") If the sweep happens to be set to a slow enough speed, you will be able to see the spot slowly move across the screen from left to right, then jump back and start again. If the sweep is set to a very high speed, the spot will move so fast that it appears as a horizontal line. Find the control labeled "sweep speed." It should be calibrated in terms of seconds, milliseconds, and microseconds per centimeter. This control changes the slope of the saw-tooth wave. When the control is turned to increase the slope, two things happen to the motion of the spot. First, it moves more rapidly across the screen because the voltage between the horizontal deflection plates is increasing more rapidly. Second, so long as the sweep circuit is free-running, the repetition rate will increase for the following reason. The sweep generator circuit is so designed that the voltage will drop back to zero when it reaches some predetermined level. When the slope is greater, that level will be reached sooner, and each sweep will occupy a shorter time. Further, when the circuit is free-running, it automatically retriggers itself each time the voltage drops to zero. Therefore the repetition rate will increase as the slope of the saw-tooth increases. Change the setting of the sweep speed control and observe its effects upon the display.

Many of the controls associated with the sweep circuit are involved in the manner in which the sweep is triggered (when it is not in the free-running state), and these controls will be discussed later.

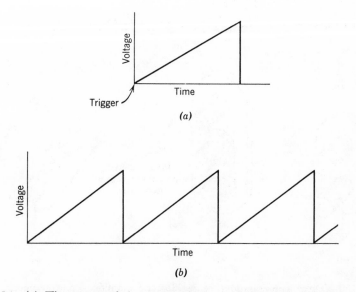

Fig. 15.4 (a) The output of the sweep circuit as a function of time after it has been triggered. (b) Sweep output when the sweep circuit is "free-running." Each time the voltage falls back to zero, it triggers another saw-tooth.

The Vertical Amplifier

The vertical and horizontal deflection plates of a well-designed cathode-ray tube have independent effects upon the position of the spot. If a voltage is applied to the vertical deflection plates at the same time as another is applied to the horizontal ones, the spot will move up or down as well as horizontally. On the front panel of the oscilloscope is a group of two or three terminals labeled "vertical (or y) input." These terminals are usually placed at the lower left side of the panel, and are arranged as shown in Fig. 15.5. They are the input terminals of an amplifier, called the vertical amplifier, whose output is impressed directly across the vertical deflection plates of the cathode-ray tube. One of them is grounded (connected to the cabinet of the oscilloscope and the cathodes of the amplifier). The ground terminals are so labeled in Fig. 15.5. If there is only one other terminal in this group, it is internally connected to the grid of the first tube in the vertical amplifier. If there are two nongrounded terminals in the group, they lead one to each of the two grids of a push-pull input stage. One of these two terminals may be connected externally to the grounded terminal, as in Fig. 15.5b, permitting the amplifier to be used with a grid-ground input.[1]

---

[1] See Chapter 14 for a discussion of push-pull and grid-ground inputs.

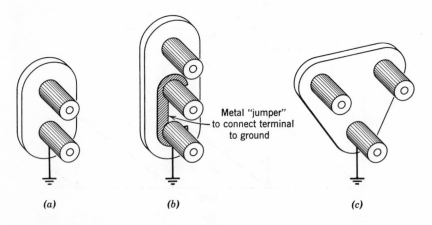

Metal "jumper" to connect terminal to ground

(a)   (b)   (c)

Fig. 15.5 Three configurations of oscilloscope amplifier input terminals. The metal "jumper" between the two terminals in the (b) configuration permits convenient connection of one side of the push-pull input to ground (producing a grid-ground input). The ground symbol indicates that the terminal is connected internally to the case of the oscilloscope.

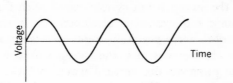

Fig. 15.6   A sine wave to be impressed across the vertical input terminals.

Now suppose a sine wave such as the one shown in Fig. 15.6 is impressed between the grounded and one of the nongrounded input terminals (the third terminal being externally connected to ground). If there is no voltage across the horizontal deflection plates, the spot will move up and down with a sinosoidal motion, and if the frequency of the sine wave is great enough, the display will appear as a vertical line. Switch the sweep circuit back to the condition in which a stationary spot is displayed. Then connect a wire at least 5 feet long to the nongrounded terminal and turn up the gain of the vertical amplifier until a vertical line appears on the screen. (Leave the other end of the wire disconnected.) All the a-c power lines in the building actually broadcast 60-cps radiation throughout the nearby space. The wire will act as an antenna, picking up some of this radiation and introducing it as a 60-cps voltage between the terminal and ground. This voltage, amplified by the vertical amplifier, thus drives the spot up and down 60 times a second.

Now if the spot is simultaneously moved horizontally across the screen, the shape of the 60-cps wave will be visible. Display it in this way by twisting the horizontal position control rapidly back and forth. If the spot is moved horizontally with a displacement directly proportional to time (i.e., with a constant velocity), the display will be a plot of the 60-cps voltage on the vertical axis against time on the horizontal axis, just as it is plotted in Fig. 15.6. Switch the sweep circuit back to free-running again, so that the spot is given a constant horizontal velocity, and the vertical wave shape should be visible.

It is unlikely that the display you now see is very informative. First, the sweep speed will probably not be optimal. Adjust it until just one or two complete cycles are visible. Now the display will probably be a ragged sine wave moving horizontally across the screen. The voltage actually picked up by the antenna has this ragged wave form. The raggedness is produced by miscellaneous equipment drawing power from the 60-cps source. The horizontal drift of the display occurs because the sweep is not synchronized with the 60-cps vertical signal. This point requires some clarification. If the period of the horizontal saw-tooth were precisely some even multiple of the period of the wave on the vertical axis, the sweep would always begin and end at the same point on the vertical wave, and the wave would be stationary on the screen. When there is a slight difference between the periods of the saw-tooth and the vertical signal, each sweep begins at a different point with respect to the vertical wave, and the wave seems to move across the screen. By making a fine adjustment of the sweep speed control, it may be possible to make the wave stop drifting for short periods of time, but the typical sweep generator is not stable enough to hold its period constant over long times. Therefore the wave will begin to move again.

When repetitive waves are to be examined and measured, it is important that they be stationary on the screen, and special circuits are built into all oscilloscopes to eliminate display drift. Some oscilloscopes have what is called a "synch" control. When this control is adjusted correctly, some of the vertical input signal is fed to the input of the sweep circuit, causing it to trigger in synchronism with the vertical signal. If your oscilloscope has such a control, you may prevent the drifting of the display by first setting the sweep speed control to minimize drift, and then turning the synch control until the wave seems to lock in place. However, most modern oscilloscopes use a different principle to stabilize displays, and that principle will be discussed in the following section.

Triggering

Each single saw-tooth wave and sweep delivered by the sweep circuit is triggered when the voltage across the input to the sweep circuit reaches some particular level. This voltage is called the trigger voltage. A selector switch, or a set of them, on the control panel of the oscilloscope allows the operator to choose any one of four different trigger voltage sources. These choices are labeled "free running," "external," "line," and "internal."

External Triggering. In the "external" position, the input to the sweep circuit is connected internally between the ground and another terminal on the control panel. This terminal is usually labeled "ext" or "ext trigger." With the switch in this position, a single sweep will be generated each time the voltage between the external input terminal and the ground reaches some particular level. Suppose, for example, that you wish to observe the nerve impulses resulting from electrical stimulation of a nerve fiber. Electrodes on the fiber are led through an external amplifier to the vertical input terminals of the oscilloscope, and part of the *stimulating* voltage is connected between the external trigger and a ground terminal. Now, each time the shock is delivered, the sweep is simultaneously triggered. When the sweep speed is properly adjusted, and if the latency of the impulses is constant, the impulses will always appear at the same place on the screen regardless of when the stimulus happens to be delivered. And if, for example, the sweep speed is 1 millisecond per centimeter and the gap between the beginning of the sweep and the first impulse is 2 centimeters, the latency is 2 milliseconds. This external trigger control may be used anytime you wish to observe the vertical input during some specified period of time, as long as the start of the period can be signaled by a voltage large enough to trigger the sweep. The actual voltage required for triggering is usually a few volts, but the level varies among oscilloscopes.

Internal Triggering. When the trigger selector is turned to "internal," the signal delivered to the vertical deflection plates is also connected across the trigger circuit. Therefore, whenever the vertical input signal reaches some particular voltage, a single sweep is triggered. Switch the trigger selector on your oscilloscope to "internal." The display should now appear as a stationary picture of the vertical input signal since the sweep begins each time at the same point on the vertical wave. If there is no sweep, and the display is simply a vertical line, find the control labeled "trigger level" and turn it until triggering occurs. (Also be sure that the gain of the vertical amplifier is great enough to give a vertical deflection of several centimeters.)

The process of internal triggering is illustrated in Fig. 15.7. The trigger-level control adjusts the voltage level of the vertical signal that just triggers the sweep. As you turn this control, the displayed wave will appear to move across the screen. What is actually happening is that the place on the wave where the sweep begins is being changed by the trigger-level control.

Associated with the trigger-level control is a switch usually labeled "trigger slope" or "polarity." The vertical signal passes through the triggering level twice each cycle, once while it is increasing and again as it is decreasing. The position of the "slope" control determines whether the sweep will begin when the vertical signal is increasing (+slope) or decreasing (−slope).

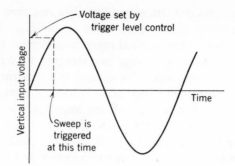

Fig. 15.7 Plot of a vertical input voltage, indicating when triggering of the sweep occurs if the sweep is set to "internal trigger." As the trigger level control is changed, the point on the wave at which triggering occurs may be shifted up or down.

The occurrence of the sweep, when it is internally triggered, depends not upon the input voltage to the vertical amplifier but rather on the output voltage of that amplifier (the input voltage to the vertical deflection plates). Therefore, as the gain of the vertical amplifier is changed, the occurrence of the sweep will shift with respect to the wave itself, beginning earlier as the gain increases. The sweep really begins when the vertical wave, *as it appears on the screen*, reaches some level on the screen, and that level is determined by the setting of the trigger level control.

The internal triggering mode is the one most often used in general laboratory work. If the signal to be examined is repetitive and regular, this mode will hold the display fixed on the screen, and the signal can easily be magnified, vertically with the vertical gain control, and horizontally (along the time dimension) with the sweep speed control. For example, the wave shape, frequency, and amplitude of a flashing light may be measured simply by connecting a phototube directly to the vertical input terminals when the sweep is in the internally triggered mode, as illustrated in Fig. 15.8.[1]

Events which are not repetitive may also be observed in this sweep mode by adjusting the trigger level control to be very sensitive. The sweep will then begin very shortly after the event begins (e.g., when the vertical voltage rises one millimeter above the zero level on the screen).

To illustrate the use of the oscilloscope in measuring the duration of a single event, set your sweep circuit to "internal triggering," the

[1] Phototube characteristics and circuits will be discussed in Chapter 16.

sweep speed to about 5 centimeters per second, and the vertical amplifier to approximately 5 volts per centimeter. Now connect one side of your 22½-volt battery to one of the oscilloscope terminals and briefly touch the other battery lead to the other terminal. When the trigger level control is properly set, the sweep will begin when the lead is first connected, and the trace will then proceed across the screen, dropping vertically when the lead is disconnected. The distance traveled before the trace drops divided by the sweep speed equals the duration of voltage applied to the oscilloscope.

Line Triggering. With the trigger mode control in the "line" position some of the 60-cps line voltage is fed to the trigger circuit. Each time the line voltage reaches some level, the sweep is triggered. The level at which triggering occurs may be adjusted with the trigger level control. This position is used whenever a signal which happens to be synchronized with the line voltage is to be observed. The principal use of line triggering in behavioral research is to observe 60-cps pickup. This pickup often appears along with the signal to be measured, and acts as noise. When the trigger selector is set on "line," this noise component may be observed easily because it is fixed on the screen while the remaining signal components are not (unless they happen to be synchronized with the line voltage). Measures may then be taken to reduce the 60 cps component.

Free Running. When the sweep generator is free-running, the cessation of each saw-tooth automatically triggers the next one, so

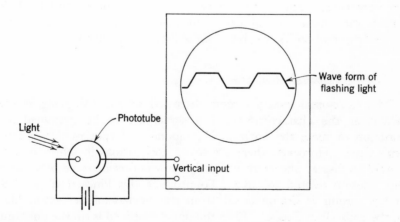

Fig. 15.8 A simple means of displaying and measuring the characteristics of a flashing light.

that the sweep is continuous. This mode is useful during the initial adjustment of the vertical gain and other controls because the trace is continuously visible.

In the other sweep modes, the sweep only occurs once each time the trigger level is reached. In the internal mode, for example, once the vertical signal has triggered a single sweep, another sweep cannot occur until the vertical signal drops below the triggering level and then reaches it again. If the vertical signal were to stay above the triggering level, no more sweeps would occur. Therefore the free-running mode is also used when the level of a d-c signal is to be measured. Measure the voltages of your battery with the oscilloscope. First set the sweep to free-running and the height of the line to some convenient level (with the vertical position control). Next set the vertical gain to a low value (e.g., 10 volts per centimeter). Now connect the voltage to be measured between the vertical input terminals. The line on the screen should move up or down, depending upon the polarity of the voltage. If it moves when the connection is first made, but then drifts back to its initial level, make sure that the vertical amplifier is direct-coupled. (There is a switch somewhere near the other vertical amplifier controls that is labeled "a-c" and "d-c." In the d-c position, the input terminals are directly coupled to the input stage of the vertical amplifier. In the a-c position, an internal capacitor is connected between the nongrounded input terminal and the grid of the first amplifier stage.) There are two knobs with which to control the vertical amplifier gain—a coarse and a fine control. The coarse control should be calibrated (volts per centimeter), and there is a position of the fine-control knob for which the coarse-control calibrations are correct. If you are not sure where that position is, refer to the oscilloscope manual.

The Horizontal Amplifier

The horizontal sweep circuit discussed in the foregoing is used whenever the characteristics of a signal are to be examined as a function of time; the horizontal component of spot motion is linear with time. However, there are many applications in which it is desirable to display the vertical signal as a function of some other signal not linearly related to time. To produce this kind of display, the sweep circuit is disconnected from the horizontal deflection plates of the cathode-ray tube. Then the signal that is to form the horizontal component is fed to the input of the "horizontal" (or x) amplifier, and the output of that amplifier is connected to drive the horizontal deflection plates. To demonstrate this procedure, follow these steps:

1. Reconnect the length of wire to the nongrounded vertical input terminal.

2. Find the horizontal input terminals. They usually have the same configuration as the vertical input terminals, and are usually at the lower right side of the control panel. Connect another length of wire to the nongrounded horizontal input terminal. Do not connect the two lengths of wire together.

3. Find the switch that disconnects the sweep circuit and connects the horizontal amplifier output across the horizontal deflection plates. This switch may be the same one that selects trigger modes, or it is sometimes an extreme position of the coarse-gain control on the horizontal amplifier. When this switch is in the correct position, the display will be a diagonal line or oval. If it is a vertical line, increase the gain of the horizontal amplifier, and if it is almost horizontal, decrease the gain.

If the vertical and horizontal deflection plates were receiving identical signals at all instants in time, the display would necessarily be a line inclined at 45 degrees to the horizontal, since, for any given vertical displacement (y value), the horizontal displacement (x value) would be identical. In another language, if the correlation between the vertical and horizontal signals is perfect, all the points will fall on a regression line at 45 degrees. When the two signals are different in amplitude only, the angle of the line will change accordingly, and if they are also different in phase, the display will become elliptical.

If you have an audio oscillator available, try the following entertaining and instructive demonstration. If you cannot borrow an oscillator, follow the first step in the demonstration anyway.

1. Impress the 60-cps line voltage across the vertical amplifier input. There are several ways to do this, but it will be good practice for you to follow the particular procedure to be described. One of the terminals of the wall socket is internally connected to the ground (i.e., water pipes, cement floor, etc.) and the other is 115 volts "above" ground. Furthermore, one of the oscilloscope input terminals is "grounded," which means that it is connected to the oscilloscope cabinet. If you were to connect the nongrounded wall terminal to the grounded oscilloscope terminal, 115 volts would appear between the cabinet and the floor, water pipes, etc., subjecting anyone who touches the cabinet to a severe shock hazard. But as long as the grounded wall terminal is connected to the grounded oscilloscope terminal and the "high" side of the wall socket to the nongrounded

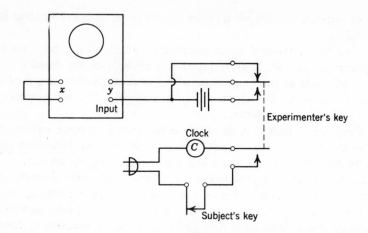

Fig. 15.9 A circuit to measure reaction time when the stimulus is a horizontal displacement of a spot of light. The vertical input terminals are connected together to insure that no vertical displacement of the spot occurs, and the horizontal terminals are connected together when the experimenter's key is not pressed to avoid unwanted horizontal displacements.

input terminal, the shock hazard is not present (unless you touch the nongrounded input terminal). To find the side of the wall socket that is grounded, connect the grounded side of the oscilloscope to a water pipe or other ground (the metal plate covering the wall socket will also serve as a ground). Then connect the nongrounded input terminal to first one and then the other wall socket terminal.[1]   When a 115-volt sine wave appears on the screen, the oscilloscope is connected to the nongrounded side of the wall, and when no vertical signal is displayed, it is connected to the grounded side. (The same test may be performed with an ordinary light bulb. Connect one terminal of the bulb to a water pipe or the wall socket cover, and the other terminal of the bulb to one of the wall terminals. The bulb will light when it is connected to the nongrounded side of the wall socket.) When the grounded wall terminal is connected to the grounded input terminal, and the nongrounded wall and input terminals are also connected together, a good (nonragged) sine wave should appear on the screen.

2. Connect the output terminals of the oscillator to the horizontal input terminals of the oscilloscope. If one of the oscillator terminals

[1] Before you make the connection, be sure that the vertical sensitivity, is low (eg. 20 volts per cm.)

is marked with a ground symbol, it should be connected to the grounded oscilloscope input terminal, but if neither oscillator terminal is so marked, either may be connected to the grounded oscilloscope terminal. (There are a number of grounded terminals on the oscilloscope, and, since all are connected together, they all are equivalent. For example, the oscillator may be connected between the nongrounded horizontal input terminal and the grounded vertical input terminal.)

3. Set the oscilloscope so that the horizontal amplifier is driving the horizontal deflection plates (sweep-disconnected), set the oscillator to approximately 60 cps, and turn up the gains of the oscillator and horizontal amplifier until a two-dimensional pattern appears on the screen. Then adjust the frequency of the oscillator until the pattern is a simple line or oval and is as stationary as possible. When the pattern is stationary, the oscillator will be generating a sine wave of exactly 60 CPS. Now set the oscillator to approximately 120 CPS

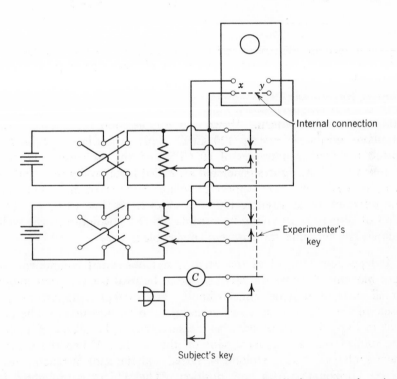

Fig. 15.10 A circuit to measure reaction time to the displacement of a visual stimulus. The circuit permits the displacement to be in any direction and of any magnitude, within the face of the screen.

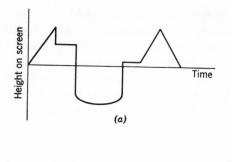

(a)

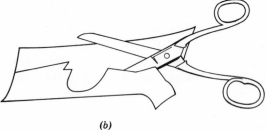

(b)

Fig. 15.11   (*a*) An arbitrary wave form to be used as a tracking stimulus.   (*b*) The wave form in Fig. 15.11*a* being cut out of opaque paper to be formed into a belt.

and observe the pattern.   When this double loop is stationary, the oscillator output is exactly 120 CPS.   This procedure may be followed for various multiples of 60 CPS, and the oscillator calibrated in this way.   The figures generated are called Lissajou figures.   Notice that, as they move, they appear to rotate in the third dimension, and the direction of apparent rotation changes from time to time.   This kind of display is a moving "reversible figure," analogous to the well-known Necker cube, staircase, etc., reversible figures.

Independent control of the vertical and horizontal components of spot movement allows the oscilloscope to be used for the presentation of all sorts of moving visual stimuli.   For example, suppose human reaction time to a silent visual stimulus is to be measured.   The circuit in Fig. 15.9 will permit this measurement to be taken.   Initially, the subject sees a stationary spot on the screen.   When the experimenter closes his key, a clock is started and the spot instantaneously moves horizontally to a new position.   The subject is instructed to press his key as soon as the spot moves, and his key stops the clock. The circuit in Fig. 15.10 allows the spot to be moved from its initial position to any other point on the screen, the new location being determined by the settings of the two potentiometers and reversing switches. (The reversing switches change the direction of movement.)

The spot may be made to move around the screen according to any predetermined pattern by using the simple principle illustrated in the following example. Let us arbitrarily decide to make the spot move up and down according to the pattern in Fig. 15.11a (say, as a stimulus for complex tracking behavior). If a voltage varying in this way as a function of time were impressed across the vertical input, the spot would move as desired. To generate such a voltage, all that is necessary is a photocell, a light bulb, and a device to drive a paper belt. The desired pattern is drawn as a line on a strip of opaque paper, and the paper is cut along the line, as shown in Fig. 15.11b. The cut pattern is then formed into a belt and driven continuously through the device shown in Fig. 15.12. In this device, rays from the bulb pass by the belt and through a slit. Some of them strike the belt, whereas others go past it and fall on a photocell. As

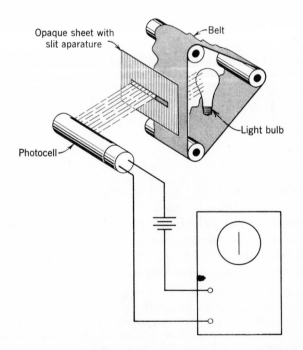

Fig. 15.12 Apparatus to produce vertical movement of the oscilloscope spot which has the temporal pattern shown in Fig. 15.11a.

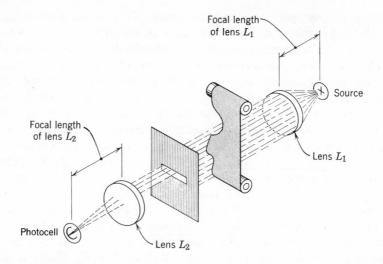

Fig. 15.13   Optical system to insure that the light arriving at the belt is uniform in intensity and to obviate inhomogeneity in the photocell surface.

the pattern on the belt moves past the slit, the amount of light reaching the photocell changes as a linear function of the belt width. Photocells will be discussed in more detail in Chapter 16, but to understand this apparatus, all that one needs to know is that a vacuum phototube, when connected in the circuit of Fig. 15.12, has an output that is linear with the incident light intensity. Therefore, as the belt moves, the spot will move on the screen with the desired motion.[1]

Z-Axis Modulation

Somewhere on the control panel or on the back of the oscilloscope there is a terminal labeled "Z axis." This terminal is connected to one of the elements in the cathode-ray tube in such a way that a voltage impressed between it and any of the grounded terminals will change the brightness of the spot. Unfortunately, in almost all oscilloscopes, the connection is a capacitance coupling. Only *changes* in the applied

[1] The optics of the device in Fig. 15.12 are not really adequate. The total amount of light falling on the photocell might not be exactly linear with belt width, and, since different parts of the photosensitive surface of the photocell are illuminated as the belt moves, inhomogeneities in that surface could introduce further nonlinearities. It is beyond the scope of this book to explain optical principles, but if the simple optical system in Fig. 15.13 is used, the output will be perfectly linear with belt width.

voltage will affect the spot brightness. The faster the applied voltage is increasing, the brighter will be the spot, and the faster it is decreasing, the dimmer will be the spot. The spot therefore cannot be extinguished or brightened for any but very short times. Z-axis modulation is most commonly used to introduce a time marker into the trace, particularly when the display is being photographed. A voltage pulse applied periodically between the Z-axis terminal and ground will generate a periodic dotting of the trace.

Phosphors

There are several different kinds of phosphors used to coat the insides of the faces of cathode-ray tubes, and the characteristics of these materials vary along two principal dimensions. Different phosphors generate light spots of different colors and persistences. The phosphors are designated by the letter P and a number. The following is a list and evaluation of the three most common ones. A complete list may be found in any booklet on cathode ray tubes, available at most electronic suppliers.

P1—*Green spot, medium persistence.* This phosphor generates most of its light in the spectral region to which human eyes are most sensitive. The spot is green, and it continues to glow for a short time after the electron beam has moved to a new region of the screen. It is often used for displays that are to be visually observed (instead of photographically recorded). However, in behavioral research, the visual efficiency of the spot on the screen is rarely of any consequence, and since the P1 phosphor has other shortcomings, it is not to be recommended.

P7—*Short persistence blue, long persistence yellow.* In the author's experience, this phosphor has proved much more useful than any of the others. When the electron beam is actually striking a point on the screen, the spot is blue. As soon as the beam leaves the point, the blue disappears (short persistence, time constant approximately 0.5 millisecond) and is replaced by a yellow afterglow which persists for a long time. The blue radiation is well matched to the spectral sensitivity of most films, and thus may be easily photographed, while the yellow is well matched to human visual sensitivity, and lasts long enough that one may actually measure the characteristics of a single sweep with a ruler after the sweep has been completed.

When a trace is being photographed with moving film, a long-persistence glow can sometimes produce a sort of smearing of the record, and, for this reason short persistence is desirable. The short-persistence blue of the *P7* phosphor is so much more actinic than the yellow for most films that the yellow afterglow will not produce smearing. However, if the film happens to be sensitive to yellow, or if the yellow afterglow is undesirable for some other reason, a color filter that passes the blue but cuts out the yellow light may be placed over the screen. Oscilloscope manufacturers sometimes supply such a filter with the cathode ray tube.

P11—Blue, short persistence. This phosphor has desirable character-istics when the oscilloscope is to be used to obtain photographic records of very fast phenomena (e.g., the shapes of nerve impulses). For this application, it is superior to the *P7* for two reasons. First, the spot is brighter and can therefore be photographed when it is moving at a greater speed. Second, the persistence is somewhat shorter than that of the blue *P7* spot, thus smearing is reduced. However, because of its short persistence, events that do not occur at high and regular repetition rates are very hard to observe visually on a *P11* screen.

When ordering a new oscilloscope, you may specify the particular phosphor you want, since any cathode-ray tube may be coated with any of the common phosphors. Should you already have an oscillo-scope with an unsuitable phosphor, you may replace the cathode-ray tube with one containing a more appropriate phosphor. A cathode-ray tube to fit any given oscilloscope, and with any common phosphor, may be ordered from the manufacturer of the oscilloscope. Instruc-tions for changing cathode-ray tubes are included in the oscilloscope manual.

POWER SUPPLIES

Most laboratory equipment is powered by the standard 115-volt, 60-cps line voltage. Should some a-c voltage other than the line voltage be required, a transformer can be used between the wall socket and the instrument. However, there are many devices that run on direct current, and these require a special power supply. Batteries may be used if very little current is drawn from them, but they are often in-convenient. Power supplies are now being manufactured which con-vert the wall power into direct current of almost any power and stability that is needed.

Power supplies may be grouped into a number of categories. High-voltage power supplies (from about 100 to several thousand volts) are usually designed to deliver relatively small amounts of current, in the milliampere range, and are used to supply power to electronic circuits. Low-voltage power supplies (up to 100 volts) are available to deliver currents as great as 50 amperes. In each of these groups, the units may be regulated or not. If a power supply simply rectifies the alternating current from the wall and filters it, it is not regulated. If, however, it contains circuits which maintain the same output voltage regardless of changes in the wall voltage or changes in the amount of current drawn from the unit, it is said to be regulated. Power supplies, therefore, are rated on each of the following properties:

1. Input voltage (usually 115 volts, 60 cps).

2. Output voltage (may be fixed, adjustable from zero to some maximum, or adjustable from a minimum not zero to a maximum).

3. Output current (the maximum amount that may be drawn without damage. The actual current drawn at any instant will depend on the voltage and the resistance of the unit getting the power).

4. Amount of ripple (that is, the amplitude of the a-c component which gets past the filtering and into the output. This is usually stated as a percentage of the output voltage).

5. Line regulation (the change in output voltage resulting from some particular change in the input voltage).

6. Load regulation (the change in output voltage resulting from a change in the output current).[1]

Before the advent of transistors, power supplies which delivered low voltages and high currents could not be very well regulated. For this reason, whenever it was required that the power to an element be extremely stable (e.g., the current through a bulb in a visual threshold experiment), batteries were used. However, modern transistorized power supplies are even more stable than batteries for applications in which currents greater than 1 milliampere or so are required.

Electronic Timers

Almost all of the cheaper electronic devices to deliver controlled time intervals, and some of the more expensive ones, operate on exactly the same principles as those of the timers discussed in Chapter 13. The temporal characteristics of the charging or discharging of a resistance-capacitance circuit are used to control a relay or set of them.

---

[1] Some regulated power supplies may also be connected so as to deliver a constant output current instead of a constant output voltage.

Commercial timers usually contain a power supply, a set of capacitors and resistors with calibrated time constants, and an amplifier. The amplifier allows the use of more rugged and reliable relays than the sensitive relays necessary for the circuits in Chapter 13. Time intervals are selected by switches on the front panel, which connect combinations of capacitors and resistors to give different time constants. This sort of timer is available to deliver intervals of from about 0.01 second to about 100 seconds. The reliability of the intervals depends very much more upon the particular make of timer. The chief source of interval variability in these timers is poor regulation of the power supply. But since most manufacturers fail to report the regulation of their built-in power supply, it is hard to select a timer on that basis. Should a timer prove unreliable, it is sometimes possible to improve it by running it from a constant-voltage transformer.

A more expensive, but far more reliable, class of timers may be built up from three basic elements—a constant frequency oscillator, a counter, and a device that operates a relay and/or sends out a pulse when the count reaches some predetermined value. Each of these elements may be bought separately, but there are commercial units that contain all three. This sort of timer starts counting the cycles of the oscillator when a switch is closed or a voltage is placed across its input, and closes a relay or delivers a voltage pulse when a number that has been preset on its control panel is reached. Therefore, its accuracy is as good as the constancy of its oscillator (plus or minus one-half the period of oscillation). Since it is fairly easy to construct a highly stable oscillator, the accuracy of the timer is usually 0.1% or better, plus or minus one-half period. If the internal frequency is 10,000 cps, for example, the time interval will never be off by more than 0.1% of the preset interval ± 0.05 millisecond.

The same unit may be used to *measure* time intervals with equally good accuracy. The unit is started with one event, stopped with another, and the count, readable on the front panel, indicates the time between events.

Counting timers may be purchased with any number of preset units working off the same counter. For example, a timer with six presets may be used to control the time of occurrence of six different events. These units may also be connected to recycle automatically when any preset count is reached, so a sequence may be repeated over and over.

Chapter 16

Sensors

The sensing devices discussed in this chapter convert various forms of information (e.g., sound) into correlated changes in electric energy. The electrical signal may then be amplified and displayed or made to control other machinery. The discussion in this chapter will be divided into sections according to the sort of information to be sensed. The sensors themselves and their appropriate amplifying devices will be included in each section.

SOUND DETECTORS

The microphone is the standard device to convert sounds into patterns of electric energy. There are a variety of principles employed in the design of microphones, but only a few will be discussed here. In general, the changes in air pressure physically defined as sound produce small movements of an element, and the element is constructed so that its output voltage is a function of its motion. The output voltage is then amplified by an audio amplifier, that is, a capacitance coupled amplifier whose frequency response lies somewhere in the audible frequency range. The output of the amplifier may drive a loudspeaker, as in a public address system, an electromagnet, as in a tape recorder, etc.

The crystal microphone contains a small section of a crystal which, by virtue of its molecular structure, generates a voltage in proportion to the pressure upon it. The crystal is mounted so that sound pressures are efficiently transmitted to it, and its output is sent through a pair of wires. (Or often a single wire, insulated, and surrounded by a

253

metal mesh sheath, called the shield. The output of the crystal is connected between the wire and the shield, so that the shield acts as the second lead.)

Another common form of microphone consists of a magnet and a coil of wire, mounted in such a way that they move with respect to each other when the air pressure changes (as with a sound). The coil lies in the magnetic field of the magnet, so that the motion of one with respect to the other generates a voltage across the coil. This voltage is brought out to the amplifier.

Good microphones are fairly expensive, since they are specifically designed to respond over the range of audible frequencies while introducing a minimum of distortion, and some are designed to be very sensitive or directional, etc. However, there are two relatively cheap and common devices that will serve as microphones if none of these special properties is required.

Permanent magnet *loudspeakers* consist of a paper cone connected to a coil of wire in a magnetic field. When the current through the coil is changed, the cone moves and produces a sound. If the leads of such a loudspeaker are connected to the *input* of an amplifier, the speaker will act as a microphone. This principle is commonly used in intercom systems, where, when a switch is in the "listen" position, the loudspeaker is connected to the output of the amplifier, and when it is in the "speak" position, the loudspeaker feeds into the input of the amplifier.

The earphone is another device that may be used in reverse to act as a microphone. Some earphones operate on the same principle as the loudspeakers just discussed. Others contain the same sort of crystal as is contained in a crystal microphone. When a changing voltage is impressed across the crystal (e.g., when it is connected to the output of an audioamplifier), it shrinks or expands, producing a sound. When a sound impinges on the crystal, it generates a voltage proportional to the sound. To see how the earphone or the loudspeaker acts as a microphone, connect the two leads of either of these devices directly across the vertical input terminals of an oscilloscope, set the oscilloscope to free-running, and turn up the vertical gain until sounds become visible as deflections of the trace. Try whistling. A whistle is interesting to look at because it is almost a pure sine wave.

PRESSURE SENSORS

The simplest pressure detector is the microswitch. This device has already been discussed in the chapter on switches. Pressure-detecting

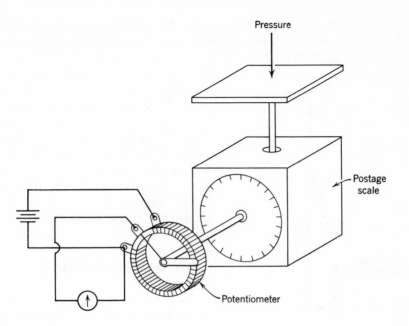

Fig. 16.1 Device to give a continuous electrical indication of pressure. The slider of a potentiometer is driven by the pointer shaft of a scale. Therefore, the voltage across the meter in the figure indicates the amount of pressure exerted on the scale table.

switches can be made fairly sensitive (e.g., to detect the presence of a mouse), and lever linkages and springs may be used to adjust the pressure at which they close.

The microswitch merely indicates presence or absence of pressure. There are a number of devices that can be made or bought to convert pressure continuously into a voltage that is proportional to the pressure. Of this class of pressure sensors, the easiest to construct is one in which pressure moves the slider on a potentiometer, and the voltage is monitored between the slider and one end of the potentiometer. One such device is shown in Fig. 16.1. The indicating needle on a postage scale is removed and the shaft that drove it is connected to the slider of a smoothly working potentiometer.

The trouble with this device, and most others that are relatively easy to build, is that changes in pressure are accompanied by fairly large changes in the position of the sensor (the measurement is not isometric). There are two ways to avoid this problem. One is to make the sensing element extremely sensitive to very small displacements, and this is what is done in most commercial pressure detectors. The other is to use a nulling procedure. For example, suppose another scale is connected mechanically to the one above, as shown in Fig. 16.2, and you simply pull the handle of scale B upward until the platform of scale A is in its original position. Then the reading on scale B, or the voltage of a potentiometer connected to it, is the isometric pressure exerted on scale A. Devices that automatically perform this sort of nulling procedure will be discussed in the next chapter.

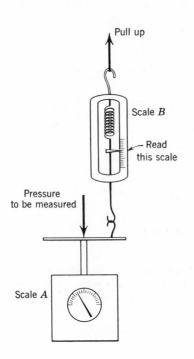

Fig. 16.2 A method for the isometric recording of pressure. The pressure to be measured is applied to the lower scale table, depressing it. The upper scale is then pulled upward until the lower scale table is in its initial position, and the upper scale is read. If the slider of a potentiometer were connected so as to be driven by the upper scale, it would permit electrical monitoring of the pressure on the lower scale.

TEMPERATURE SENSORS

The device in Fig. 16.3 indicates when a temperature has reached any one of a number of predetermined levels. It is simply a mercury thermometer into which a set of contacts have been introduced. When the column of mercury expands, it connects successively higher contacts together. This sort of sensing thermometer is available commercially.

The most widely used device for indicating electrically when the temperature reaches some level is shown in Fig. 16.4. The bar is made by fastening together strips of two different metals. When the bar is heated, the metals expand at different rates, and the bar bends. When it bends far enough, the contacts are connected together. The temperature at which contact is made may be changed by moving the adjustable contact with respect to the bar. This form of sensing device is the basic element in almost all thermostats used to control the temperature of buildings. Take the cover off any thermostat and you will probably be able to see the bimetallic strip and contacts.

To convert continuous changes in temperature into a usable analogous voltage requires more complicated equipment. The thermocouple consists essentially of three wires, two made of one kind of metal, and the third of a different metal. When these three wires are connected as shown in Fig. 16.5, a voltage will be generated across the output which is proportional to the difference in temperature between the two junctions. Thus, if one junction is kept at a known temperature (e.g., in ice water), the output voltage indicates the temperature of the other. The thermocouple is used very extensively in industry. Because the power output of most thermocouples is extremely low, a very sensitive amplifier and detector are required. Thermocouples, and special amplifiers designed to operate from them, are manufactured by most producers of bioelectronic equipment.

The resistance of any resistor changes a little with its temperature, and some resistive compounds are especially sensitive to temperature changes. Resistors made of these substances are called thermistors. When a thermistor is connected in a circuit that gives a sensitive and continuous reading of its resistance, it acts as a temperature

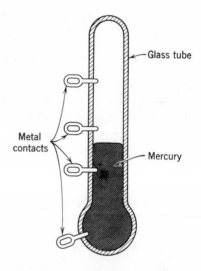

Fig. 16.3 A simple device to give an electric signal when the temperature reaches each of three different levels. As the temperature increases, the column of mercury expands and connects successively higher contacts.

sensor. In order to measure the resistance of any element, a current must be passed through it, and that current tends to heat the element. Therefore it is important to pass as little current as possible through a thermistor. Some thermistors can safely pass as much as 1 milliampere, permitting their resistance (and temperature) to be displayed on an ordinary milliammeter. Other thermistors require more sensitive measuring apparatus.

Thermistors are available in a wide variety of resistances. Their change in resistance is usually linear with temperature over a range of

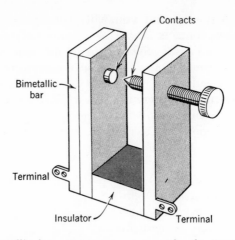

Fig. 16.4 A bimetallic bar temperature sensor. As the temperature increases, the bar bends, until the contacts touch at a temperature determined by the position of the screw-mounted contact.

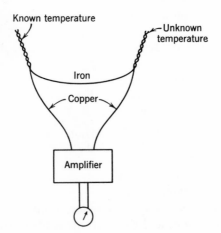

Fig. 16.5 A thermocouple circuit. Any difference in the temperature between the two junctions results in a proportional voltage across the input of the amplifier. Iron and copper wires are used in this figure, but commercial thermocouples are usually constructed of more exotic metals.

about 10°C, and nonlinear for changes in temperature greater than that (this property varies considerably among different thermistors). Most important for behavioral work, some thermistors are very small and respond very rapidly to changes in temperature. For example, they have been implanted in the nasal cavities of rats, where their changes in resistance follow the rat's inspiration and expiration.

LIGHT SENSORS

The common photoelectric sensors may be divided into three functional categories. For those in one category, a voltage is generated which is related to the intensity of light falling on the sensor. The second type is essentially a resistor whose resistance changes as the light intensity changes. In the third type, light striking a surface releases electrons, which are then collected by a positively charged plate. Various members of each of these types will be discussed as well as some operational circuits.

Vacuum Phototubes

Figure 16.6 contains photographs of a number of vacuum phototubes and a sketch of the structure of a typical one. Light passes through the glass envelope (the envelope is sometimes made of quartz when ultraviolet light is to be detected) and strikes a metal surface coated with one of a number of substances. For light of a given wave length, some particular proportion of the incident quanta is lost, and each of the remaining quanta releases an electron from the surface. The tube is normally connected to a power supply such that the photosensitive area is negative with respect to the other element, the anode. Thus, when light strikes the photosensitive surface, the electrons released from that surface pass through the vacuum and reach the anode, and current flows around the circuit.

For any particular wave length, a constant proportion of the incident quanta is lost and a constant proportion actually releases electrons. When the voltage between the cathode (photosensitive surface) and the anode exceeds some critical level (typically 22½ volts), all of the electrons released at the cathode reach the anode. Therefore, if the intensity of the light, i.e., the number of quanta incident per second, is increased, the current flow is also increased by the same proportion. As long as the voltage across a vacuum phototube exceeds some critical value, the current that the tube passes will be linear with the light

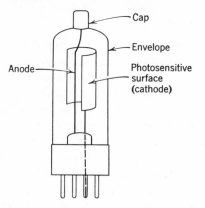

Fig. 16.6 A selection of vacuum phototubes. (Photograph *courtesy* Helen E. Howell, Berkeley, Calif.)

intensity. This is a very important and relatively unique property of vacuum phototubes. Very few other types of photosensors are linear with intensity.

The above linearity statement applies to the intensity of a light of any fixed wave length. However, for any given cathode, the proportion of incident quanta that releases electrons depends upon the wave length characteristics of those quanta. Some wave lengths are more efficient at releasing quanta than others. Each phototube has its own spectral sensitivity curve. The particular curve depends upon the material coating the cathode and the spectral transmission of the envelope (e.g., glass absorbs ultraviolet, thus tubes designed to detect ultraviolet generally have quartz envelopes). The phototube charac-

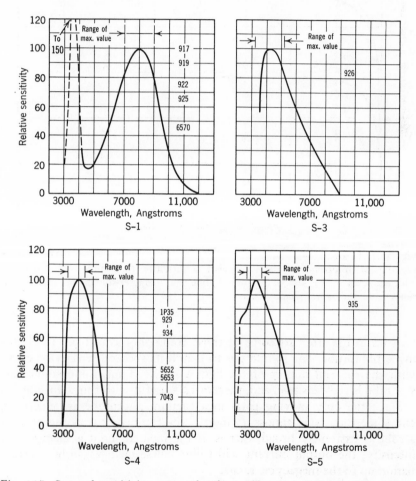

Fig. 16.7 Spectral sensitivity curves for four different cathode coatings. Some of the phototubes employing these various coatings are listed on each of the graphs. The dotted portions of some of the curves indicate that, although the coatings themselves may be sensitive in the near ultraviolet region of the spectrum, the glass envelopes absorb light at those wave lengths, so the tubes as a whole do not respond.

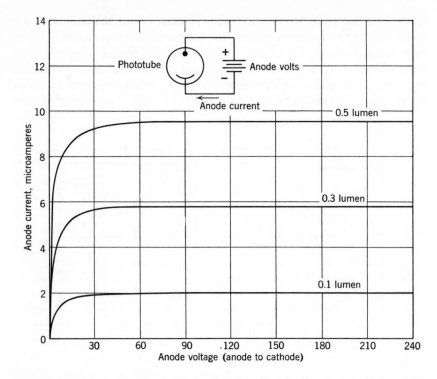

Fig. 16.8 Characteristic curves for a typical vacuum phototube (917). Other vacuum phototubes may have different sensitivities (e.g., tube 929 delivers 5 microamperes at 0.1 lumen, 100 volts), but the characteristic curves of all such tubes have the same general shapes.

teristics in Fig. 16.7 are some of those commonly available. In choosing a phototube, one should try to match its spectral sensitivity curve with the spectral output of the light source. Thus, for example, the 917 tube is red-sensitive, and, therefore, is useful with tungsten sources.

Since the only moving parts in a vacuum phototube are electrons, and since they have almost no inertia, the frequency response of such a tube is extremely broad; that is, if the incident light is changing in intensity, the output current will follow these changes without attenuation up to the megacycle range.

Because of the way in which light is converted into electric energy, vacuum phototubes have one special property the understanding of which is crucial to their proper use. The curves in Fig. 16.8 are typical of almost all vacuum phototubes. Consider the lowest curve. It represents the fact that, with a fixed incident light intensity, the current through the tube and circuit increases as the applied voltage is increased from zero up to about 25 volts.   Increases in voltage above that value do not substantially change the current, as long as the intensity of light is constant.   The fact that the curve is flat above 25 volts means that, above that voltage, all of the electrons that are released by the cathode reach the anode.   Further increases in voltage cannot increase the current (except for certain second-order effects not worth discussing here).   Because of this characteristic, the stability of the source of power is very unimportant.   For example, if the source is a 45-volt battery, it can age until its actual voltage is only 25 volts and still leave the circuit unaffected.   The fact that the other curves in Fig. 16.8 are regularly displaced upwards indicates that, as long as the voltage is greater than about 25 volts, the current output is directly proportional to the light intensity.

Now suppose that the supply voltage is 90 volts, and the output of the photocell is fed into a resistance of 1 megohm (e.g., the input impedance of a typical oscilloscope), as shown in Fig. 16.9.   When the cell is dark, virtually no current flows.   Therefore there will be no voltage drop across the resistor, and the full 90 volts will be across the tube.   When the cell is lighted so that 0.5 lumen falls on its sensitive area, 10 microamperes will flow through the circuit (see Fig. 16.8).   Therefore the voltage across the resistor will increase from zero to 10 volts, and the voltage across the tube will decrease from 90 to 80 volts.   Since this decrease in tube voltage does not change its current output, it will continue to deliver 10 microamperes.   If the resistor were increased to two megohms, the same light intensity would produce a change of 20 volts across it, still leaving the phototube current unchanged.   In other words, as long as the voltage across the tube remains above 25 volts, raising the resistance of the load increases the voltage change resulting from a particular change in light

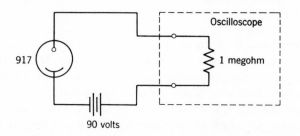

Fig. 16.9   Circuit in which a phototube drives an oscilloscope whose input impedance is 1 megohm.

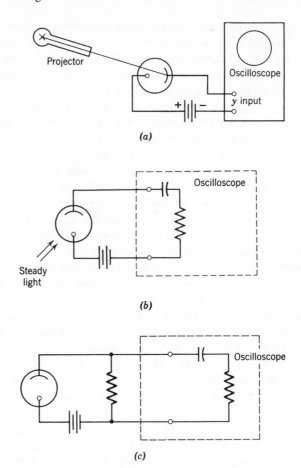

Fig. 16.10   (a) Simple system to detect the breaking of a beam of light.   (b) The same circuit when the oscilloscope amplifier is capacitance-coupled to the phototube. This circuit will not operate, as explained in the text.   (c) A circuit that will operate properly.

level.   Therefore, if a vacuum phototube is to run some voltage-sensing device, the higher the impedance of the device, the better. This property of the phototube can be summed up by stating that, at any given light intensity, it is a constant-*current* device.   In this sense it is very different from almost all other sensors.   One common difficulty arising from a lack of appreciation of this property is as follows. Suppose that you wish to monitor the changes in light intensity that occur when a rat walks past a light beam.   A vacuum phototube is placed in the beam and connected as shown in Fig. 16.10a.   Every time the light is interrupted, the changes in intensity are displayed on the oscilloscope. Now suppose that there is some ambient light falling on the phototube (i.e., light that always falls on the cell regardless of the rat's presence), and suppose that this light is fairly intense compared with the light that is affected by the rat. The output of the photocell then will consist of a large d-c component and a small a-c one. When you increase the gain of the oscilloscope enough to see the changes in light level (a-c component), the d-c level will push the spot all the way off the screen. Ordinarily this problem can be solved simply by capacitance-coupling the input to the oscilloscope, thereby blocking the d-c component while passing the a-c one. Then all that will be displayed are changes in voltage. But if a vacuum phototube is capacitance-coupled, no deflection at all will appear on the oscilloscope, even when the light intensity changes. An examination of the circuit in Fig. 16.10*b* will clarify the reasons for this. The phototube will "try" to drive a fixed amount of current through the capacitor because of the steady light incident upon it. But the capacitor has an almost infinite resistance to steady current. Therefore, the voltage across the capacitor will approach the full voltage of the battery, and the voltage across the phototube will drop below the knee in its response curve. In fact, it will drop almost to zero, and subsequent changes in the light level will, therefore, not produce changes in the output current. In general, vacuum phototubes cannot be capacitance-coupled. However, if a resistor is connected as in Fig. 16.10*c*, the circuit will operate correctly. The circuit in Fig. 16.11

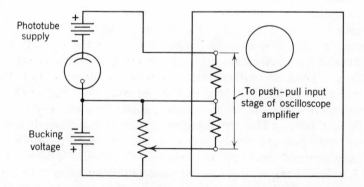

Fig. 16.11 Circuit to detect small changes in incident light. The voltage due to the ambient light falling on the photocell is opposed by an adjustable bucking voltage. Since the push-pull input of the oscilloscope actually subtracts one of these voltages from the other, the net steady component may be adjusted to zero by manipulating the slider of the potentiometer.

illustrates another way to nullify the ambient output of a vacuum phototube when its output is displayed on an oscilloscope with a push-pull input. This circuit circumvents the distortion sometimes introduced by capacitative coupling.

Since vacuum phototubes are perfectly linear with light intensity, they are very useful in measuring changes in light levels (e.g., calibrating neutral density filters in visual research). Because of their extremely broad frequency response, they may be used to measure very short flash durations (for example, in tachistoscopic experiments). It is only necessary to connect the photocell, a 45-volt battery, and an oscilloscope in series, as in Fig. 16.10a, to accomplish either of these functions. The light levels and flash durations will be directly displayed on the oscilloscope screen.

Multiplier Phototubes

The ordinary vacuum phototube does not deliver very much power, and its output must be amplified considerably in order to be useful (e.g., by the vertical amplifier of an oscilloscope). A device which has the same excellent linearity and frequency response as the vacuum phototube, but which puts out vastly more power (e.g., enough to operate relays directly), is the multiplier phototube. This device is essentially a vacuum phototube and amplifier all in one small envelope. The multiplier tube consists of a coated cathode and an anode, as in the ordinary phototube. However, between those two elements is a series of specially coated plates called dynodes. The tube voltages are connected in such a way that each of these dynodes is more positive than the preceding one, as diagrammed in Fig. 16.12. When a quantum strikes the cathode and releases an electron, the electron is attracted to the first dynode. The coating on the dynode is such that two or more electrons are released for each single electron that strikes it. These secondary electrons then hit the next dynode, and are multiplied again. By the time the electrons strike the anode, there are anywhere from 100,000 to several million for each single one that left the cathode. (The actual multiplication factor depends upon the coating and upon the number of dynodes. Standard multiplier tubes are manufactured with up to fourteen dynodes.) There are two very big disadvantages to the use of photomultiplier tubes. One is that they require a high-voltage power supply (from 600 to 1500 volts). More important, unlike the ordinary vacuum phototube, the output current is very sensitive to changes in the supply voltage. A change of one percent in the supply voltage can change the output current by

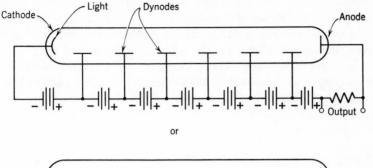

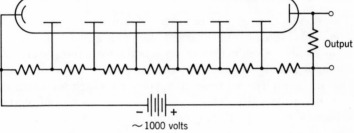

Fig. 16.12 Two circuits that provide the necessary voltages between elements in a photomultiplier tube.

10%. Therefore, if a photomultiplier tube is to be used for measuring light intensities, its power supply must be extremely well regulated. Photomultiplier tubes and their power supplies are expensive and somewhat tricky to use. They are discussed here primarily because they are used more and more in commercial light-detecting equipment, and the user of such equipment should be familiar with their properties.

Gas Phototubes

When a standard vacuum phototube is filled with certain gases, it is called a gas phototube, and its properties are considerably different from those of the vacuum phototube. In the gas tube, electrons leaving the cathode ionize the gas, and the process of ionization actually produces some multiplication of the energy that was initially controlled by the incident light. Thus, for a given light intensity and voltage, a gas phototube will put out more current than a vacuum tube. However, the ionization of the gas depends very strongly upon the voltage across the tube, and the output, therefore, changes with

the supply voltage. The gas tube has two other unfortunate properties. Again, because of the characteristics of the ionization process,
the output current is not linear with the light intensity, and because
gas ions have appreciable mass, the tube will not respond fully to very
fast changes in light level. Gas phototubes are used frequently in the
sound pickup units of sound movie projectors, but, for general laboratory use, the vacuum tube and some of the devices discussed below
are much more suitable.

Photoconductive Cells

The conduction of current through substances involves the interaction and exchange of charged particles among the molecules of
the substance. Conduction in semiconductors, those materials having
resistances somewhere between that of good conductors and of insulators, has many special properties, some of which are taken advantage
of in the production of transistors. A property of certain semiconductors is the fact that incident light quanta change the availability of movable charged particles, so the resistance of a properly
constructed semiconductor unit will change with the intensity of
incident light. When a power source and a sensitive meter are
connected in series with such a cell, the circuit acts as a light sensor.

For a long time, selenium cells were the most common representatives of photoconductive light sensors. However, for most applica

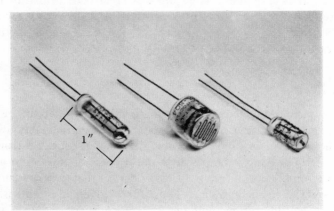

Fig. 16.13 Various photoresistive units. The small ones may carry up to 75
milliwatts, and the large one 500 milliwats. (*Courtesy* Clairex Corp.)

tions, they have now been supplanted by a variety of much more sensitive cells. These cells are usually referred to as photodiodes.

The cadmium sulfide cells shown in Fig. 16.13 are photodiodes. The particular characteristics of these cells vary widely among individual units, but typically, for the smallest cell pictured, the resistance in the dark is several megohms and it falls to about 10,000 ohms when lighted, for example, by a 60-watt incandescent light bulb a few feet away. The larger cell changes from approximately 50,000 ohms in the dark to 500 ohms in the light.

Since the resistance of the cell varies with incident light, the greater the voltage across it, the greater the change in current for a given change in light. However, the voltage cannot be increased indefinitely. The small cells pictured in Fig. 16.13 are rated at 75 milliwatts. This means that the unit will get too hot if the product of the current through the cell and the voltage across it exceeds 0.075. Seventy-five milliwatts is sufficient to drive a moderately sensitive relay directly, as in the circuit shown in Fig. 16.14. The larger unit in Fig. 16.13 is rated at 0.5 watt, so this unit will easily operate an ordinary relay or counter when connected as in Fig. 16.14.

Photoconductive cells such as these are extremely well suited as light sensors to drive relays. However, since their output curves are not linear with light intensity, and since many of them are subject to gradual drifts in output when the light intensity is constant (very much as the eye light and dark adapts), they are not well suited for the measurement of light intensities unless special precautions are taken.

Photoconductive cells are available with a number of different spectral sensitivity curves, ranging from the far infrared to x-rays. Cadmium selenide cells are sensitive in the red and near infrared, and are therefore particularly well suited for the detection of light from incandescent lamps.

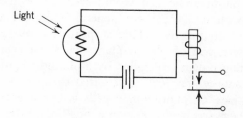

Fig. 16.14 Circuit in which a relay closes when the light falling on the photodiode exceeds some threshold level.

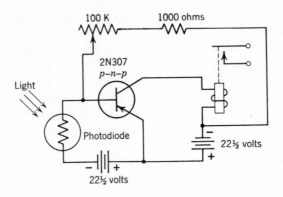

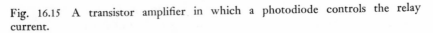

Fig. 16.15   A transistor amplifier in which a photodiode controls the relay current.

The characteristics of photodiodes make them extremely useful in transistor circuits. For example, the circuit in Fig. 16.15 is one which will amplify the output of a 50-milliwatt cadmium sulfide cell sufficiently to operate an ordinary relay reliably. The changing resistance of the cell changes the base to emitter current of the transistor, and this, in turn, results in an even greater change in the current through the relay.

Photovoltaic Cells

The sensing of light by a photoconductive cell requires the use of an external source of power. There is another type of photosensor, called the photovoltaic cell, which actually generates its own voltage when struck by light. This kind of cell is commonly used in photographic light meters, where it directly drives a sensitive meter. Although the photovoltaic cell would seem to be more convenient than the photoconductive cell for general laboratory work, it is actually used less frequently. This is primarily because the power output of a given size of photovoltaic cell is not nearly so great as the corresponding power controlled by a photodiode of the same size. A very large photovoltaic cell is required to operate a relay. Since the output voltage of photovoltaic cells is not linear with light intensity, and their frequency response does not extend to the high frequencies, they have no compensating advantages, except that they happen not to require a power source. (Some photovoltaic cells have a current output that is linear with light intensity when the resistance of the external circuit is zero, but that is not very helpful.)

There is, however, one sort of photovoltaic cell that is particularly useful. This cell has a spectral sensitivity curve that is fairly closely matched to the phototopic luminosity curve of the human eye, and is, therefore, useful for the measurement of luminosity. The matching of response curves is achieved by combining a particular inherent response curve of the photovoltaic material with a special filter. A cell of this type, manufactured by the Weston Electrical Instrument Corporation, is called the "photronic cell."

Summary Table

Use	Type of Cell
Measure relative amounts of light of fixed spectral composition	Vacuum phototube
Measure duration of flash for short flashes	Vacuum phototube
Examine temporal characteristics of light pulse	Vacuum phototube
Operate relay or counter when light beam is interrupted	Photoconductive cell
Measure relative luminosities of lights of different spectral composition	"Photronic cell"

Chapter 17

Feedback and null-sensing devices

The principles of servomechanics are used extensively in modern commercial instruments. Some of these principles are very simple, but they involve a fundamentally different approach to certain instrumentation problems. If you are planning to design apparatus, it is extremely worthwhile to be familiar with servomechanical principles, for the use of these principles often allows the apparatus to be greatly simplified while actually performing its function better.

For the purposes of this chapter, there is one property that defines a servomechanism. A servomechanism is error-actuated. In other words, it senses the difference between its actual performance and the desired performance and acts to reduce that error. Suppose, for example, that you wish to maintain your laboratory at 105 degrees Fahrenheit. It is clear that a heater is needed, and let us say that it is an electrically operated one. You might carefully insulate the laboratory from as many external sources of temperature change as possible, and then determine some on-off cycle of the heater that maintains the temperature near 105 degrees. The heater could then be controlled by a simple timer to maintain that cycle. Or you can use a thermostat, that is, a device that turns off the heater whenever the temperature rises above 105 degrees and turns it on when it is colder. The timer control is probably somewhat simpler to construct, but it is obvious that it is not so satisfactory as the thermostat. Any change in the line voltage, the external temperature, wear on the timer, etc., could result in temperature errors, while thermostatic control is relatively independent of these factors. The thermostat and heater combination is one of the best-known examples of a servomechanism. It constantly senses the direction of the difference between the actual and the desired temperature, and changes the temperature accordingly.

Although most people are acquainted with thermostats, and it is clear that this method of temperature control is superior to nonservo-controlled systems, the same principles are too often ignored when other kinds of apparatus are to be designed. This chapter includes a set of specific examples of the uses of servomechanical principles in situations where they are not so commonly employed. The examples are discussed not because they are solutions to specific problems but rather to give you a mental set such that, when you are about to design any piece of apparatus, you will consider the possibilities of using servomechanical principles.

HOLDING A DOOR OPEN

Suppose it is necessary electrically to control the opening and closing of a start box door in a maze. The door may be designed as shown in Fig. 17.1, so that it swings about a vertical axis and is pulled on by one of two solenoids, one opening and the other closing the door. The circuit in Fig. 17.2 will open or close the door simply, but it has the following drawback. When the door is open, a large current must flow through one of the solenoids in order to pull it

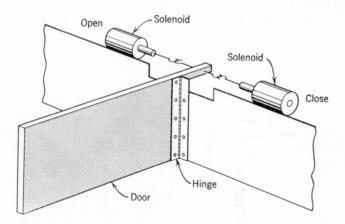

Fig. 17.1 Mechanical arrangement to open and close a door electrically. Current through the solenoid on the left pulls the door open. The right solenoid pulls it closed.

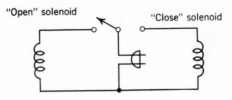

Fig. 17.2 Simple circuit to permit remote opening and closing of the door.

closed, but once it is closed, very little current (none if the door were perfectly balanced) is required to hold it closed. A current great enough to pull the door closed might overheat the solenoid in a short time, unless the solenoid were a very large one. This difficulty may be overcome and small solenoids may be used by employing servomechanical principles. If a large current were driven through the solenoid until the door closed, and then the current were greatly reduced, the mechanism would still operate correctly, and it would have the advantage that, since the current would flow for only a very short time, the solenoid would not become overheated. In other words, a current greatly exceeding the rated current of the solenoids could be used without doing any damage. A set of contacts mounted on the door and the walls could sense whether or not the door was closed when it was supposed to be (i.e., they would sense its error), and the current could be regulated accordingly. The circuit in Fig. 17.3 will accomplish this. When the door reaches the desired position, it opens a pair of contacts, reducing the current

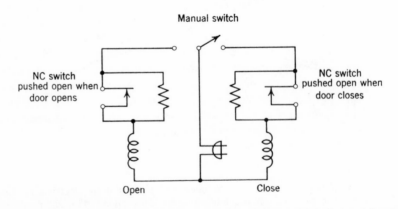

Fig. 17.3 Circuit employing error-sensing for positive action in opening and closing the door.

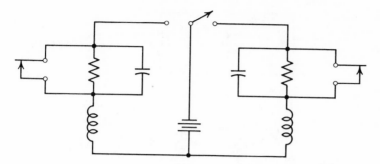

Fig. 17.4   Circuit to reduce hunting, using capacitative damping.

through the solenoid. The entire device is then a simple servo-mechanism.

There are certain problems which enter into the design of many error-actuated devices, and some would enter into this one. When the door swings over and hits the stop at the end of its travel, it will have a tendency to bounce away. If this bounce is too large, it will allow the sensing contacts to close, and another pulse of current will flow through the solenoid. This second pulse may also cause the door to bounce, and if the second, third, etc., bounces are too big, the door will chatter continuously. This kind of behavior is called "hunting"; the device continues to hunt for its zero-error position, and repeatedly overshoots it. There are a large number of ways to reduce or elimi-nate hunting. In this apparatus, the door stops can be covered with some relatively nonelastic material (e.g., felt), and the contacts can then be made with enough spring that they remain open over the amount of bounce that still occurs. Another type of solution to prob-lems of hunting involves operating on the electrical characteristics of the system. For example, if the solenoids are run from a d-c source, and capacitors are placed in the circuit, as shown in Fig. 17.4, the current will drop gradually from the high to the low level during the time that the bounce would have occurred. The introduction of elements (e.g., felt pads or capacitors) which make the electrical or mechanical actions of the system more sluggish and, consequently, reduce hunting is called "damping" the system.

MOTOR SPEED CONTROL

Suppose that you want to produce a light that will flash at a number of different, precisely fixed frequencies. The light may be interrupted

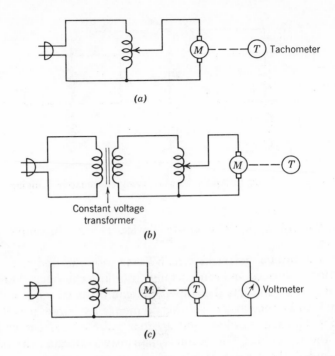

Fig. 17.5 (a) Simple circuit to control the speed of a motor. (b) The introduction of a constant-voltage transformer to reduce speed changes caused by line-voltage fluctuations. (c) Control circuit using an electric tachometer and voltmeter for visual monitoring of speed.

by a motor-driven sectored disk.   One way to achieve different flash rates is to drive the motor from a variable voltage transformer, as in Fig. 17.5a. By using a tachometer, you can determine the speed of the motor that corresponds to each of the readings on the dial of the transformer, and calibrate the system in this way.   However, should the line voltage change, this calibration will no longer hold.   The trouble could be eliminated by running the variable-voltage transformer from a constant-voltage transformer, as in Fig. 17.5b, but the motor will still not run at precisely fixed speeds.   Transformers heat up as they are operated, and this results in a change in their output current.   Furthermore, this heating up depends upon the room temperature.   Even more important, small changes in the temperature and general condition of the motor will cause it to change its speed even when the current through it is constant.

It is clearly important to monitor the speed of the motor constantly.

This is easily done by mounting a tachometer on the motor shaft.   If the tachometer is one which generates a voltage in proportion to its speed (any permanent magnet motor, such as the toy motor on your circuit board, will do this), then the speed of the motor may be monitored by connecting a voltmeter across the output of the tachometer, as shown in Fig. 17.5c.   As long as the voltmeter and tachometer are calibrated, a given speed may be maintained by constantly adjusting the variable-voltage transformer to keep the meter at a given reading.   This method is satisfactory as long as the tachometer and meter are subject to less drift than the limits of permissible error in the experiment, and this is generally true of meters and tachometers.

The kind of motor control diagrammed in Fig. 17.5c is an error-actuated one.   The servosystem, or servoloop, includes the motor, the variable voltage transformer, the meter and tachometer, and you.   It is superior to the nonservosystems described above so long as your skill is sufficient.   The speed is independent of line voltage changes, changes in the motor, etc.

The kind of system that includes a human operator in the servoloop is often adequate.   However, if the operator has other things to do, or if he is not fast enough, it may be worthwhile to replace him with an automatic sensing device that does exactly what he was doing.   The operator is actually performing a very simple task.   He is turning up the voltage when the voltmeter needle is too low and turning it down when it is too high.   The same function might be performed by a set of contacts mounted on the meter needle, as shown in Fig. 17.6.   However, since the typical meter movement does not have enough force to close a pair of contacts effectively, the meter must be replaced by a special kind of relay, called a polarized relay, as diagrammed in Fig. 17.7.   The relay consists of a coil and a set of SPDT contacts.   The common contact c is mounted on a movable permanent magnet in such a way that, when there is no current through the coil, c is disconnected from the remaining two contacts a and b, but when current flows through the coil, c will touch either a or b, depending upon the direction of current flow.

The circuit in Fig. 17.7 also illustrates a different method of speed control.   The bucking circuit applies a voltage across the relay which is in opposition to the voltage generated by the tachometer.   When the two voltages are equal, no current will flow through the relay coil, and normal voltage will act upon the motor.   If the speed of the motor is too low, current will flow through the relay coil, causing c and a to make contact, short-circuiting R_1 in the motor circuit, and causing the motor to run faster.   If the motor should run too fast,

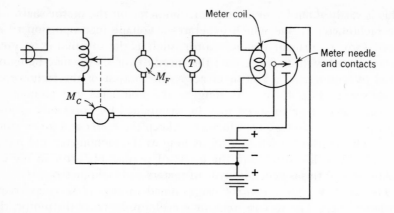

Fig. 17.6 Circuit to hold speed constant automatically. If the speed of the flicker motor (M_F) should fall below that desired, the meter needle will touch the upper contact. The control motor (M_C) will then begin to rotate in a clockwise direction. The shaft of the control motor is mechanically coupled to the slider of the variable voltage transformer in such a way that clockwise rotation of the motor increases the voltage to the flicker motor, causing it to speed up. Should the flicker motor run too fast, the control motor will be driven counterclockwise, decreasing the voltage to the flicker motor.

current will flow in the opposite direction through the relay coil, c will contact b, placing resistor R_2 in parallel with the motor, and it will slow down.

The setting of the potentiometer in the bucking circuit ultimately determines the speed of the motor, and may be so calibrated. The

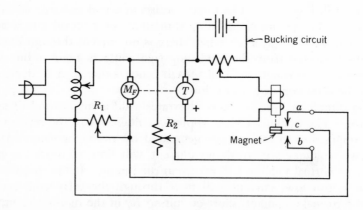

Fig. 17.7 Another circuit to hold motor speed constant.

variable-voltage transformer setting does *not* determine the motor speed. However, when the circuit is in actual operation, it will run most smoothly (with a minimum of hunting) if, for each speed, the variable-voltage transformer is set to a level which would drive the motor at approximately the correct speed even if the remaining control circuit were not present.

CONTROL OF LIGHT INTENSITY

The amount of light radiated from any light bulb depends upon several factors. First, small changes in the supply voltage produce relatively large changes in brightness. This source of variance may be avoided by the use of a stable power supply (e.g., constant-voltage transformer for moderately good constancy, a transistorized regulated supply for extreme stability). However, there are two other important sources of intensity change that cannot be handled in this way. As an incandescent lamp ages, its filament evaporates and is deposited as a dark film on the inside of the envelope. That is why the glass in old bulbs often looks dark. Evaporation of the filament not only changes brightness by the deposition of a light-absorbing film; as the evaporation continues, the filament wires become smaller, and this too changes the brightness of the bulb. To compensate for these changes in brightness, the actual intensity of the lamp must be monitored. This may be done by mounting a photocell of some sort where light from the bulb falls upon it, and metering the output of the photocell. Since evaporative changes are fairly gradual, at least during the early stages of aging, it is usually sufficient to place the experimenter in the servoloop. That is, he can check the intensity regularly, and small changes may be corrected by appropriate changes in the voltage across the bulb. But there are some situations in which human control may be inadequate. For example, suppose that, in order to maximize the light intensity through an optical system, the bulb is being run above its rated voltage. This will greatly increase the brightness and greatly decrease the life of a bulb. (Most photographic lamps are essentially bulbs so designed that they run "too hot" on the normal line voltage.) Under these circumstances, intensity may require constant monitoring and control.

The circuit in Fig. 17.8 is a servosystem for maintaining a bulb at a constant intensity. Light from the bulb to be controlled falls on a photoconductive cell (*ph*), whose resistance changes with the intensity of light falling upon it. The circuit constantly compares the resistance

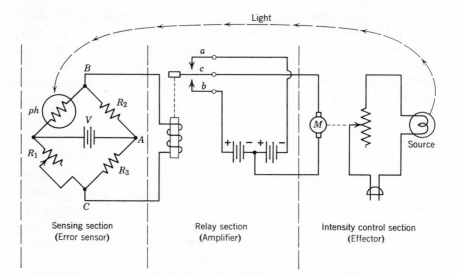

Fig. 17.8   Circuit to maintain the brightness of a lamp at a constant level.

of the photocell with a standard resistance, and adjusts the current through the bulb to keep the two resistances equal. The circuit may be conceptually divided into three parts (and it is a basic principle of good apparatus design to build the circuit, physically, in the same three sections, so that sources of trouble may be more easily located). The first part, on the left in Fig. 17.8, contains a sensing system. The second is a polarized relay, and the third changes the light intensity.

The sensing system is called a bridge circuit, and operates in the following way. R_2 and R_3 are equal resistances. If R_1 is adjusted until it has the same resistance as the photocell, the battery will drive the same amount of current through the upper loop (containing the photocell and R_2) and the lower one (containing R_1 and R_3). Since the same amount of current is flowing through R_2 and R_3, and since their resistances are equal, the voltage between the points labeled A and B will equal the voltage between A and C. Therefore the voltage between B and C will be zero. If the resistance of the photocell then increases, less current will flow through R_2 than R_3, the voltage from A to B will be smaller than from A to C, and the voltage between B and C will be nonzero. If the resistance of the photocell were reduced below that of R_1, the voltage between B and C would again be non-zero, but of the opposite polarity. Thus the voltage between B and C, that is, the output voltage of the sensing section, will indicate the relation between the resistances of R_1 and the photocell.   The remaining parts of the circuit are designed to change the current through the bulb in such a way as to maintain the voltage between B and C at zero.

The output of the sensing section is fed to the coil of a polarized relay of the sort discussed earlier in this chapter.   When such a relay is connected between B and C, the contact labeled c will be disconnected when the photocell resistance equals R_1, that is, when the light intensity is at the desired level.   If the light is more or is less intense, c will be connected to a or b.   The contacts of this polarized relay control the current through a reversible motor which, in turn, drives the slider of a variable resistor in series with the bulb.   When the bulb is at the desired intensity, the relay is open and no current flows through the motor.   If the intensity drops, the relay turns on the motor in the direction that decreases the resistance in series with the bulb, and when the bulb reaches the correct intensity again, the motor stops.   Should the bulb become too bright, the motor will increase the resistance in series with it until its intensity is correct again.

The output of the sensing system could be coupled directly to the motor and the circuit would theoretically still work properly, since the current through the motor would be zero when the intensity is correct, and would be nonzero in one direction or the other if the intensity were too high or too low.   However, a fairly powerful motor is required to drive the variable resistor in this kind of circuit, and the current that can be controlled by most photocells would not be sufficient to operate such a motor.   The relay allows the small current of the sensing system to control the larger current required by the motor and, therefore, acts basically as an amplifier.   Thus this circuit, like most servomechanical circuits, contains three elements: an error sensor, an amplifier, and an "effector."

The circuit in Fig. 17.8 is called a null-sensing circuit because it operates only when the difference between two quantities, in this case two resistances, is not zero.   The only factors that determine the constancy of the light intensity are the stabilities of the photocell and resistors.   A change in the line voltage to the bulb will be automatically compensated, as will be changes due to evaporation, dust, etc.   Changes in the voltage V are of secondary importance.   If V were reduced, the only effect would be that of making the circuit less *sensitive* to small changes in intensity, but the mean intensity level would be unaffected.   The linearity of the photocell is also irrelevant as long as its resistance changes monotonically with changes in light intensity.   To change the brightness of the bulb, the value of R_1 must be changed. The intensity will then change until the resistance of the photocell again equals R_1.

The logical aspects of the operation of this circuit are independent of the particular values of the resistors in the sensing section. However, the current that operates the relay must flow through the resistors in the sensing circuit. Therefore those resistances cannot be too great. The circuit in Fig. 17.8 will operate well when a high-power photoresistor, such as a ½-watt cadmium sulfide photodiode, is used as the photosensor and the other resistances are set to have roughly the same resistance as the photodiode shows under operating conditions. (A bridge circuit operates most efficiently when all the resistances are equal, and this may be proved from Ohm's law, if you want to.)   If a photocell that controls less power is used, it may be necessary to amplify the voltage between B and C in order for it to operate the relay.

SOME GENERAL PROPERTIES OF NULL-SENSING SYSTEMS

The null-sensing principle is a very generally useful one, and variants of it are easy to apply.   If the photoresistive cell in Fig. 17.8 is replaced by a photovoltaic cell, R_1 is replaced by a variable voltage source, and V is omitted, the circuit will perform the same function (see Fig. 17.9).   In fact, any kind of sensor whose voltage or resistance varies with the quantity to be controlled may be used in just this kind of circuit.   And the linearity of the sensor is irrelevant.   The only requirement of the sensor is that its resistance or voltage change monotonically with the quantity to be controlled.

The same system may be used to position an object by remote con-

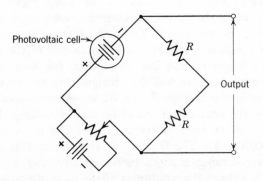

Fig. 17.9 Bridge circuit employing a photovoltaic cell.

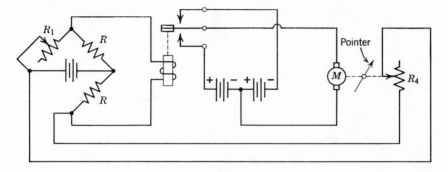

Fig. 17.10 Circuit to permit remote control of the angle of a pointer. The pointer will automatically "follow" changes in the setting of R_1.

trol.   Suppose that a subject sitting on one side of a room is to adjust the angle to the vertical of a pointer on the other side of the room. He is given a variable resistor R_1 in the circuit of Fig. 17.10.   The pointer is driven by the motor in this figure, and the pointer is also clamped to another variable resistor R_4, which is equivalent to the resistance of the photocell in Fig. 17.8.   When the subject rotates the slider of his control resistor, the motor will drive the pointer until its resistor has the same value as the one set by the subject.

It is important to realize that each of these devices, taken as a whole, is really an amplifier. For example, the pointer in the last example can be a very large, heavy one, or it can be the rudder of an ocean liner.   The very small force required to turn the controlling knob is amplified by the system until it is great enough to move the pointer or rudder.   Similarly, the very small changes in light energy impinging on the photocell are amplified enough to drive the variable resistor in the lamp control circuit.

An important characteristic of this kind of amplifier is that its response will be a linear function of the input, even when some of the components of the system are very nonlinear.   The input-vs.-output characteristic for the polarized relay in Fig. 17.10 is shown in Fig. 17.11a.   The relay is as nonlinear as a device can be, and it is the basic amplifying device in the circuit.   Yet, as long as R_1 and R_4 are identical resistors, the input-vs.-output characteristic for the device as a whole is almost perfectly linear, as shown in Fig. 17.11b.   Furthermore, the curve in Fig. 17.11b is virtually unaffected by changes in any of the voltages in the circuit as long as the voltages are large enough to make it operate at all.   Many modern all-electronic amplifiers use this same null-sensing principle.   Their input-output characteristic

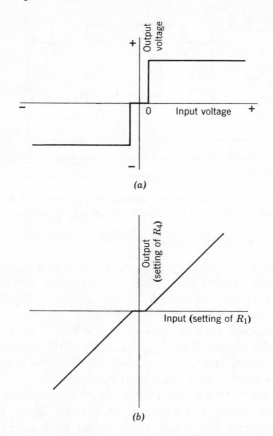

Fig. 17.11 (a) Input-vs-output curve for the polarized relay in Fig. 17.10. The short segment near the origin represents the range of voltages that are below the threshold for relay operation. (b) The input-vs.-output curve for the circuit in Fig. 17.10, taken as a whole. This curve is linear except in the region of the threshold of the relay. (The short, horizontal segment is called the "dead zone" of the system.)

may be linear, even though most of the circuit components may be nonlinear.

CAPTURED SPOT TRACKING

When the motion of an object is to be measured or used to control some other quantity, but no sensing device can be attached to the object, servomechanical principles may be used in what is called captured spot tracking. A small spot of light is projected on to an edge or contour of the moving object, the spot is automatically made to stay on that edge even when the object moves, and a voltage proportional to the movement of the spot (and the object) is supplied at the output of the tracker.

The following demonstration is a useful one for developing an understanding of the behavior of servomechanisms (of which almost all animal behavior is an example). It is a simplified captured-spot-tracking system. You will need an oscilloscope with a direct-coupled vertical amplifier and some kind of photocell. The particular type of photocell is not important, although it is advisable to find one whose spectral sensitivity matches the spectral output of the spot on the oscilloscope screen (e.g., $P11$ screen and 929 vacuum phototube).

1. Adjust the oscilloscope until a moderately intense spot is stationary on the screen (sweep circuit disconnected), and mount the photocell in front of the screen in a position where it receives some of the light from the spot.

2. Set the vertical gain of the oscilloscope to a low value and connect the output of the photocell circuit to the vertical input terminals. As you change the vertical gain or the spot intensity, the spot will move up and down. If the spot moves downward when the spot intensity is increased, the polarity is correct for this demonstration. If the spot moves upward, reverse the connections at the oscilloscope input.

3. Turn the vertical gain to its least sensitive position and place a piece of cardboard against the screen, as shown in Fig. 17.12, so that its upper horizontal edge is near the middle of the screen, but a little below the spot.

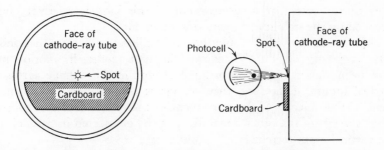

Fig. 17.12 Cardboard, photocell, and oscilloscope arranged for the captured-spot-tracking demonstration.

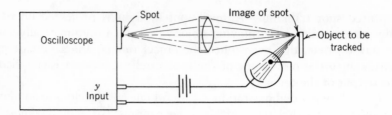

Fig. 17.13 Semischematic diagram of an electrical and optical system for captured spot tracking of an object that cannot be placed directly against the face of the cathode ray tube.

4. Increase the vertical gain.   When the gain begins to increase, the spot will move downward until it is just at a level with the edge of the cardboard.   Further increases in gain will cause the spot to move only slightly.   Increase the gain to ten or twenty times the gain required to move the spot to the edge of the cardboard.

5. Move the vertical position control a little in the direction that would normally move the spot downward. (The spot will not actually move.)

6. Move the cardboard up and down, and the spot will follow it. The spot acts as though it were captured by the edge.

7. Set the oscilloscope to free-running at a moderate speed (e.g., 10 centimeters per second) and tilt the cardboard until one corner is upward.   The spot should trace out the profile of the card (or your finger, or any other object just in front of the screen).

Three properties of this device should be noted.   Within limits, the position of the spot is only slightly affected by: (1) moving the vertical position control; (2) changing the vertical gain; and (3) changing the intensity of the spot.   These properties are manifestations of the fact that a servosystem of this kind is relatively uninfluenced by the stability of many of its elements.

This device provides a spot on an oscilloscope screen that moves with a moving object.   Whenever the spot moves, its motion must have been caused by a proportional change in the voltage across the vertical input.   Therefore, that voltage is proportional to the movement of the object.   If the movement of the object is to control some other apparatus, the other apparatus may be connected in parallel with the vertical input terminals.

Applications of captured spot tracking usually employ an optical system such as the one diagrammed in Fig. 17.13.   The lens forms an image of the oscilloscope spot on the object to be tracked, and light reflected from the object is used to control the position of the spot on the screen. This apparatus operates on exactly the same principles as the one in the demonstration just described, but permits the tracking of objects at some distance from the oscilloscope screen.

A MODEL OF A MUSCLE-STRETCH CONTROL SYSTEM

The lengths of many and possibly all skeletal muscles in animals are controlled by servosystems similar to some of those discussed in this chapter. The actual control system for any muscle involves a number of overlapping and interacting servoloops, but only the general aspects of one of these loops will be discussed here. The mechanical structure of a skeletal muscle and the part of its control system under consideration are schematized in Fig. 17.14. When the muscle fibers in this diagram contract, they reduce the distance between their origin and insertion, as represented by the walls. Stretch receptors, scattered

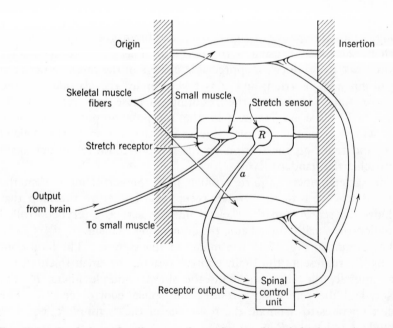

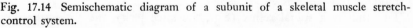

Fig. 17.14 Semischematic diagram of a subunit of a skeletal muscle stretch-control system.

throughout the muscle, are mechanically connected in parallel with the fibers, as in Fig. 17.14. There are two basic elements in the stretch receptor that are of relevance to this discussion—a small muscle fiber and a unit that is responsive to stretching. The output of the receptor, as indicated by the rate of firing of its afferent nerve fiber (labeled a), is a function of the amount by which the sensing unit itself is stretched. Its output will therefore increase when the small muscle contracts, and decrease when the skeletal muscle fibers contract. The amount of tension in the small muscle is set by various centers in the brain, but the tension in the skeletal fibers is controlled through a spinal loop whose input is the output of the receptor. The operation of this control loop is similar to that of a null-sensing system, in that the output of the receptor always tends to be maintained at a standard level. Whenever its output is greater than the standard, the skeletal fibers contract, tending to reduce the output, and when the output is too low, the fibers relax, tending to increase the level. If the skeletal fibers are suddenly stretched (e.g., when the tendon in the knee is struck by a reflex hammer), the output of the receptor is increased. This results in a compensating increase in the tension of the skeletal fibers (the knee jerk).

When the command is to be given for the origin and insertion to be brought closer together, a signal from the brain goes directly to the small muscle fiber, causing it to contract. This contraction in itself is too weak to produce an appreciable change in the distance between the origin and insertion, and it is taken up by the elasticity of the receptor unit. However, the resulting increase in stretch of the sensor will cause an increase in the receptor output. The spinal loop will then come into play, increasing the tension in the skeletal fibers and reducing the tension on the receptor until its output again approaches the standard level.

The skeletal fibers require a much more powerful input than the small muscle fiber in the stretch receptor. Therefore the loop that includes the sensor and the skeletal muscles acts as a servocontrolled amplifier, the small muscle being the controlling element.

The circuit in Fig. 17.15 is a model of this system. The loop containing R_1 represents the brain control system, the small solenoid the small muscle, the large solenoids the skeletal muscle fibers, R_2 the sensor, and the remaining circuitry the spinal control center. The circuit operates to maintain the resistance of the "sensor" R_2 equal to a standard resistance R_4.

To simulate a spinal reflex (e.g., the knee jerk), the walls may be suddenly pushed apart and then released. The resulting increase in

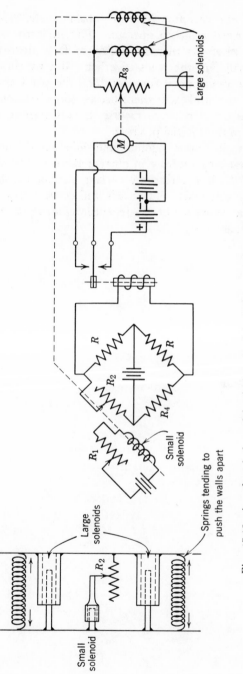

Fig. 17.15 An electrical model of the physiological control system shown in Fig. 17.14.

the resistance of the receptor R_2 will unbalance the "spinal" bridge, causing the polarized relay to operate. This, in turn, will drive the motor in such a direction that the resistance R_3 is decreased, and the large solenoids will pull the walls together. But by the time all that has occurred, the momentary force pushing the walls apart will have disappeared, and the walls will therefore be too close together. This will cause the polarized relay to reverse its connections, etc., and the walls will return to their initial position.

To move the walls closer together, the slider on R_1 must be moved upward. The resulting increase in current through the small solenoid will move R_2 to the left, ultimately causing an increase in the current through the large solenoids. The walls will come to rest in their new position when the resistance of the receptor again equals the resistance of the standard resistor R_4.

Appendix I

Output curves for dry batteries, from Burgess Engineering Manual (second edition).

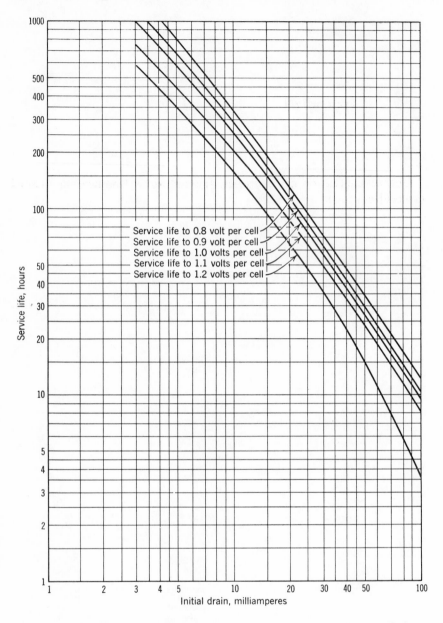

Fig. AI.1   #5 cells (ASA cell size *B*).   Service life when continuous discharge is at 70°F.   (*Courtesy* Burgess Battery Co.)

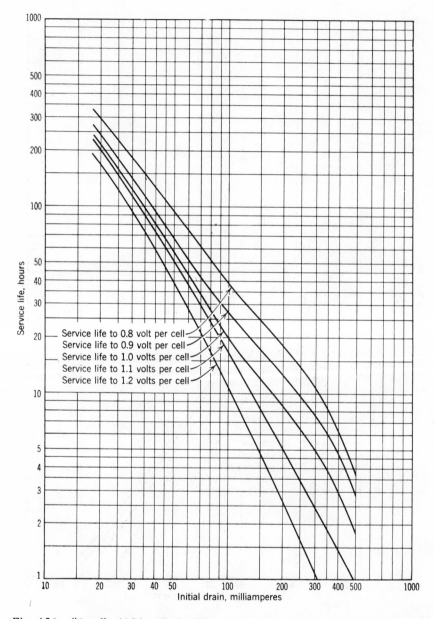

Service life to 0.8 volt per cell
Service life to 0.9 volt per cell
Service life to 1.0 volts per cell
Service life to 1.1 volts per cell
Service life to 1.2 volts per cell

Service life, hours

Initial drain, milliamperes

Fig. AI.2   #2 cells (ASA cell size *D*). Service life when continuous discharge is at 70°F. (*Courtesy* Burgess Battery Co.)

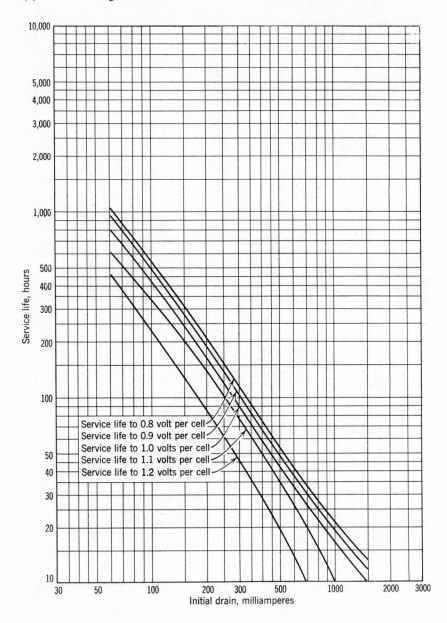

Fig. AI.3   #6 ignition (ASA cell size 6). Service life when continuous discharge is at 70°F.   (*Courtesy* Burgess Battery Co.)

Appendix II

Resistor Color Code

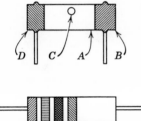

Fixed composition resistors

Color	Significant Figure	Decimal Multiplier	Tolerance (%)
Black	0	1	—
Brown	1	10	
Red	2	100	
Orange	3	1,000	
Yellow	4	10,000	
Green	5	100,000	
Blue	6	1,000,000	
Violet	7	10,000,000	
Gray	8	100,000,000	
White	9	1,000,000,000	
Gold	—	0.1	5
Silver	—	0.01	10
No color	—	—	20

Example: A resistor banded
is a $20 \times 10^4 = 0.2$ megohm $\pm 5\%$ resistor.

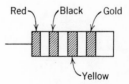

Fig. A II-1—Color coding of fixed composition resistors. The color code is given in the table. The colored areas have the following significance:

A—First significant figure of resistance in ohms.
B—Second significant figure.
C—Decimal multiplier.
D—Resistance tolerance in per cent. If no color is shown the tolerance is $\pm 20\%$.

Appendix III

Partial list of general electrical suppliers who mail catalogues.

1. Allied Radio, 100 North Western Ave., Chicago, Ill.
2. Burstein-Applebee Co., 1012 McGee St., Kansas City, Mo.
3. Herbach and Rademan, Inc., 1204 Arch St., Philadelphia, Pa.
4. Newark Electronics Corp., 233 West Madison St., Chicago, Ill.
5. Radio Shack, 167 Washington St., Boston, Mass., and 230 Crown St., New Haven, Conn.
6. Universal Relay Corp., 42 White St., New York, N.Y.

Also see advertisements in the following magazines which may be purchased on the newsstands or at electronic supply houses.

1. *Electronics World*.
2. *Radio Electronics*.
3. *Popular Electronics*.

Appendix IV

Table of wire sizes, numbering code, and current capacities.

Copper-wire Table

Wire Size A.W.G. (B & S)	Diam., mils[1]	Circular-Mil Area	Ohms per 1000 feet, 25°C	Approx. Current-Carrying Capacity	Diam., mm	Nearest British S.W.G. No.
1	289.3	83690	0.1264	119.6	7.348	1
2	257.6	66370	0.1593	94.8	6.544	3
3	229.4	52640	0.2009	75.2	5.827	4
4	204.3	41740	0.2533	59.6	5.189	5
5	181.9	33100	0.3195	47.3	4.621	7
6	162.0	26250	0.4028	37.5	4.115	8
7	144.3	20820	0.5080	29.7	3.665	9
8	128.5	16510	0.6405	23.6	3.264	10
9	114.4	13090	0.8077	18.7	2.906	11
10	101.9	10380	1.018	14.8	2.588	12
11	90.74	8234	1.284	11.8	2.305	13
12	80.81	6530	1.619	9.33	2.053	14
13	71.96	5178	2.042	7.40	1.828	15
14	64.08	4107	2.575	5.87	1.628	16
15	57.07	3257	3.247	4.65	1.450	17
16	50.82	2583	4.094	3.69	1.291	18
17	45.26	2048	5.163	2.93	1.150	18
18	40.30	1624	6.510	2.32	1.024	19
19	35.89	1288	8.210	1.84	0.9116	20
20	31.96	1022	10.35	1.46	0.8118	21
21	28.46	810.1	13.05	1.16	0.7230	22
22	25.35	642.4	16.46	0.918	0.6438	23
23	22.57	509.5	20.76	0.728	0.5733	24
24	20.10	404.0	26.17	0.577	0.5106	25
25	17.90	320.4	33.00	0.458	0.4547	26
26	15.94	254.1	41.62	0.363	0.4049	27
27	14.20	201.5	52.48	0.288	0.3606	29
28	12.64	159.8	66.17	0.228	0.3211	30
29	11.26	126.7	83.44	0.181	0.2859	31
30	10.03	100.5	105.2	0.144	0.2546	33
31	8.928	79.70	132.7	0.114	0.2268	34
32	7.950	63.21	167.3	0.090	0.2019	36
33	7.080	50.13	211.0	0.072	0.1798	37
34	6.305	39.75	266.0	0.057	0.1601	38
35	5.615	31.52	335.0	0.045	0.1426	38–39
36	5.000	25.00	423.0	0.036	0.1270	39–40
37	4.453	19.83	533.4	0.028	0.1131	41
38	3.965	15.72	672.6	0.022	0.1007	42
39	3.531	12.47	848.1	0.018	0.0897	43
40	3.145	9.88	1069	0.014	0.0799	44

[1] A mil is 1/1000 (one-thousandth) of an inch.

Appendix V

Answers to problems

Chapter 2

1. The resistor must have a resistance of 27.5 ohms, and a wattage of at least 110 watts.

2.

Relative Loudness	R (ohms)
16	11 (given)
8	26
4	56
2	116
1	236

Chapter 3

1. $R = 5$ ohms.
2. $R_1 = 3.33$ ohms.
3. $I_1 = 1$ ampere, $I_2 = 2$ amperes, $I_3 = 3$ amperes.
4. $I_2 = 3.33$ amperes, $I_3 = 7.33$ amperes, $R = 2.5$ ohms.
5. $I_1 = 0.267$ ampere, $I_2 = 0.333$ ampere, $I_3 = 0.600$ ampere.
6. $E = 6.45$ volts.
7. $R = 22$ ohms.
8. $E = 32.75$ volts.
9. Reading $= 1.43$ volts.
10. $I = 5.22$ amperes.
11. $R = 6540$ ohms.

12. (*Chapter 3*)

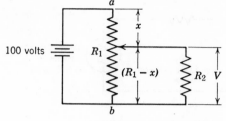

General equation $V = 100 - \dfrac{100\,x\,(R_1 - x + R_2)}{x\,(R_1 - x + R_2) + R_2\,(R_1 - x)}$

when $R_2 >> R_1$ (eg. $R_1 = 10$ ohms, $R_2 = 10,000$ ohms)

$$V \approx 100 - \frac{100\,x}{R_1}$$

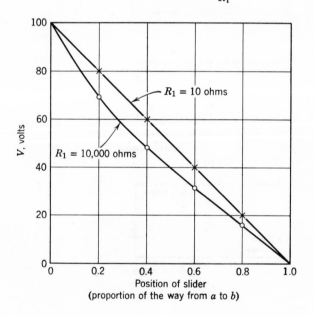

$R_1 = 10$ ohms

$R_1 = 10,000$ ohms

V, volts

Position of slider
(proportion of the way from *a* to *b*)

13. (*Chapter 3*)

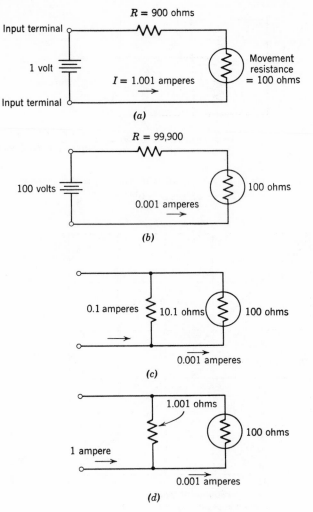

(a)

(b)

(c)

(d)

Chapter 6

1.

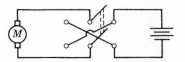

2. (*Chapter 6*)

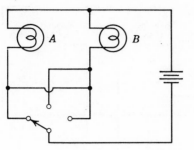

Not correct
(*A* and *B* both
will always be lit.)

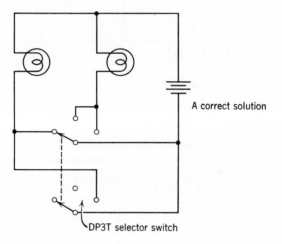

A correct solution

DP3T selector switch

3. (*Chapter 6*)

4.

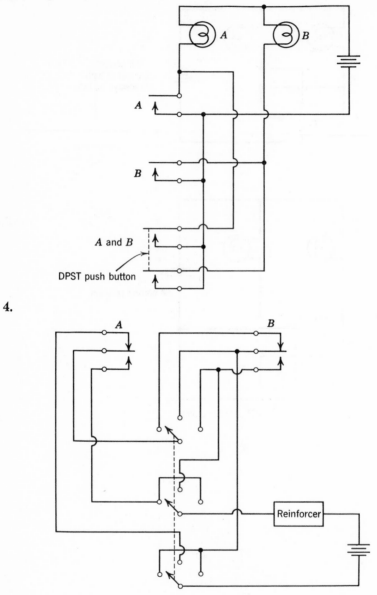

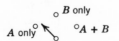

5a. (*Chapter 6*)

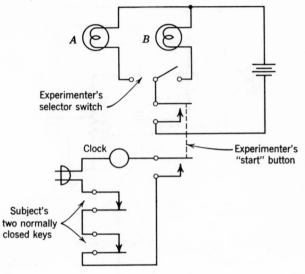

Experimenter's
selector switch

Clock

Experimenter's
"start" button

Subject's
two normally
closed keys

5b.

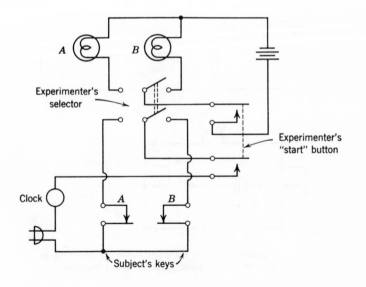

Experimenter's
selector

Experimenter's
"start" button

Clock

A   *B*

Subject's keys

6. *(Chapter 6)*

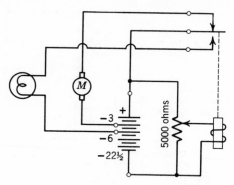

7.

Subject's toggles

Experimenter's selector toggles

Relay

Push button

Buzz

Experimenter closes his toggle switch corresponding to
the incorrect subject switch before each trial.

Chapter 7

1.

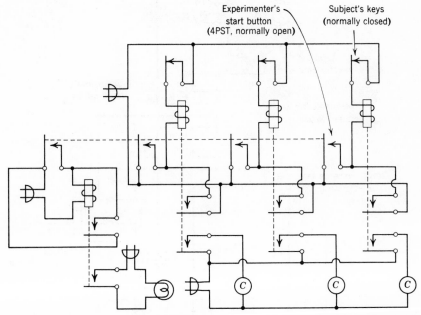

2. (*Chapter* 7)

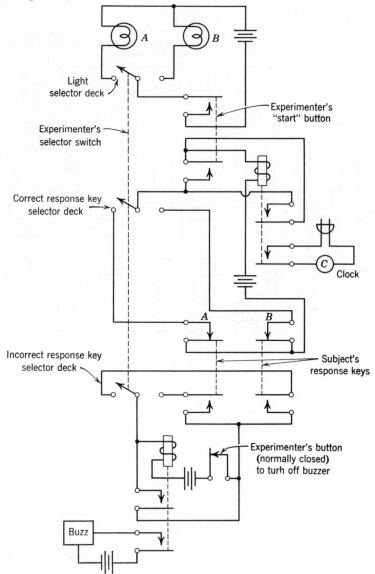

Light selector deck

Experimenter's "start" button

Experimenter's selector switch

Correct response key selector deck

Clock

Incorrect response key selector deck

Subject's response keys

Experimenter's button (normally closed) to turh off buzzer

Buzz

3. (*Chapter* 7)

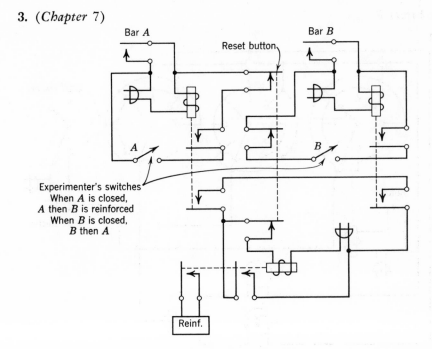

Chapter 8

1.

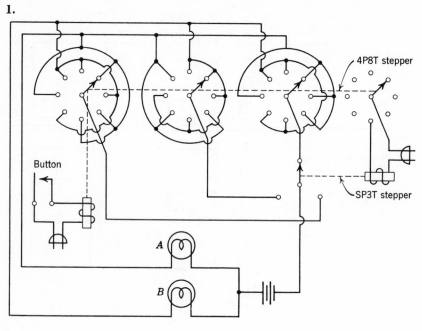

2.

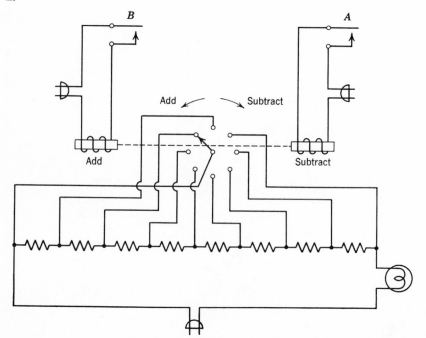

3. *(Chapter 8)*

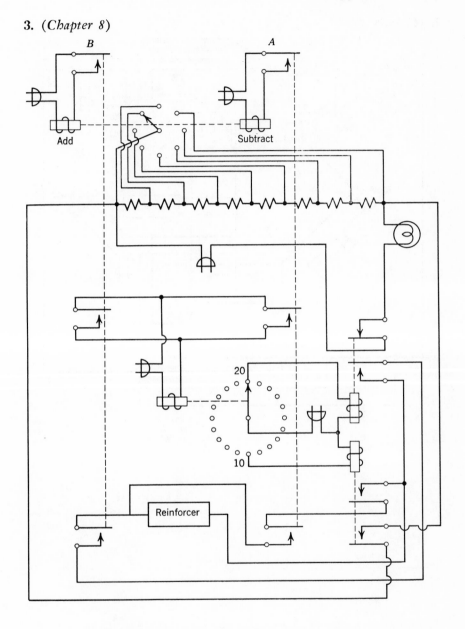

4. (*Chapter 8*)

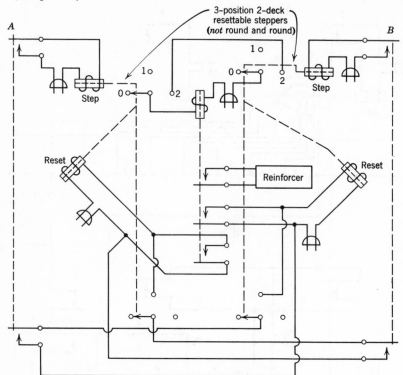

Chapter 13

1.

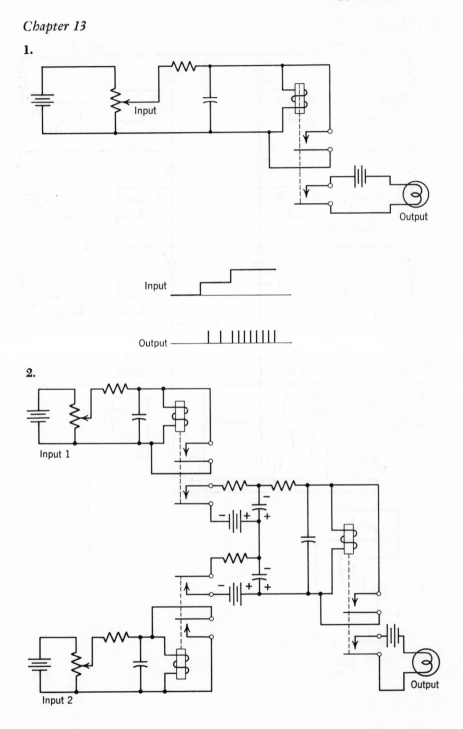

2.

3. (*Chapter 13*)

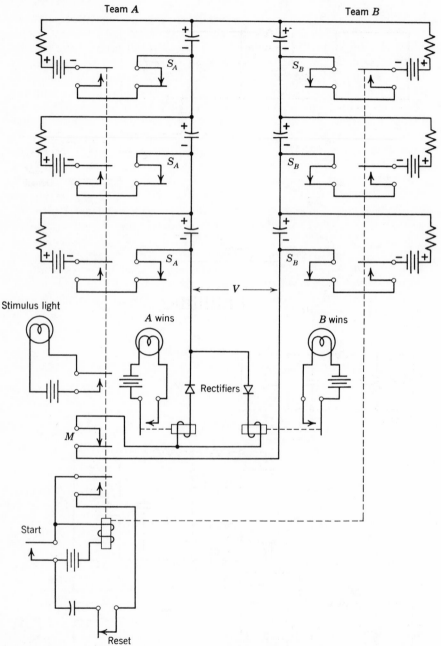

3. (*Chapter 13*) (*cont.*)

When the experimenter momentarily presses the key labeled "start," the relay in that circuit closes and holds itself closed for 3 seconds. That relay also turns on the stimulus light and completes each of the six subject's subcircuits. Since the subject's keys, labeled S_A and S_B, are normally closed, each of the six capacitors in the subjects' circuits will begin to charge up. As soon as each subject presses his key, his capacitor will stop charging. Thus, during the interval after all subjects have responded but before 3 seconds are up, all of the capacitors will carry voltages proportional to the subject's reaction times. If the total voltage across team A's capacitors is greater than across team B's, the voltage V will be of one polarity, and if B's voltage sum is greater, the polarity of V will be opposite.

When the 3 seconds are over, the start relay opens, closing the normally closed contacts labeled M. Therefore current will flow in one of the two paths containing the rectifiers, the conducting path depending upon the polarity of V. Since these paths contain the relays that drive the winners' lights, the bulb will light that corresponds to the team with the lower total voltage, that is, the lower total reaction time. *Note:* In order for this circuit to operate correctly, the voltage across each capacitor must be linearly related to the charging time. This will be approximately true if the time constants of the subjects' subcircuits are large relative to the subjects' reaction times.

Index